COMPOUND AMOUNT

If P dollars is deposited for n time periods at a compound interest rate i per period, the **compound amount** A is

$$A = P(1 + i)^n.$$

Consider an ordinary annuity of n payments of R dollars each at the end of consecutive interest periods with interest compounded at a rate of i per period. The **future value** S of the annuity is:

$$S = R\left[\frac{(1 + i)^n - 1}{i}\right].$$

The **present value** P of the annuity is:

$$P = R\left[\frac{1 - (1 + i)^{-n}}{i}\right].$$

The **matrix** version of the elimination method uses the following **matrix row operations** to obtain the augmented matrix of an equivalent system. They correspond to using elementary row operations on a system of equations.

1. Interchange any two rows.
2. Multiply each element of a row by a nonzero constant.
3. Replace a row by the sum of itself and a constant multiple of another row in the matrix.

UNION RULE

For any events E and F from a sample space S.

$$P(E \cup F) = P(E) + P(F) - P(E \cap F).$$

PROPERTIES OF PROBABILITY

Let S be a sample space consisting of n distinct outcomes $s_1, s_2, \ldots, s_n$. An acceptable probability assignment consists of assigning to each outcome s_1 a number p_1 (the probability of s_1) according to these rules.

1. The probability of each outcome is a number between 0 and 1.

$$0 \le p_1 \le 1, \quad 0 \le p_2 \le 1, \quad \ldots, \quad 0 \le p_n \le 1.$$

2. The sum of the probabilities of all possible outcomes is 1.

$$p_1 + p_2 + p_3 + \cdots + p_n = 1.$$

BAYES' FORMULA

For any events E and $F_1, F_2, \ldots, F_n$, from a sample space S, where $F_1 \cup F_2 \ldots \cup F_n = S$,

$$P(F_i|E) = \frac{P(F_i) \cdot P(E|F_i)}{P(F_1) \cdot P(E|F_1) + \cdots + P(F_n) \cdot P(E|F_n)}.$$

Mathematics with Applications and Logic

Custom Edition for Winthrop University

Margaret L. Lial

Thomas W. Hungerford

John P. Holcomb, Jr.

Charles D. Miller

Vern E. Heeren

John Hornsby

Taken from:
Mathematics with Applications, Tenth Edition
by Margaret L. Lial, Thomas W. Hungerford, and John P. Holcomb, Jr.

Mathematical Ideas, Eleventh Edition
by Charles D. Miller, Vern E. Heeren, and John Hornsby

Learning Solutions

New York   Boston   San Francisco
London   Toronto   Sydney   Tokyo   Singapore   Madrid
Mexico City   Munich   Paris   Cape Town   Hong Kong   Montreal

Cover Art: *Regatta Single,* by Angela Sciaraffa

Taken from:

Mathematics with Applications, Tenth Edition
by Margaret L. Lial, Thomas W. Hungerford, and John P. Holcomb, Jr.
Copyright © 2011, 2007, 2004 by Pearson Education, Inc.
Published by Addison Wesley
Boston, Massachusetts 02116

Mathematical Ideas, Eleventh Edition
by Charles D. Miller, Vern E. Heeren, and John Hornsby
Copyright © 2008 by Pearson Education, Inc.
Published by Addison Wesley
Boston, Massachusetts 02116

This special edition published in cooperation with Pearson Learning Solutions.

The information, illustrations, and/or software contained in this book, and regarding the above-mentioned programs, are provided "As Is," without warranty of any kind, express or implied, including without limitation any warranty concerning the accuracy, adequacy, or completeness of such information. Neither the publisher, the authors, nor the copyright holders shall be responsible for any claims attributable to errors, omissions, or other inaccuracies contained in this book. Nor shall they be liable for direct, indirect, special, incidental, or consequential damages arising out of the use of such information or material.

All trademarks, service marks, registered trademarks, and registered service marks are the property of their respective owners and are used herein for identification purposes only.

Pearson Learning Solutions, 501 Boylston Street, Suite 900, Boston, MA 02116
A Pearson Education Company
www.pearsoned.com

Printed in the United States of America

1 2 3 4 5 6 7 8 9 10 V382 15 14 13 12 11 10

0002000102706511 05

KB

ISBN 10: 0-558-92763-7
ISBN 13: 978-0-558-92763-9

Contents

Taken from:
Mathematics with Applications, Tenth Edition
by Margaret L. Lial, Thomas W. Hungerford, and John P. Holcomb, Jr.

Taken from:
Mathematical Ideas, Eleventh Edition
by Charles D. Miller, Vern E. Heeren, and John Hornsby

Preface

Mathematics with Applications is an applications-oriented text for students in business, management, and natural and social sciences. The text can be used for a variety of different courses, and the only prerequisite is a course in algebra. Chapter 1 provides a thorough review of basic algebra for those students who need it.

It has been our primary goal to present sound mathematics in an understandable manner, proceeding from the familiar to new material and from concrete examples to general rules and formulas. There is an ongoing focus on real-world problem solving, and almost every section includes relevant, contemporary applications.

▶ New to This Edition

This edition covers the same topics as the previous one, but with the following significant additions and changes to both content and presentation:

- ▶ Chapter 5 (Mathematics of Finance) has been substantially rewritten to introduce material that plays a significant role in today's business environment. It includes new material on treasury bills, corporate bonds, zero-coupon bonds, pension distributions, bond pricing, and annuities due. The discussion of the present value of an annuity has been completely redone so that the topic is much more understandable.

- ▶ The first two sections of Chapter 6 (Systems of Linear Equations and Matrices) have been expanded to three. Systems of two equations in two variables are now in a section by themselves—to satisfy both those instructors who want to omit this discussion and proceed directly to larger systems, and those who requested expanded coverage of this topic. Both the elimination method and the Gauss–Jordan method for solving large systems of equations are now in the same section, since many instructors prefer to get to the Gauss–Jordan method as soon as possible. Finally, an entire section is devoted to applications of systems of equations.

- ▶ At the request of a number of users, the discussion of frequency probability has been moved from Section 8.4 to 8.3.

- ▶ Some requested changes have also been made in Chapter 10 (Introduction to Statistics). The first section has been split into two to give separate treatment to two important topics. Section 10.1 has an expanded discussion of frequency distributions, and Section 10.2 covers measures of central tendency.

- ▶ Three of the end-of-chapter Cases are new and several others have been updated.

- ▶ Approximately 20% of the real data examples have been updated. Updates were focused on situations in which data could be updated to reflect current conditions.

- ▶ Approximately 18% of the 5,288 exercises in the book are new and 11% more have been updated. 15% of the 623 examples in the text are new and 24% have been updated.

▶ The margin exercises that have always been a part of this book have been renamed *Checkpoints,* to more accurately reflect their pedagogical purpose. The checkpoint icons (such as $\overset{3}{\checkmark}$) within the body of the text indicate when it's appropriate to work the Checkpoint exercise. Their answers have been moved to the end of the section to provide a more open and inviting page layout and to encourage students to work the problems before looking at the answers.

▶ In the Examples real-world applications now carry titles corresponding to the ones used in the Exercises (Business, Finance, Health, Social Science, etc.).

▶ Continuing Pedagogical Features

▶ *Balanced Approach*   Multiple representations of a topic (symbolic, numerical, graphical, verbal) are given when appropriate. However, we do not believe that all representations are useful for all topics, so effective alternatives are discussed only when they are likely to increase student understanding.

▶ *Real-Data Examples and Explanations*   Real-data exercises have long been a popular feature of this book. A significant number of new real-data examples have also been introduced into the text.

▶ *Cautions* highlight common student difficulties or warn against frequently made mistakes.

▶ *Exercises*   In addition to the drill, conceptual, application-based exercises, as well as questions from past CPA exams, there are some specially-marked exercises:

> Writing Exercises 🖊 (see page 241)
>
> Connection Exercises 🔁 that relate current topics to earlier sections (see page 317); and
>
> exercises that require technology 🖱 (see page 152).

▶ *Selected exercises* include a reference back to related example(s) within the section (see, e.g., examples 6 and 7). This helps students as they get started with homework.

▶ *End-of-Chapter* materials include a summary of key terms and symbols and key concepts, as well as a set of chapter-review exercises.

▶ *Cases* appear at the end of each chapter and offer contemporary real-world applications of some of the mathematics presented in the chapter. Not only do these provide an opportunity for student to see the mathematics they are learning in action, but they also provide at least a partial answer to the question, "What's this stuff good for?"

▶ Technology

It is assumed that all students have a calculator that will handle exponential and logarithmic functions. Beyond that, however, *the use of technology in this text is optional.* Examples and exercises that definitely require some sort of technology (graphing calculators, spreadsheets, or other computer programs) are marked with the icon ⌨, so instructors who want to omit these discussions and exercises can easily do so.

Instructors who routinely use technology in their courses will find more than enough material here to satisfy their needs. Here are some of the features they may want to incorporate into their courses:

▸ *Examples and Exercises marked with* ⌨ A number of examples show students how various features of graphing calculators and spreadsheets can be applied to the topics in this book.

▸ *Technology Tips* These are placed at appropriate points in the text to inform students of various features of their graphing calculator, spreadsheet, or other computer programs. Note that

Technology Tips for	**Also apply to**
TI-84+	TI-83+, TI-Nspire, and usually TI-83
Casio	Casio 9750 GII and 9860 GII, and usually other models.

▸ *Appendix A: Graphing Calculators* This consists of a brief introduction to the relevant features of the latest Texas Instruments and Casio graphing calculators. An outline of the appendix is on page 951, and the full appendix is available in MyMathLab or at pearsonhighered.com/MWA10. Additionally, the Web sites contain downloadable programs for both TI and Casio calculators that add functionality that is specifically relevant to this course.

▸ A separate Graphing Calculator and Excel Spreadsheet Manual is also available. This manual, correlated to examples in the textbook, provides students with the support they need to make use of graphing calculators and Excel.

▸ Course Flexibility

The content of the text is divided into three parts:

- College Algebra (Chapters 1–4),
- Finite Mathematics (Chapters 5–10),
- Calculus (Chapters 11–14)

This coverage of the material offers flexibility, making the book appropriate for a variety of courses, including:

Finite Mathematics and Calculus (one year or less). Use the entire book; cover topics from Chapters 1–4 as needed before proceeding to further topics.

Finite Mathematics (one semester or two quarters). Use as much of Chapters 1–4 as needed, and then go into Chapters 5–10 as time permits and local needs require.

Calculus (one semester or quarter). Cover the precalculus topics in Chapters 1–4 as necessary, and then use Chapters 11–14.

College Algebra with Applications (one semester or quarter). Use Chapters 1–8, with Chapters 7 and 8 being optional.

Chapter interdependence is as follows:

Chapter	Prerequisite
1 Algebra and Equations	None
2 Graphs, Lines, and Inequalities	Chapter 1
3 Functions and Graphs	Chapters 1 and 2
4 Exponential and Logarithmic Functions	Chapter 3
5 Mathematics of Finance	Chapter 4
6 Systems of Linear Equations and Matrices	Chapters 1 and 2
7 Linear Programming	Chapters 3 and 6
8 Sets and Probability	None
9 Counting, Probability Distributions, and Further Topics in Probability	Chapter 8
10 Introduction to Statistics	Chapter 8
11 Differential Calculus	Chapters 1–4
12 Applications of the Derivative	Chapter 11
13 Integral Calculus	Chapters 11 and 12
14 Multivariate Calculus	Chapters 11–13

Contact your local Pearson Education sales representative to order a customized version of this text.

Student Supplements

Student's Solutions Manual

▶ By Beverly Fusfield and James J. Ball, Indiana State University
▶ This manual contains detailed, carefully worked out solutions to all odd-numbered section exercises and all Chapter Review and Case exercises.
ISBN 13: 978-0-321-64582-1;
ISBN 10: 0-321-64582-0

Graphing Calculator and Excel Spreadsheet Manual

▶ By Victoria Baker, Nicholls State University and Stela Pudar-Hozo, Indiana University—Northwest
▶ The Graphing Calculator portion contains detailed instruction for using the TI-83/TI-83+/TI-84+, TI-Nspire, and Casio 9750 GII and Casio 9860 GII with this textbooks. Instructions are organized by chapter and section.
▶ The Excel spreadsheet portion contains detailed instructions for using Excel with this textbook. Available in MyMathLab or through www.coursesmart.com
ISBN-13: 978-0-321-65513-3
ISBN-10: 0-321-65513-4

Instructor Supplements

Instructor's Edition

▶ This book contains answers to all exercises in the text.
ISBN 13: 978-0-321-64632-3;
ISBN 10: 0-321-64632-0

Online Instructor's Solutions Manual (downloadable only)

▶ By Beverly Fusfield and James J. Ball, Indiana State University
▶ This manual contains detailed solutions to all text exercises, suggested course outlines, and a chapter interdependence chart.
Go to www.pearsonhighered.com/educator or MyMathLab.

Online Test Bank (downloadable only)

▶ By David Bridge, University of Central Oklahoma
▶ This test bank includes four alternate tests per chapter that parallel the text's Chapter Tests. Available through http://www.pearsonhighered.com/educator or in MyMathLab,

(continued)

Instructor Supplements (*continued*)

TestGen®

▸ TestGen enables instructors to build, edit, print, and administer tests using a computerized bank of questions developed to cover all the objectives of the text. TestGen is algorithmically based, allowing instructors to create multiple equivalent versions of the same question or test with the click of a button. Instructors also can modify test bank questions or add new questions. Tests can be printed or administered online. Available for download through http://www.pearsonhighered.com/educator.

PowerPoint® Lecture Slides

▸ These slides present key concepts and definitions from the text. They are available in MyMathLab or at http://www.pearsonhighered.com/educator.

Media Supplements

MyMathLab® Online Course (access code required)
MyMathLab is a text-specific, easily customizable online course that integrates interactive multimedia instruction with textbook content. MyMathLab gives you the tools you need to deliver all or a portion of your course online, whether your students are in a lab setting or working from home.

▸ **Interactive homework exercises,** correlated to your textbook at the objective level, are algorithmically generated for unlimited practice and mastery. Most exercises are free-response and provide guided solutions, sample problems, and learning aids for extra help.

▸ **Personalized Study Plan,** generated when students complete a test or quiz, indicates which topics have been mastered and links to tutorial exercises for topics students have not mastered.

▸ **Multimedia learning aids,** such as video lectures, animations, and complete multimedia textbook, help students independently improve their understanding and performance.

▸ **Assessment Manager** lets you create online homework, quizzes, and tests that are automatically graded. Select just the right mix of questions from the MyMathLab exercise bank, instructor-created custom exercises, and/or TestGen test items.

▸ **Gradebook,** designed specifically for mathematics and statistics, automatically tracks students' results and give you control over how to calculate final grades. You can also add offline (paper-and-pencil) grades to the gradebook.

▸ **MathXL® Exercise Builder** allows you to create static and algorithmic exercises for your online assignments. You can use the library of sample exercises as an easy starting point.

▸ **Pearson Tutor Center** (www.pearsontutorsercvices.com) access is automatically included with MyMathLab. The Tutor Center is staffed by qualified math instructors who provide textbook-specific tutoring for students via toll-free phone, fax, email, and interactive Web sessions.

MyMathLab is powered by CourseCompass™, Pearson Education's online teaching and learning environment, and by MathXL, our online homework, tutorial, and assessment system. MyMathLab is available to qualified adopters. For more information, visit www.mymathlab.com or contact your Pearson sales representative.

MathXL Online Course (access code required)

MathXL is an online homework, tutorial, and assessment system that accompanies Pearson's textbooks in mathematics or statistics.

- **Interactive homework exercises,** correlated to your textbook at the objective level, are algorithmically generated for unlimited practice and mastery. Most exercises are free-response and provide guided solutions, sample problems, and learning aids for extra help.
- **Personalized Study Plan,** generated when students complete a test or quiz, indicates which topics have been mastered and links to tutorial exercises for topics students have not mastered.
- **Multimedia learning aids,** such as video lectures and animations, help students independently improve their understanding and performance.
- **Gradebook,** designed specifically for mathematics and statistics, automatically tracks students' results and gives you control over how to calculate final grades.
- **MathXL Exercise Builder** allows you to create static and algorithmic exercises for your online assignments. You can use the library of sample exercises as an easy starting point.
- **Assessment Manager** lets you create online homework, quizzes, and tests that are automatically graded. Select just the right mix of questions from the MathXL exercise bank, instructor-created custom exercises, and/or TestGen test items.

MathXL is available to qualified adopters. For more information, visit our Web site www.mathxl.com, or contact your Pearson sales representative.

New! *Video Lectures on DVD with Optional Subtitles*

The video lectures for this text are available on DVD, making it easy and convenient for students to watch the videos from a computer at home or on campus. The videos feature engaging chapter summaries and worked-out examples. This format provides distance-learning students with critical video instruction. The videos have optional English subtitles; they can easily be turned on or off for individual student needs.
ISBN-13: 978-0-321-64577-7; ISBN 10: 0-321-64577-4

Acknowledgments

The authors wish to thank the following reviewers for their helpful comments and suggestions for this and previous editions of the text (reviewers of the 10th edition are noted with an asterisk):

Erol Barbut, University of Idaho

Bob Beul, St. Louis University–Metropolitan College

Richard Bieberich, Ball State University

Chris Boldt, Eastfield College

Michael J. Bradley, Merrimack College

James F. Brown, Midland College

Tarek Buhagiar, University of Central Florida*

James E. Carpenter, Iona College

Jesus Carreon, Mesa Community College

Faith Y. Chao, Golden Gate University

Jan S. Collins, Embry-Riddle University

Jerry Currence, University of South
  Carolina–Lancaster

Juli D'Ann Ratheal, Western Texas
  A & M University

Frederick Davidson, Old Dominion
  University

Jean Davis, Southwest Texas State University

Duane E. Deal, Ball State University

Richard D. Derderian, Providence College

Carol E. DeVille, Louisiana Tech University

Wayne Ehler, Anne Arundel Community
  College

George A. Emerson, National University

Garret Etgen, University of Houston

George Evanovich, Iona College

Richard Fast, Mesa Community College

Gordon Feathers, Iona College

J. Franklin Fitzgerald, Boston University

Leland J. Fry, Kirkwood Community College

Dauhrice K. Gibson, Gulf Coast Community
  College

Robert E. Goad, Sam Houston State University

Mark Goldstein, West Virginia Northern
  Community College*

Richard E. Goodrick, University of Washington

Kim Gregor, Delaware Technical and
  Community College

Kay Gura, Ramapo College of New Jersey

Joseph A. Guthrie, University of Texas
  at El Paso

Patricia Hirschy, Delaware Technical and
  Community College

Arthur M. Hobbs, Texas A & M University

Irene Hollman, Southwestern College

Miles Hubbard, St. Cloud State University

Katherine J. Huppler, St. Cloud State University

Carol M. Hurwitz, Manhattan College

Donald R. Ignatz, Lorain County
  Community College

Alec Ingraham, New Hampshire College

Robert H. Johnston, Virginia Commonwealth
  University

June Jones, Macon College

Paul Kaczur, Phoenix College

Michael J. Kallaher, Washington State
  University

Akihiro Kanamori, Boston University

Terence J. Keegan, Providence College

Hubert C. Kennedy, Providence College

Raja Khoury, Collin County Community
  College

Clint Kolaski, University of Texas
  at San Antonio

Archille J. Laferriere, Boston College

Steve Laroe, University of Alaska–Fairbanks

Jeffrey Lee, Texas Tech University

Arthur M. Lieberman, Cleveland State
  University

Norman Lindquist, Western Washington
  University

Laurence P. Maher, Jr., North Texas State
  University

Norman R. Martin, Northern Arizona University

Donald Mason, Elmhurst College

James Mazzarella, Holy Family College

Walter S. McVoy, Illinois State University

C. G. Mendez, Metropolitan State College
  of Denver

Shannon Michaux, University of Colorado
  at Colorado Springs

W. W. Mitchell, Jr., Phoenix College

Robert A. Moreland, Texas Tech University

Ruth M. Murray, College of DuPage

Kandasamy Muthuvel, University of
  Wisconsin–Oshkosh

Javad Namazi, Fairleigh Dickinson University*

Carol Nessmith, Georgia Southern College

Peter Nicholls, Northern Illinois University

Ann O'Connell, Providence College

Kathy O'Dell, University of Alabama
  at Huntsville

Charles Odion, Houston Community College

Thomas J. Ordoyne, University of South
  Carolina at Spartanburg

Marian Paysinger, University of Texas
at Arlington
Julienne K. Pendleton, Brookhaven College
Sandra Peskin, Queensborough Community
College
S. Pierce, West Coast University
John M. Plachy, Metropolitan State College
Elizabeth Polenzani, Pasadena City College
Donald G. Poulson, Mesa Community College
Wayne B. Powell, Oklahoma State University
Michael I. Ratliff, Northern Arizona University
Clark P. Rhoades, Loyola University at
New Orleans
Sarah Sabinson, Queensborough Community
College
Leon Sagan, Anne Arundel Community College
C. Edward Sandifer, Western Connecticut
State University*
Warren Sargent, College of the Sequoias*
Subhash C. Saxena, University of South
Carolina, Coastal Carolina College
Harold Schachter, Queensborough
Community College
Steven A. Schonefeld, Tri-State University
Robert Seaver, Lorain County Community
College
Surinder Sehgal, Ohio State University
Gordon Shilling, University of Texas
at Arlington

Calvin Shipley, Henderson State University
Pradeep Shukla, Suffolk University
James L. Southam, San Francisco State
University
John Spellman, Southwest Texas State
University
Joan M. Spetich, Baldwin-Wallace College
William D. Stark, Navarro College
Jo Steig, Phoenix College
David Stoneman, University
of Wisconsin–Whitewater
David P. Sumner, University of South Carolina
Daniel F. Symancyk, Anne Arundel
Community College
Giovanni Viglino, Ramapo College
of New Jersey
Deborah A. Vrooman, Coastal Carolina
College
H. J. Wellenzohn, Niagara University
Stephen H. West, Coastal Carolina College
Thelma West, University of Louisiana
at Lafayette
Richard J. Wilders, North Central College
John L. Wisthoff, Anne Arundel Community
College
Hing-Sing Yu, University of Texas
at San Antonio
Cathy Zucco-Teveloff, Trinity College

We also wish to thank our accuracy checkers, who did an excellent job of checking both text and exercise answers: Paul Lorczak, Debra McGivney, John and Ann Corbeil. Thanks also to the supplements authors: Jim Ball, Beverly Fusfield, David Bridge, Victoria Baker and Stela Pudar-Hozo. Special thanks to Becky Troutman, who carefully compiled the Index of Applications.

We want to thank the staff of Pearson Education for their assistance with, and contributions to, this book, particularly Greg Tobin, Deirdre Lynch, Jennifer Crum, Jeff Weidenaar, Sheila Spinney, Elizabeth Bernardi, Joanne Wendelken, Kendra Bassi, and Jean Choe. Finally, we wish to express our appreciation to Denise Showers of Aptara Corporation, who was a pleasure to work with.

Margaret L. Lial
Thomas W. Hungerford
John P. Holcomb, Jr.

To the Student

This book has several features designed to help you understand and apply the mathematics presented here.

Checkpoints These problems appear in the margin and are keyed to the discussion in the text. When you see the symbol ✔ in the text, you are advised to work the corresponding checkpoint problem in the margin. Doing so will help you to understand and apply new concepts.

Technology Examples and exercises that require graphing calculators, spreadsheets, or other technology are marked with the icon. Some instructors may make this material part of the course, whereas others will not require you to use technology other than a calculator that can handle exponential functions and logarithms.

For those who use technology, there is a *Graphing Calculator Appendix* that covers the basics of calculator use and provides a number of helpful programs for working with some of the topics in the text. An outline of the appendix is on page 951 and the full appendix is available in MyMathLab or at http://www.pearsonhighered.com/MWA10.

Finally, there are *Technology Tips* throughout the text that describe the proper menu or keys to use for various procedures on a graphing calculator. Note that

Technology Tips for	Also apply to
TI-84+	TI-83+, TI-Nspire, and usually TI-83
Casio	Casio 9750 GII and 9860 GII, and usually other models.

The key to succeeding in this course is to remember that

mathematics is not a spectator sport.

You can't expect to learn mathematics without *doing* mathematics any more than you could learn to swim without getting wet. You have to take an active role, making use of all the resources at your disposal: your instructor, your fellow students, and this book. To get the most out of the book, you need to read it regularly (preferably *before* starting the exercises).

Finally, remember the words of the great Hillel: "The bashful do not learn." There is no such thing as a "dumb question" (assuming, of course, that you have read the book and your class notes and attempted the homework). Your instructor will welcome questions that arise from a serious effort on your part. So get your money's worth: Ask questions.

Sets and Probability

We often use the relative frequency of an event from a survey to estimate unknown probabilities. For example, we can estimate the probability that a high-earning chief executive officer is in his sixties; see Example 10 in Section 8.4. Other applications of probability occur in the health and social sciences. Examples include estimating the probability of having a healthy weight, owning two cars within a household, or working full time; see Exercises 45, 52, and 57 on pages 504–505.

CASE 8: Medical Diagnosis

Federal officials cannot predict exactly how the number of traffic deaths is affected by the trend toward fewer drunken drivers and the increased use of seat belts. Economists cannot tell exactly how stricter federal regulations on bank loans affect the U.S. economy. The number of traffic deaths and the growth of the economy are subject to many factors that cannot be predicted precisely.

Probability theory enables us to deal with uncertainty. The basic concepts of probability are discussed in this chapter, and applications of probability are discussed in the next chapter. Sets and set operations are the basic tools for the study of probability, so we begin with them.

8.1 ▶ Sets

Think of a set as a well-defined collection of objects. A set of coins might include one of each type of coin now put out by the U.S. government. Another set might be made up of all the students in your English class. By contrast, a collection of young adults does not constitute a set unless the designation "young adult" is clearly defined. For example, this set might be defined as those aged 18–29.

In mathematics, sets are often made up of numbers. The set consisting of the numbers 3, 4, and 5 is written as

$$\{3, 4, 5\},$$

where **set braces**, { }, are used to enclose the numbers belonging to the set. The numbers, 3, 4, and 5 are called the **elements**, or **members**, of this set. To show that 4 is an element of the set $\{3, 4, 5\}$, we use the symbol $\in$ and write

$$4 \in \{3, 4, 5\},$$

read, "4 is an element of the set containing 3, 4, and 5."

Also, $5 \in \{3, 4, 5\}$. Place a slash through the symbol $\in$ to show that 8 is *not* an element of this set:

$$8 \notin \{3, 4, 5\}.$$

This statement is read, "8 is not an element of the set $\{3, 4, 5\}$."

Sets are often named with capital letters, so that if

$$B = \{5, 6, 7\},$$

then, for example, $6 \in B$ and $10 \notin B$. ✔

Sometimes a set has no elements. Some examples are the set of female presidents of the United States in the period 1788–2008, the set of counting numbers less than 1, and the set of men more than 10 feet tall. A set with no elements is called the **empty set**. The symbol $\varnothing$ is used to represent the empty set.

Answers: See page 475.

✔**Checkpoint 1**

Indicate whether each statement is *true* or *false*.

(a) $9 \in \{8, 4, -3, -9, 6\}$.

(b) $4 \notin \{3, 9, 7\}$.

(c) If $M = \{0, 1, 2, 3, 4\}$, then $0 \in M$.

⊘ **CAUTION** Be careful to distinguish between the symbols 0, $\varnothing$, and {0}. The symbol 0 represents a *number*; $\varnothing$ represents a *set* with no elements; and {0} represents a *set* with one element, the number 0. Do not confuse the empty set symbol $\varnothing$ with the zero symbol 0 on a computer screen or printout.

Two sets are **equal** if they contain exactly the same elements. The sets $\{5, 6, 7\}$, $\{7, 6, 5\}$, and $\{6, 5, 7\}$ all contain exactly the same elements and are equal. In symbols,

$$\{5, 6, 7\} = \{7, 6, 5\} = \{6, 5, 7\}.$$

This means that the ordering of the elements in a set is unimportant. Sets that do not contain exactly the same elements are *not equal*. For example, the sets $\{5, 6, 7\}$ and $\{5, 6, 7, 8\}$ do not contain exactly the same elements and are not equal. We show this by writing

$$\{5, 6, 7\} \neq \{5, 6, 7, 8\}.$$

Sometimes we describe a set by a common property of its elements rather than by a list of its elements. This common property can be expressed with **set-builder notation**; for example,

$$\{x \mid x \text{ has property } P\}$$

(read, "the set of all elements x such that x has property P") represents the set of all elements x having some property P.

Example 1   List the elements belonging to each of the given sets.

(a) $\{x \mid x \text{ is a natural number less than } 5\}$

Solution The natural numbers less than 5 make up the set $\{1, 2, 3, 4\}$.

(b) $\{x \mid x \text{ is a state that borders Florida}\}$

Solution The states that border Florida make up the set $= \{\text{Alabama, Georgia}\}$.

✓**Checkpoint 2**

List the elements in the given sets.

(a) $\{x \mid x \text{ is a counting number more than 5 and less than 8}\}$

(b) $\{x \mid x \text{ is an integer, and } -3 < x \leq 1\}$

Answers: See page 475.

The **universal set** in a particular discussion is a set that contains all of the objects being discussed. In grade-school arithmetic, for example, the set of whole numbers might be the universal set, whereas in a college calculus class the universal set might be the set of all real numbers. When it is necessary to consider the universal set being used, it will be clearly specified or easily understood from the context of the problem.

Sometimes, every element of one set also belongs to another set. For example, if

$$A = \{3, 4, 5, 6\}$$

and

$$B = \{2, 3, 4, 5, 6, 7, 8\},$$

then every element of A is also an element of B. This is an example of the following definition.

A set A is a **subset** of a set B (written $A \subseteq B$) provided that every element of A is also an element of B.

Example 2   For each case, decide whether $M \subseteq N$.

(a) M is the set of all businesses making a profit in the last calendar year. N is the set of all businesses.

Solution Each business making a profit is also a business, so $M \subseteq N$.

(b) M is the set of all first-year students at a college at the end of the academic year, and N is the set of all 18-year-old students at the college at the end of the academic year.

Solution By the end of the academic year, some first-year students are older than 18, so there are elements in M that are not in N. Thus, M is not a subset of N, written $M \nsubseteq N$.

Every set A is a subset of itself, because the statement "every element of A is also an element of A" is always true. It is also true that the empty set is a subset of every set.*

For any set A,

$$\emptyset \subseteq A \quad \text{and} \quad A \subseteq A.$$

A set A is said to be a **proper subset** of a set B (written $A \subset B$) if every element of A is an element of B, but B contains at least one element that is not a member of A.

Example 3 Decide whether $E \subset F$.

(a) $E = \{2, 4, 6, 8\}$ and $F = \{1, 2, 3, 4, 5, 6, 7, 8, 9, 10\}$.

Solution Since each element of E is an element of F and F contains several elements not in E, $E \subset F$.

(b) E is the set of registered voters in Texas. F is the set of adults aged 18 years or older.

Solution To register to vote, one must be at least 18 years old. Not all adults at least 18 years old, however, are registered. Thus, every element of E is contained in F and F contains elements not in E. Therefore, $E \subset F$.

(c) E is the set of diet soda drinks. F is the set of diet soda drinks sweetened with Nutrasweet®.

Solution Some diet soda drinks are sweetened with the sugar substitute Splenda®. In this case, E is not a proper subset of F (written $E \not\subset F$), nor is it a subset of F at all ($E \not\subseteq F$). **3** ✓

Example 4 List all possible subsets for each of the given sets.

(a) $\{7, 8\}$

Solution A good way to find the subsets of $\{7, 8\}$ is to use a **tree diagram**—a systematic way of listing all the subsets of a given set. The tree diagram in Figure 8.1(a) shows there are four subsets of $\{7, 8\}$:

$$\emptyset, \quad \{7\}, \quad \{8\}, \quad \text{and} \quad \{7, 8\}.$$

(b) $\{a, b, c\}$

Solution The tree diagram in Figure 8.1(b) shows that there are 8 subset of $\{a, b, c\}$:

$$\emptyset, \quad \{a\}, \quad \{b\}, \quad \{c\}, \quad \{a, b\}, \quad \{a, c\}, \quad \{b, c\}, \quad \text{and} \quad \{a, b, c\}.$$ **4** ✓

✓**Checkpoint 3**

Indicate whether each statement is *true* or *false*.

(a) $\{10, 20, 30\} \subseteq \{20, 30, 40, 50\}$.

(b) $\{x | x$ is a minivan$\} \subseteq \{x | x$ is a motorvehicle$\}$.

(c) $\{a, e, i, o, u\} \subset \{a, e, i, o, u, y\}$.

(d) $\{x | x$ is a U.S. state that begins with the letter "A"$\} \subset$ {Alabama, Alaska, Arizona, Arkansas}.

Answers: See page 475.

✓**Checkpoint 4**

List all subsets of $\{w, x, y, z,\}$.

Answer: See page 475.

*This fact is not intuitively obvious to most people. If you wish, you can think of it as a convention that we agree to adopt in order to simplify the statements of several results later.

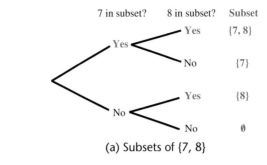

(a) Subsets of {7, 8}

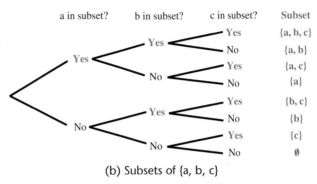

(b) Subsets of {a, b, c}

FIGURE 8.1

✔**Checkpoint 5**

Find the number of subsets for each of the given sets.

(a)
$\{x \mid x \text{ is a season of the year}\}$

(b)
$\{-6, -5, -4, -3, -2, -1, 0\}$

(c) $\{6\}$

Answers: See page 475.

By using the fact that there are two possibilities for each element (either it is in the subset or it is not), we have found that a set with 2 elements has 4 $(= 2^2)$ subsets and a set with 3 elements has 8 $(= 2^3)$ subsets. Similar arguments work for any finite set and lead to the following conclusion.

A set of n distinct elements has 2^n subsets.

Example 5   Find the number of subsets for each of the given sets.

(a) {blue, brown, hazel, green}

Solution Since this set has 4 elements, it has $2^4 = 16$ subsets.

(b) $\{x \mid x \text{ is a month of the year}\}$

Solution This set has 12 elements and therefore has $2^{12} = 4096$ subsets.

(c) $\varnothing$

Solution Since the empty set has 0 elements, it has $2^0 = 1$ subset, $\varnothing$ itself. ⁵✓

✔**Checkpoint 6**

Refer to sets A, B, C, and U in the diagram.

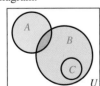

(a) Is $A \subseteq B$?

(b) Is $C \subseteq B$?

(c) Is $C \subseteq U$?

(d) Is $\varnothing \subseteq A$?

Answers: See page 475.

Venn diagrams are sometimes used to illustrate relationships among sets. The Venn diagram in Figure 8.2, on the next page, shows a set A that is a subset of a set B, because A is entirely in B. (The areas of the regions are not meant to be proportional to the sizes of the corresponding sets.) The rectangle represents the universal set U. ⁶✓

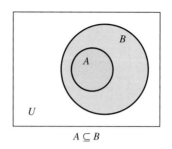

$A \subseteq B$

FIGURE 8.2

Some sets have infinitely many elements. We often use the notation "..." to indicate such sets. One example of an infinite set is the set of natural numbers, $\{1, 2, 3, 4, \ldots\}$. Another infinite set is the set of integers, $\{\ldots, -3, -2, -1, 0, 1, 2, 3, \ldots\}$.

OPERATIONS ON SETS

Given a set A and a universal set U, the set of all elements of U that do *not* belong to A is called the **complement** of set A. For example, if A is the set of all the female students in your class and U is the set of all students in the class, then the complement of A would be the set of all male students in the class. The complement of set A is written A' (read "A-prime"). The Venn diagram in Figure 8.3 shows a set B. Its complement, B', is shown in color.

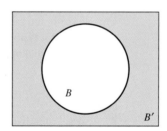

FIGURE 8.3

Some textbooks use $\overline{A}$ to denote the complement of A. This notation conveys the same meaning as A'.

Example 6   Let $U = \{1, 2, 3, 4, 5, 6, 7\}, A = \{1, 3, 5, 7\}$, and $B = \{3, 4, 6\}$. Find the given sets.

(a) A'

   Solution Set A' contains the elements of U that are not in A:

$$A' = \{2, 4, 6\}.$$

(b) B'

   Solution $B' = \{1, 2, 5, 7\}$.

(c) $\varnothing'$ and U'

   Solution $\varnothing' = U$ and $U' = \varnothing$. ✓

✔**Checkpoint 7**

Let $U = \{a, b, c, d, e, f, g\}$, with $K = \{c, d, f, g\}$ and $R = \{a, c, d, e, g\}$. Find

(a) K';

(b) R'.

Answers: See page 475.

Given two sets A and B, the set of all elements belonging to *both* set A and set B is called the **intersection** of the two sets, written $A \cap B$. For example, the elements that belong to both $A = \{1, 2, 4, 5, 7\}$ and $B = \{2, 4, 5, 7, 9, 11\}$ are 2, 4, 5, and 7, so

$$A \text{ and } B = A \cap B$$
$$= \{1, 2, 4, 5, 7\} \cap \{2, 4, 5, 7, 9, 11\}$$
$$= \{2, 4, 5, 7\}.$$

The Venn diagram in Figure 8.4 shows two sets A and B, with their intersection, $A \cap B$, shown in color.

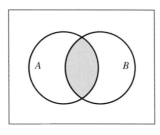

$A \cap B$

FIGURE 8.4

Checkpoint 8

Find the following.

(a) $\{1, 2, 3, 4\} \cap \{3, 5, 7, 9\}$

(b) Suppose K is the set of all blue-eyed blondes in a class and J is the set of all blue-eyed brunettes in the class. Let $P = \{x | x$ is a brown-eyed redhead$\}$. If the class has only blondes or brunettes, find $K \cap P$.

Answers: See page 475.

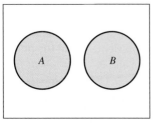

A and B are disjoint sets.

FIGURE 8.5

Example 7 Find the given sets.

(a) $\{9, 15, 25, 36\} \cap \{15, 20, 25, 30, 35\}$

Solution $\{15, 25\}$. The elements 15 and 25 are the only ones belonging to both sets.

(b) $\{x | x$ is a teenager$\} \cap \{x | x$ is a senior citizen$\}$

Solution $\varnothing$ since no teenager is a senior citizen.

Two sets that have no elements in common are called **disjoint sets**. For example, there are no elements common to both $\{50, 51, 54\}$ and $\{52, 53, 55, 56\}$, so these two sets are disjoint, and

$$\{50, 51, 54\} \cap \{52, 53, 55, 56\} = \varnothing.$$

The result of this example can be generalized as follows.

For any sets A and B,

if A and B are disjoint sets, then $A \cap B = \varnothing$.

Figure 8.5 is a Venn diagram of disjoint sets.

The set of all elements belonging to set A or to set B, or to both sets, is called the **union** of the two sets, written $A \cup B$. For example, for sets $A = \{1, 3, 5\}$ and $B = \{3, 5, 7, 9\}$,

$$A \text{ or } B = A \cup B$$
$$= \{1, 3, 5\} \cup \{3, 5, 7, 9\}$$
$$= \{1, 3, 5, 7, 9\}.$$

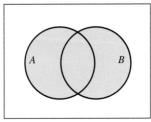

$A \cup B$

FIGURE 8.6

✓**Checkpoint 9**

Work the given union problems.

(a) Find $\{a, b, c\} \cup \{a, c, e\}$.

(b) Describe $K \cup J$ in words for the sets given in Checkpoint 8(b).

―――――――――

Answers: See page 475.

The Venn diagram in Figure 8.6 shows two sets A and B, with their union, $A \cup B$, shown in color.

Example 8 Find the given sets.

(a) $\{1, 2, 5, 9, 14\} \cup \{1, 3, 4, 8\}$.

 Solution Begin by listing the elements of the first set, $\{1, 2, 5, 9, 14\}$. Then include any elements from the second set *that are not already listed.* Doing this gives

$$\{1, 2, 5, 9, 14\} \cup \{1, 3, 4, 8\} = \{1, 2, 3, 4, 5, 8, 9, 14\}.$$

(b) {terriers, spaniels, chows, dalmatians} $\cup$ {spaniels, collies, bulldogs}

 Solution {terriers, spaniels, chows, dalmatians, collies, bulldogs}.

 Finding the complement of a set, the intersection of two sets, or the union of two sets is an example of a *set operation.*

Operations on Sets

Let A and B be any sets, with U signifying the universal set. Then

the **complement** of A, written A', is

$$A' = \{x \mid x \notin A \text{ and } x \in U\};$$

the **intersection** of A and B is

$$A \cap B = \{x \mid x \in A \text{ and } x \in B\};$$

the **union** of A and B is

$$A \cup B = \{x \mid x \in A \text{ or } x \in B \text{ or both}\}.$$

⊙ **CAUTION** As shown in the preceding definitions, an element is in the intersection of sets A and B if it is in *both* A and B at the same time, but an element is in the union of sets A and B if it is in *either* set A or set B, *or* in both sets A and B.

Example 9 The following table gives the 52-week high and low prices, the last price, and the change in price from the day before for five stocks on a recent day.*

―――――――――

*Morningstar.com, February 15, 2009.

Stock	High	Low	Last	Change
Allstate	52.16	17.12	21.23	−.30
Apple	192.24	78.20	98.99	−.11
Microsoft	32.10	16.75	19.09	−.17
Pepsi	75.25	43.78	52.57	+.57
UPS	75.08	41.40	44.84	−.06

Let the universal set U consist of the five stocks listed in the table. Let A contain all stocks with a high price greater than $60, B all stocks with a last price between $25 and $55, and C all stocks with a negative change. Find the results of the given set operations.

(a) B'

Solution Set B consists of Pepsi and UPS. Set B' contains all the listed stocks that are not in set B, so

$$B' = \{\text{Allstate, Apple, Microsoft}\}.$$

(b) $A \cap C$

Solution Set A consists of Apple, Pepsi, and UPS, and set C consists of Allstate, Apple, Microsoft, and UPS. Hence,

$$A \cap C = \{\text{Apple, UPS}\}.$$

(c) $A \cup B$

Solution $A \cup B = \{\text{Apple, Pepsi, UPS}\}$.   10✓

✓**Checkpoint 10**

In Example 9, find the given set of stocks.

(a) All stocks with a last price between $25 and $55 and with a negative price change

(b) All stocks with a last price between $25 and $55 or with a negative price change

Answers: See page 475.

8.1 ▶ **Exercises**

Write true or false for each statement.

1. $3 \in \{2, 5, 7, 9, 10\}$

2. $6 \in \{-2, 6, 9, 5\}$

3. $9 \notin \{2, 1, 5, 8\}$

4. $3 \notin \{7, 6, 5, 4\}$

5. $\{2, 5, 8, 9\} = \{2, 5, 9, 8\}$

6. $\{3, 7, 12, 14\} = \{3, 7, 12, 14, 0\}$

7. $\{\text{all whole numbers greater than 7 and less than 10}\} = \{8, 9\}$

8. $\{\text{all counting numbers not greater than 3}\} = \{0, 1, 2\}$

9. $\{x \mid x \text{ is an odd integer}, 6 \le x \le 18\} = \{7, 9, 11, 15, 17\}$

10. $\{x|x \text{ is a vowel}\} = \{a, e, i, o, u\}$

11. The elements of a set may be sets themselves, as in $\{1, \{1, 3\}, \{2\}, 4\}$. Explain why the set $\{\varnothing\}$ is not the same set as $\{0\}$.

12. What is set-builder notation? Give an example.

Let $A = \{-3, 0, 3\}$, $B = \{-2, -1, 0, 1, 2\}$, $C = \{-3, -1\}$, $D = \{0\}$, $E = \{-2\}$, and $U = \{-3, -2, -1, 0, 1, 2, 3\}$. Insert $\subseteq$ or $\not\subseteq$ to make the given statements true. (See Example 2.)

13. A____U

14. E____A

15. A____E

16. B____C

17. $\varnothing$____A

18. $\{0, 2\}$____D

19. D____B

20. A____C

Find the number of subsets of the given set. (See Example 5.)

21. $\{A, B, C\}$

22. {red, yellow, blue, black, white}

23. $\{x|x \text{ is an integer strictly between 0 and 8}\}$

24. $\{x|x \text{ is a whole number less than 4}\}$

Find the complement of each set. (See Example 6.)

25. The set in Exercise 23 if U is the set of all integers.

26. The set in Exercise 24 if U is the set of all whole numbers.

27. Describe the intersection and union of sets. How do they differ?

Insert $\cap$ or $\cup$ to make each statement true. (See Examples 7 and 8.)

28. $\{5, 7, 9, 19\}$____$\{7, 9, 11, 15\} = \{7, 9\}$

29. $\{8, 11, 15\}$____$\{8, 11, 19, 20\} = \{8, 11\}$

30. $\{2, 1, 7\}$____$\{1, 5, 9\} = \{1\}$

31. $\{6, 12, 14, 16\}$____$\{6, 14, 19\} = \{6, 14\}$

32. $\{3, 5, 9, 10\}$____$\varnothing = \varnothing$

33. $\{3, 5, 9, 10\}$____$\varnothing = \{3, 5, 9, 10\}$

34. $\{1, 2, 4\}$____$\{1, 2, 4\} = \{1, 2, 4\}$

35. $\{1, 2, 4\}$____$\{1, 2\} = \{1, 2, 4\}$

36. Is it possible for two nonempty sets to have the same intersection and union? If so, give an example.

Let $U = \{a, b, c, d, e, f, 1, 2, 3, 4, 5, 6\}$, $X = \{a, b, c, 1, 2, 3\}$, $Y = \{b, d, f, 1, 3, 5\}$, and $Z = \{b, d, 2, 3, 5\}$.

List the members of each of the given sets, using set braces. (See Examples 6–8.)

37. $X \cap Y$

38. $X \cup Y$

39. X'

40. Y'

41. $X' \cap Y'$

42. $X' \cap Z$

43. $X \cup (Y \cap Z)$

44. $Y \cap (X \cup Z)$

Let $U = \{$all students in this school$\}$,
$M = \{$all students taking this course$\}$,
$N = \{$all students taking accounting$\}$, and
$P = \{$all students taking philosophy$\}$.

Describe each of the following sets in words.

45. M'

46. $M \cup N$

47. $N \cap P$

48. $N' \cap P'$

49. Refer to the sets listed in the directions for Exercises 13–20. Which pairs of sets are disjoint?

50. Refer to the sets listed in the directions for Exercises 37–44. Which pairs of sets are disjoint?

Refer to Example 9 in the text. Describe each of the sets in Exercises 51–54 in words; then list the elements of each set.

51. A'

52. $B \cup C$

53. $A' \cap B'$

54. $B' \cup C$

Business *An electronics store classifies credit applicants by sex, marital status, and employment status. Let the universal set be the set of all applicants, M be the set of male applicants, S be the set of single applicants, and E be the set of employed applicants. Describe the following sets in words.*

55. $M \cap E$

56. $M' \cap S$

57. $M' \cup S'$

Business *The U.S. advertising volume (in millions of dollars) spent by certain types of media in 2006 and 2007 is shown in the following table:**

Medium	2006	2007
Newspapers	46,555	42,133
Magazines	13,168	13,787
Broadcast Television	46,880	44,521
Cable Television	25,025	26,319
Radio	19,643	19,152
Direct Mail	58,642	60,225
Internet	9,100	10,529

List the elements of each set.

58. The set of all media that collected more than $40,000 million in both 2006 and 2007.

59. The set of all media that collected less than $11,000 million in 2006 or 2007 (or both years).

60. The set of all media that had revenues rise from 2006 to 2007.

Business *The top seven cable television providers as of September 2008 are listed here.*† *Use this information for Exercises 61–66.*

Rank	Cable Provider	Subscribers
1	Comcast Cable Communications	24,406,000
2	Time Warner Cable	13,266,000
3	Cox Communications	5,382,125
4	Charter Communications	5,146,100
5	Cablevision Systems	3,112,000
6	Bright House Networks LLC	2,331,089
7	Suddenlink Communications	1,395,189

**Statistical Abstract of the United States*: 2009.

†National Cable Television Association, www.ncta.com.

List the elements of the following sets.

61. F, the set of cable providers with more than 8 million subscribers.

62. G, the set of cable providers with between 2 and 5 million subscribers.

63. H, the set of cable providers with over 2.5 million subscribers.

64. $F \cup G$ **65.** $H \cap F$ **66.** G'

Health   *The following table shows some symptoms of an underactive thyroid and an overactive thyroid:*

Underactive Thyroid	Overactive Thyroid
Sleepiness, s	Insomnia, i
Dry hands, d	Moist hands, m
Intolerance of cold, c	Intolerance of heat, h
Goiter, g	Goiter, g

Let U be the smallest possible set that includes all the symptoms listed, N be the set of symptoms for an underactive thyroid, and O be the set of symptoms for an overactive thyroid. Use the lowercase letters in the table to list the elements of each set.

67. O' **68.** N'

69. $N \cap O$ **70.** $N \cup O$

✓Checkpoint Answers

1. (a) False   (b) True   (c) True
2. (a) $\{6, 7\}$ (b) $\{-2, -1, 0, 1\}$
3. (a) False   (b) True   (c) True   (d) False
4. $\varnothing$, $\{w\}$, $\{x\}$, $\{y\}$, $\{z\}$, $\{w, x\}$, $\{w, y\}$, $\{w, z\}$, $\{x, y\}$, $\{x, z\}$, $\{y, z\}$, $\{w, x, y\}$, $\{w, x, z\}$, $\{w, y, z\}$, $\{x, y, z\}$, $\{w, x, y, z\}$
5. (a) 16   (b) 128   (c) 2
6. (a) No   (b) Yes   (c) Yes   (d) Yes
7. (a) $\{a, b, e\}$ (b) $\{b, f\}$ **8.** (a) $\{3\}$ (b) $\varnothing$
9. (a) $\{a, b, c, e\}$
     (b) All members of the class who have blue eyes
10. (a) $\{UPS\}$ (b) $\{Allstate, Apple, Microsoft, Pepsi, UPS\}$

8.2 ▶ Applications of Venn Diagrams

We used Venn diagrams in the last section to illustrate set union and intersection. The rectangular region in a Venn diagram represents the universal set U. Including only a single set A inside the universal set, as in Figure 8.7, divides U into two nonoverlapping regions. Region 1 represents A', those elements outside set A, while region 2 represents those elements belonging to set A. (The numbering of these regions is arbitrary.)

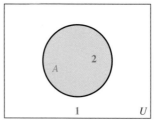

One set leads to 2 regions.
(Numbering is arbitrary.)

FIGURE 8.7

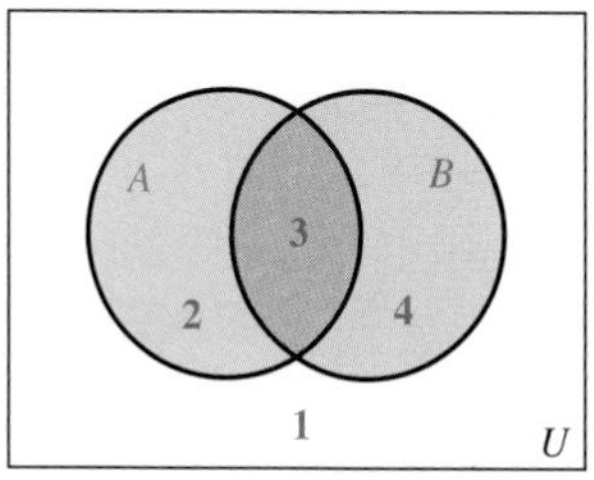

Two sets lead to 4 regions.
(Numbering is arbitrary.)

FIGURE 8.8

The Venn diagram of Figure 8.8 shows two sets inside U. These two sets divide the universal set into four nonoverlapping regions. As labeled in Figure 8.8, region 1 includes those elements outside both set *A* and set *B*. Region 2 includes those elements belonging to *A* and not to *B*. Region 3 includes those elements belonging to both *A* and *B*. Which elements belong to region 4? (Again, the numbering is arbitrary.)

Example 1 Draw a Venn diagram similar to Figure 8.8, and shade the regions representing the given sets.

(a) $A' \cap B$

Solution Set A' contains all the elements outside set *A*. As labeled in Figure 8.8, A' is represented by regions 1 and 4. Set *B* is represented by the elements in regions 3 and 4. The intersection of sets A' and *B*, the set $A' \cap B$, is given by the region common to regions 1 and 4 and regions 3 and 4. The result, region 4, is shaded in Figure 8.9.

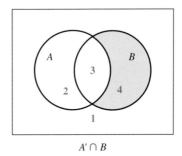

$A' \cap B$

FIGURE 8.9

(b) $A' \cup B'$

Solution Again, set A' is represented by regions 1 and 4 and set B' by regions 1 and 2. To find $A' \cup B'$, identify the region that represents the set of all elements in A', B', or both. The result, which is shaded in Figure 8.10, includes regions 1, 2, and 4. ✓

✓**Checkpoint 1**

Draw Venn diagrams for the given set operations.

(a) $A \cup B'$

(b) $A' \cap B'$

Answers: See page 485.

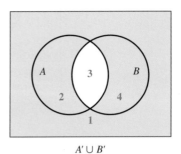

$A' \cup B'$

FIGURE 8.10

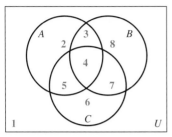

Three sets lead to 8 regions.

FIGURE 8.11

✓**Checkpoint 2**

Draw Venn diagrams for the given set operations.

(a) $(B' \cap A) \cup C$

(b) $(A \cup B)' \cap C$

Answers: See page 485.

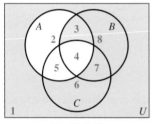

$A' \cup (B \cap C')$

FIGURE 8.12

✓**Checkpoint 3**

(a) Place numbers in the regions on a Venn diagram if the data on the 100 households in Example 2 showed

    35 DVD players;
    28 DCs;
    20 with both.

(b) How many have a DC, but not a DVD player?

Answers: See page 485.

Venn diagrams also can be drawn with three sets inside U. These three sets divide the universal set into eight nonoverlapping regions that can be numbered (arbitrarily) as in Figure 8.11.

Example 2   Shade $A' \cup (B \cap C')$ in a Venn diagram.

Solution First find $B \cap C'$; see Figure 8.12. Set B is represented by regions 3, 4, 7, and 8, and set C' by regions 1, 2, 3, and 8. The overlap of these regions, regions 3 and 8, represents the set $B \cap C'$. Set A' is represented by regions 1, 6, 7, and 8. The union of regions 3 and 8 and regions 1, 6, 7, and 8 contains regions 1, 3, 6, 7, and 8, which are shaded in Figure 8.12. 2✓

Venn diagrams can be used to solve problems that result from surveying groups of people. As an example, suppose a researcher collecting data on 100 households finds that

    29 have a DVD player (DVD),

    21 have a digital camera (DC), and

    15 have both.

The researcher wants to answer the following questions:

(a) How many do not have a digital camera?

(b) How many have neither a DVD player nor a digital camera?

(c) How many have a DVD player, but not a digital camera?

A Venn diagram like the one in Figure 8.13 will help sort out the information. In Figure 8.13(a), we put the number 15 in the region common to both a digital camera and a DVD player, because 15 households have both. Of the 29 with a DVD player, $29 - 15 = 14$ have no digital camera, so in Figure 8.13(b) we put 14 in the region for a DVD player, but no digital camera. Similarly, $21 - 15 = 6$ households have a digital camera, but not a DVD player, so we put 6 in that region. Finally, the diagram shows that $100 - 6 - 15 - 14 = 65$ households have neither a digital camera nor a DVD player. Now we can answer the questions:

(a) $65 + 14 = 79$.

(b) 65 have neither.

(c) 14 have a DVD player, but not a digital camera. 3✓

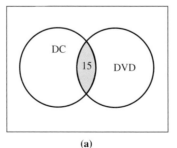

(a)

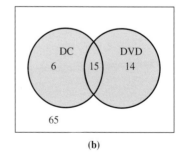

(b)

FIGURE 8.13

Example 3   A group of 60 freshman business students at a large university was surveyed, with the following results:

19 of the students read *Business Week*;

18 read the *Wall Street Journal*;

50 read *Fortune*;

13 read *Business Week* and the *Journal*;

11 read the *Journal* and *Fortune*;

13 read *Business Week* and *Fortune*;

9 read all three magazines.

Use the preceding data to answer the following questions:

(a) How many students read none of the publications?

(b) How many read only *Fortune*?

(c) How many read *Business Week* and the *Journal*, but not *Fortune*?

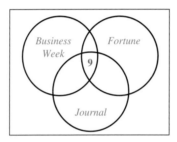

FIGURE 8.14(a)

Solution   Once again, use a Venn diagram to represent the data. Since 9 students read all three publications, begin by placing 9 in the area in Figure 8.14(a) that belongs to all three regions.

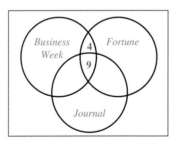

FIGURE 8.14(b)

Of the 13 students who read *Business Week* and *Fortune*, 9 also read the *Journal*. Therefore, only $13 - 9 = 4$ students read just *Business Week* and *Fortune*. So place a 4 in the region common only to *Business Week* and *Fortune* readers, as in Figure 8.14(b).

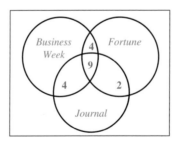

FIGURE 8.14(c)

In the same way, place a 4 in the region of Figure 8.14(c) common only to *Business Week* and the *Journal* readers, and 2 in the region common only to *Fortune* and the *Journal* readers.

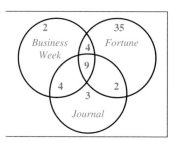

FIGURE 8.14(d)

The data shows that 19 students read *Business Week*. However, $4 + 9 + 4 = 17$ readers have already been placed in the *Business Week* region. The balance of this region in Figure 8.14(d) will contain only $19 - 17 = 2$ students. These 2 students read *Business Week* only—not *Fortune* and not the *Journal*.

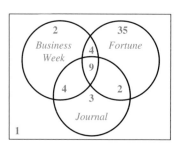

FIGURE 8.14(e)

In the same way, 3 students read only the *Journal* and 35 read only *Fortune*, as shown in Figure 8.14(e).

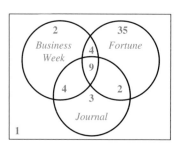

FIGURE 8.14(f)

A total of $2 + 4 + 3 + 4 + 9 + 2 + 35 = 59$ students are placed in the various regions of Figure 8.14(e). Since 60 students were surveyed, $60 - 59 = 1$ student reads none of the three publications, and so 1 is placed outside the other regions in Figure 8.14(f).

Figure 8.14(f) can now be used to answer the questions asked at the beginning of this example:

(a) Only 1 student reads none of the publications.

(b) There are 35 students who read only *Fortune*.

(c) The overlap of the regions representing *Business Week* and the *Journal* shows that 4 students read *Business Week* and the *Journal*, but not *Fortune*. ✓

✓ **Checkpoint 4**

In Example 3, how many students read exactly,

(a) 1 of the publications?

(b) 2 of the publications?

Answers: See page 485.

Example 4 **Health** Mark McCloney, M.D., saw 100 patients exhibiting flu symptoms such as fever, chills, and headache. Dr. McCloney reported the following information on patients exhibiting symptoms:

Of the 100 patients,

74 reported a fever;

72 reported chills;

67 reported a headache;

55 reported both a fever and chills;

47 reported both a fever and a headache;

49 reported both chills and a headache;

35 reported all three;

3 thought they had the flu, but did not report fever, chills, or headache.

Create a Venn Diagram to represent this data. It should show the number of people in each region.

Solution Begin with the 35 patients who reported all three symptoms. This leaves $55 - 35 = 20$ who reported fever and chills, but not headache; $47 - 35 = 12$ who reported fever and headache, but not chills; and $49 - 35 = 14$ who reported chills and headache, but not fever. With this information, we have $74 - (35 + 20 + 12) = 7$ who reported fever alone; $72 - (35 + 20 + 14) = 3$ with chills alone; and $67 - (35 + 12 + 14) = 6$ with headache alone. The remaining 3 patients who thought they had the flu, but did not report fever, chills, or headache are denoted outside the 3 circles. See Figure 8.15. ✓

✓**Checkpoint 5**

In Example 4, suppose 75 patients reported a fever and only 2 thought they had the flu, but did not report fever, chills, or headache. Then how many

(a) reported only a fever?

(b) reported a fever or chills?

(c) reported a fever, chills, or headache?

Answers: See page 485.

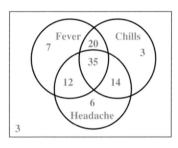

FIGURE 8.15

📄 **NOTE** In all the preceding examples, we started in the innermost region with the intersection of the categories. This is usually the best way to begin solving problems of this type.

We use the symbol $n(A)$ to denote the *number* of elements in A. For instance, if $A = \{w, x, y, z\}$, then $n(A) = 4$. Next, we prove the following useful fact.

> **Addition Rule for Counting**
> $$n(A \cup B) = n(A) + n(B) - n(A \cap B).$$

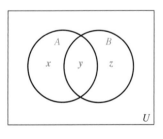

FIGURE 8.16

For example, if $A = \{r, s, t, u, v\}$ and $B = \{r, t, w\}$, then $A \cap B = \{r, t\}$, so that $n(A) = 5$, $n(B) = 3$, and $n(A \cap B) = 2$. By the formula in the box, $n(A \cup B) = 5 + 3 - 2 = 6$, which is certainly true, since $A \cup B = \{r, s, t, u, v, w\}$.

Here is a proof of the statement in the box: Let x be the number of elements in A that are not in B, y be the number of elements in $A \cap B$, and z be the number of elements in B that are not in A, as indicated in Figure 8.16. That diagram shows that $n(A \cup B) = x + y + z$. It also shows that $n(A) = x + y$ and $n(B) = y + z$, so that

$$n(A) + n(B) - n(A \cap B) = (x + y) + (z + y) - y$$
$$= x + y + z$$
$$= n(A \cup B).$$

Example 5 A group of 10 students meets to plan a school function. All are majoring in accounting or economics or both. Five of the students are economics majors, and 7 are majors in accounting. How many major in both subjects?

Solution Let A represent the set of accounting majors and B represent the set of economics majors. Use the union rule, with $n(A) = 5$, $n(B) = 7$, and $n(A \cup B) = 10$. We must find $n(A \cap B)$:

$$n(A \cup B) = n(A) + n(B) - n(A \cap B)$$
$$10 = 5 + 7 - n(A \cap B).$$

So,

$$n(A \cap B) = 5 + 7 - 10 = 2. \quad \boxed{6} ✓$$

✔ **Checkpoint 6**

If $n(A) = 10$, $n(B) = 7$, and $n(A \cap B) = 3$, find $n(A \cup B)$.

Answer: See page 485.

Example 6 **Natural Science** The following table gives the amounts (in thousand short tons) of air pollutant emission in 2007 for highway vehicles (cars, trucks, etc., denoted A) and off-highway machines (farm equipment, construction equipment, industrial machinery, etc., denoted B), where the air pollutants are sulfur dioxide (denoted C), volatile organic compounds (denoted D), carbon monoxide (denoted E), and nitrogen oxides (denoted F).*

		C Sulfur Dioxide	D Volatile Organic Compounds	E Carbon Monoxide	F Nitrogen Oxides	Total
A	**Highway**	91	3602	41,610	5563	50,866
B	**Off Highway**	396	2650	18,762	4164	25,972
	Total	487	6252	60,372	9727	76,838

Find the number of short tons of pollutants in the given sets.

(a) $A \cap E$

Solution The set $A \cap E$ consists of all pollutants that are generated by highway vehicles *and* that are carbon monoxide. From the table, we see there were 41,610 thousand such short tons.

(b) $A \cup E$

Solution The set $A \cup E$ consists of all pollutants that are generated from highway vehicles *or* that are carbon monoxide. Using the addition rule for

---

*Statistical Abstract of the United States: 2009.

counting, we have $n(A \cup E) = n(A) + n(E) - n(A \cap E)$. From the table, we have $n(A) = 50,866$ and $n(E) = 60,372$. From part (a), we have $n(A \cap E) = 41,610$. Thus,

$$n(A \cup E) = n(A) + n(E) - n(A \cap E)$$
$$= 50,866 + 60,372 - 41,610$$
$$= 69,628 \text{ thousand short tons.}$$

✓**Checkpoint 7**

Refer to Example 6 and find the number of short tons in each set.

(a) $B \cup C$

(b) $(B \cap D) \cup C'$

Answers: See page 485.

(c) $(E \cup F) \cap A'$

Solution Begin with the set $E \cup F$, which contains all the carbon monoxide and nitrogen oxide pollutants. Of this set, take those amounts that are *not* for highway vehicles, for a total of $18,762 + 4164 = 22,926$ thousand short tons. ✓

8.2 ▶ Exercises

Sketch a Venn diagram like the one shown, and use shading to show each of the given sets. (See Example 1.)

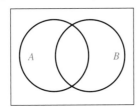

1. $A \cap B'$ **2.** $A \cup B'$ **3.** $B' \cup A'$ **4.** $A' \cap B'$
5. $B' \cup (A \cap B')$ **6.** $(A \cap B) \cup A'$
7. U' **8.** $\varnothing'$
9. Three sets divide the universal set into at most _____ regions.
10. What does the notation $n(A)$ represent?

Sketch a Venn diagram like the one shown, and use shading to show each of the given sets. (See Example 2.)

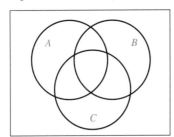

11. $(A \cap C') \cup B$ **12.** $A \cap (B \cup C')$
13. $A' \cap (B \cap C)$ **14.** $(A' \cap B') \cap C$
15. $(A \cap B') \cup C$ **16.** $(A \cap B') \cap C$

Use Venn diagrams to answer the given questions. (See Examples 2 and 4.)

17. Social Science In 2007, the percentage of children under 18 years of age who lived with both parents was 70.7, the percentage of children under 18 years of age who lived only with their mother was 22.6, and the percentage of children under 18 years of age who lived with neither parent was 3.5.* What percentage of children under age 18 lived with their father only?

18. Business In 2007, the total number of union members (in thousands) age 16 and above was 129,766. There were 29,409 members ages 25 to 34 years old, 30,296 ages 35 to 44 years old, 29,731 members ages 45 to 54 years old, 16,752 members ages 55 to 64 years old, and 4183 members ages 65 years and over.* How many union members were in the age group 16 to 24?

19. Business The human resources director for a commercial real estate company received the following numbers of applications from people with the given information:

66 with sales experience;

40 with a college degree;

23 with a real estate license;

26 with sales experience and a college degree;

16 with sales experience and a real estate license;

15 with a college degree and a real estate license;

11 with sales experience, a college degree, and a real estate license;

Statistical Abstract of the United States: 2009.

22 with neither sales experience, a college degree, nor a real estate license.

(a) How many applicants were there?
(b) How many applicants did not have sales experience?
(c) How many had sales experience and a college degree, but not a real estate license?
(d) How many had only a real estate license?

20. **Business**   A pet store keeps track of the purchases of customers over a four-hour period. The store manager classifies purchases as containing a dog product, a cat product, a fish product, or a product for a different kind of pet. She found that:

83 customers purchased a dog product;

101 customers purchased a cat product;

22 customers purchased a fish product;

31 customers purchased a dog and a cat product;

8 customers purchased a dog and a fish product;

10 customers purchased a cat and a fish product;

6 customers purchased a dog, a cat, and a fish product;

34 customers purchased a product for a pet other than a dog, cat, or fish.

(a) How many purchases were for a dog product only?
(b) How many purchases were for a cat product only?
(c) How many purchases were for a dog or fish product?
(d) How many purchases were there in total?

21. **Natural Science**   A marine biologist surveys people who fish on Lake Erie and caught at least one fish to determine whether they had caught a walleye, a smallmouth bass, or a yellow perch in the last year. He finds:

124 caught at least one walleye;

133 caught at least one smallmouth bass;

146 caught at least one yellow perch;

75 caught at least one walleye and at least one smallmouth bass;

67 caught at least one walleye and at least one yellow perch;

79 caught at least one smallmouth bass and at least one yellow perch;

45 caught all three.

(a) Find the total number of people surveyed.
(b) How many caught at least one walleye or at least one smallmouth bass?
(c) How many caught only walleye?

22. **Health**   Human blood can contain either no antigens, the A antigen, the B antigen, or both the A and B antigens. A third antigen, called the Rh antigen, is important in human reproduction and, like the A and B antigens, may or may not be present in an individual. Blood is called

type A positive if the individual has the A and Rh antigens, but not the B antigen. A person having only the A and B antigens is said to have type AB-negative blood. A person having only the Rh antigen has type O-positive blood. Other blood types are defined in a similar manner. Identify the blood type of the individuals in regions (a)–(g) of the Venn diagram.

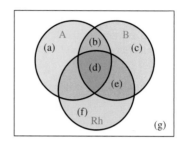

23. **Natural Science**   Use the diagram from Exercise 22. In a certain hospital, the following data was recorded:

25 patients had the A antigen;

17 had the A and B antigens;

27 had the B antigen;

22 had the B and Rh antigens;

30 had the Rh antigen;

12 had none of the antigens;

16 had the A and Rh antigens;

15 had all three antigens.

How many patients
(a) were represented?
(b) had exactly one antigen?
(c) had exactly two antigens?
(d) had O-positive blood?
(e) had AB-positive blood?
(f) had B-negative blood?
(g) had O-negative blood?
(h) had A-positive blood?

24. **Business**   In reviewing the portfolios of 365 of its clients, a mutual funds company categorized whether the clients were invested in international stock funds, domestic stock funds, or bond funds. It found that,

125 were invested in domestic stocks, international stocks, and bond funds;

145 were invested in domestic stocks and bond funds;

300 were invested in domestic stocks;

200 were invested in international and domestic stocks;

18 were invested in international stocks and bond funds, but not domestic stocks;

35 were invested in bonds, but not in international or domestic stocks;

87 were invested in international stocks, but not in bond funds.

(a) How many were invested in international stocks?

(b) How many were invested in bonds, but not international stocks?

(c) How many were not invested in bonds?

(d) How many were invested in international or domestic stocks?

25. Social Science The table lists the cross-classification of marital status and sex for the adults chosen for the 2006 General Social Survey (GSS).*

Marital Status	Male (M)	Female (F)
Married (A)	1018	1152
Widowed (B)	65	301
Divorced (C)	320	412
Separated (D)	61	95
Never Married (E)	534	546

Using the letters given in the table, find the number of respondents in each set.

(a) $A \cap M$

(b) $C \cap (F \cup M)$

(c) $D \cup F$

(d) $B' \cap E'$

26. Social Science The number of active-duty service-women in different segments of the U.S. armed forces as of September 2006 is given in the table:†

	Army (A)	Air Force (B)	Navy (C)	Marines (D)
Officers (O)	12,459	12,836	7649	1101
Enlisted (E)	57,825	54,957	42,400	10,049

Use this information and the letters given to find the number of female military personnel in each of the given sets.

(a) $A \cup B$

(b) $E \cup (C \cup D)$

(c) $O' \cap B'$

27. Business The table gives the number (rounded to the nearest thousand) of manufacturing firms (A) and construction firms (B) cross-classified by level of income and industry type.‡

Industry Type	Under $1 million ($C$)	$1 to $4.9 million ($D$)	$5 to $9.9 million ($E$)
A	165,000	70,000	18,000
B	573,000	137,000	21,000

Industry Type	$10 to $49.9 million ($F$)	More than $50 million ($G$)
A	18,000	7000
B	18,000	3000

Using the letters given in the table, find the number of firms in each of the given sets.

(a) $C \cup D$

(b) $B \cap G$

(c) $A \cap (E \cup F)$

(d) $(F \cup G)'$

(e) $A' \cap C'$

28. Health The top four causes of death in the United States for persons ages 16–34 are motor vehicle crash, homicide, suicide, and accidental poisoning. The table gives the numbers of these deaths in 2005:*

Cause of Death	Age Group		
	16–20 (A)	21–24 (B)	25–34 (C)
Motor Vehicle Crash (D)	5665	4587	7047
Homicide (E)	2571	2717	4752
Suicide (F)	1905	2120	4990
Accidental Poisoning (G)	896	1553	4386

Using the letters given in the table, find the number of deaths in each of the given sets.

(a) $A \cup B$

(b) $D \cup E$

(c) $E \cap B$

(d) $D' \cap C$

29. Restate the union rule in words.

Use Venn diagrams to answer the given questions. (See Example 5.)

30. If $n(A) = 5$, $n(B) = 8$, and $n(A \cap B) = 4$, what is $n(A \cup B)$?

31. If $n(A) = 12$, $n(B) = 27$, and $n(A \cup B) = 30$, what is $n(A \cap B)$?

32. Suppose $n(B) = 7$, $n(A \cap B) = 3$, and $n(A \cup B) = 20$. What is $n(A)$?

33. Suppose $n(A \cap B) = 5$, $n(A \cup B) = 35$, and $n(A) = 13$. What is $n(B)$?

*www.norc.org/GSS&Website/.

†www.infoplease.com.

‡*Statistical Abstract of the United States*: 2009.

*www.nhtsa.gov.

Draw a Venn diagram and use the given information to fill in the number of elements for each region.

34. $n(U) = 48, n(A) = 26, n(A \cap B) = 12, n(B') = 30$

35. $n(A) = 28, n(B) = 12, n(A \cup B) = 30, n(A') = 19$

36. $n(A \cup B) = 17,\qquad n(A \cap B) = 3,\qquad n(A) = 8,$
$n(A' \cup B') = 21$

37. $n(A') = 28,\qquad n(B) = 25,\qquad n(A' \cup B') = 45,$
$n(A \cap B) = 12$

38. $n(A) = 28,\quad n(B) = 34,\quad n(C) = 25,\quad n(A \cap B) = 14,$
$n(B \cap C) = 15,\quad n(A \cap C) = 11,\quad n(A \cap B \cap C) = 9,$
$n(U) = 59$

39. $n(A) = 54,\qquad n(A \cap B) = 22,\qquad n(A \cup B) = 85,$
$n(A \cap B \cap C) = 4,\quad n(A \cap C) = 15,\quad n(B \cap C) = 16,$
$n(C) = 44, n(B') = 63$

In Exercises 40–43, show that the statements are true by drawing Venn diagrams and shading the regions representing the sets on each side of the equals signs.*

40. $(A \cup B)' = A' \cap B'$ **41.** $(A \cap B)' = A' \cup B'$

42. $A \cap (B \cup C) = (A \cap B) \cup (A \cap C)$

43. $A \cup (B \cap C) = (A \cup B) \cap (A \cup C)$

44. Explain in words the statement about sets in question 40.

45. Explain in words the statement about sets in question 41.

46. Explain in words the statement about sets in question 42.

47. Explain in words the statement about sets in question 43.

---

*The statements in Exercises 40 and 41 are known as De Morgan's laws. They are named for the English mathematician Augustus De Morgan (1806–71).

✓ Checkpoint Answers

1. (a)   **(b)**

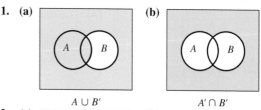

$A \cup B'$ $A' \cap B'$

2. (a)   **(b)**

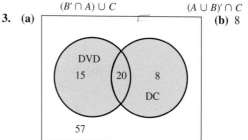

$(B' \cap A) \cup C$ $(A \cup B)' \cap C$

3. (a)   **(b)** 8

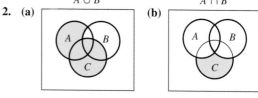

4. (a) 40 **(b)** 10   **5. (a)** 8 **(b)** 92 **(c)** 98

6. 14

7. (a) 26,063 thousand short tons
   (b) 76,351 thousand short tons

8.3 ▶ Introduction to Probability

If you go to a pizzeria and order two large pizzas at $14.99 each, you can easily find the *exact* price of your purchase: $29.98. For the manager at the pizzeria, however, it is impossible to predict the *exact* number of pizzas to be purchased daily. The number of pizzas purchased during a day is *random*: The quantity cannot be predicted exactly. A great many problems that come up in applications of mathematics involve random phenomena—phenomena for which exact prediction is impossible. The best that we can do is determine the *probability* of the possible outcomes.

RANDOM EXPERIMENTS AND SAMPLE SPACES

A **random experiment** (sometimes called a random phenomenon) has outcomes that we cannot predict, but that nonetheless have a regular distribution in a large number of repetitions. We call a repetition from a random experiment a **trial**. The possible results of each trial are called **outcomes**. For instance, when we flip a coin, the outcomes are heads and tails. We do not know whether a particular flip will yield heads or tails, but we do know that if we flip the coin a large a number of times, about half the flips will be heads and half will be tails. Each flip of the coin is a trial. The **sample space** (denoted by S) for a random experiment is the set of all possible outcomes. For the coin flipping, the sample space is

$$S = \{\text{heads, tails}\}.$$

Example 1 Give the sample space for each random experiment.

(a) Use the spinner in Figure 8.17.

FIGURE 8.17

Solution The 7 outcomes are 1, 2, 3, . . . 7, so the sample space is

$$\{1, 2, 3, 4, 5, 6, 7\}.$$

(b) For the purposes of a public opinion poll, respondents are classified as young, middle aged, or senior and as male or female.

Solution A sample space for this poll could be written as a set of ordered pairs:

{(young, male), (young, female), (middle aged, male),

(middle aged, female), (senior, male), (senior, female)}.

(c) An experiment consists of studying the numbers of boys and girls in families with exactly 3 children. Let *b* represent *boy* and *g* represent *girl*.

Solution For this experiment, drawing a tree diagram can be helpful. First, we draw two starting branches to the left to indicate that the first child can be either a boy or a girl. From each of those outcomes, we draw two branches to indicate that the second child can be either a boy or girl. Last, we draw two branches from each of those outcomes to indicate that after the second child, the third child can be either a boy or a girl. The result is the tree in Figure 8.18.

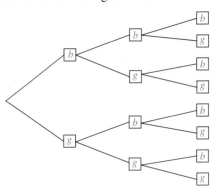

FIGURE 8.18

We can now easily list the members of the sample space *S*. We follow the eight paths of the branches to yield

$$S = \{bbb, bbg, bgb, bgg, gbb, gbg, ggb, ggg\}.$$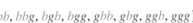

✓ Checkpoint 1

Draw a tree diagram for the random experiment of flipping a coin two times, and determine the sample space.

Answer: See page 495.

EVENTS

An **event** is an outcome, or a set of outcomes, of a random experiment. Thus, an event is a subset of the sample space. For example, if the sample space for tossing a coin is $S = \{h, t\}$, then one event is $E = \{h\}$, which represents the outcome "heads."

An ordinary die is a cube whose six different faces show the following numbers of dots: 1, 2, 3, 4, 5, and 6. If the die is fair (not "loaded" to favor certain faces over others), then any one of the faces is equally likely to come up when the die is rolled. The sample space for the experiment of rolling a single fair die is $S = \{1, 2, 3, 4, 5, 6\}$. Some possible events are as follows:

The die shows an even number: $E_1 = \{2, 4, 6\}$.

The die shows a 1: $E_2 = \{1\}$.

The die shows a number less than 5: $E_3 = \{1, 2, 3, 4\}$.

The die shows a multiple of 3: $E_4 = \{3, 6\}$.

Example 2   For the sample space S in Example 1(c) on the previous page, write the given events in set notation.

(a) Event H: The family has exactly two girls.

Solution Families with three children can have exactly two girls with either bgg, gbg, or ggb, so that event H is

$$H = \{bgg, gbg, ggb\}.$$

(b) Event K: The three children are the same sex.

Solution Two outcomes satisfy this condition: all boys and all girls, or

$$K = \{bbb, ggg\}.$$

(c) Event J: The family has three girls.

Solution Only ggg satisfies this condition, so

$$J = \{ggg\}. \quad ✔2$$

✔**Checkpoint 2**

Suppose a die is tossed. Write the given events in set notation.

(a) The number showing is less than 3.

(b) The number showing is 5.

(c) The number showing is 8.

Answers: See page 495.

If an event E equals the sample space S, then E is a **certain event**. If event $E = \varnothing$, then E is an **impossible event**.

Example 3   Suppose a fair die is rolled. Then the sample space is $\{1, 2, 3, 4, 5, 6\}$. Find the requested events.

(a) The event "the die shows a 4."

Solution $\{4\}$.

(b) The event "the number showing is less than 10."

Solution The event is the entire sample space $\{1, 2, 3, 4, 5, 6\}$. This event is a certain event; if a die is rolled, the number showing (either 1, 2, 3, 4, 5, or 6) must be less than 10.

(c) The event "the die shows a 7."

Solution The empty set, ∅; this is an impossible event.

✓ **Checkpoint 3**

Which of the events listed in Checkpoint 2 is

(a) certain?

(b) impossible?

Answers: See page 495.

Since events are sets, we can use set operations to find unions, intersections, and complements of events. Here is a summary of the set operations for events.

> **Set Operations for Events**
>
> Let E and F be events for a sample space S. Then
>
> $E \cap F$ occurs when both E **and** F occur;
> $E \cup F$ occurs when E **or** F **or both** occur;
> E' occurs when E does **not** occur.

Example 4 A study of college students grouped the students into various categories that can be interpreted as events when a student is selected at random. Consider the following events:

  E: The student is under 20 years old;
  F: The student is male;
  G: The student is a business major.

Describe each of the following events in words.

(a) E'

Solution E' is the event that the student is 20 years old or older.

(b) $F' \cap G$

Solution $F' \cap G$ is the event that the student is not male and the student is a business major—that is, the student is a female business major.

(c) $E' \cup G$

Solution $E' \cup G$ is the event that the student is 20 or over or is a business major. Note that this event includes all students 20 or over, regardless of major. ✓

✓ **Checkpoint 4**

Write the set notation for the given events for the experiment of rolling a fair die if $E = \{1, 3\}$ and $F = \{2, 3, 4, 5\}$.

(a) $E \cap F$

(b) $E \cup F$

(c) E'

Answers: See page 495.

Two events that cannot both occur at the same time, such as getting both a head and a tail on the same toss of a coin, are called **disjoint events**. (Disjoint events are sometimes referred to as *mutually exclusive events*.)

> **Disjoint Events**
>
> Events E and F are disjoint events if $E \cap F = \varnothing$.

For any event E, E and E' are disjoint events.

Example 5   Let $S = \{1, 2, 3, 4, 5, 6\}$, the sample space for tossing a die. Let $E = \{4, 5, 6\}$, and let $G = \{1, 2\}$. Are E and G disjoint events?

Solution Yes, because they have no outcomes in common; $E \cap G = \varnothing$. See Figure 8.19. ✓

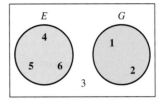

FIGURE 8.19

✔**Checkpoint 5**

In Example 5, let $F = \{2, 4, 6\}$, $K = \{1, 3, 5\}$, and G remain the same. Are the given events disjoint?

(a) F and K

(b) F and G

Answers: See page 495.

PROBABILITY

For sample spaces with *equally likely* outcomes, the probability of an event is defined as follows.

> ### Basic Probability Principle
>
> Let S be a sample space of equally likely outcomes, and let event E be a subset of S. Then the **probability that event E occurs** is
>
> $$P(E) = \frac{n(E)}{n(S)}.$$

By this definition, the **probability of an event** is a number that indicates the relative likelihood of the event.

⚠ **CAUTION** The basic probability principle applies only when the outcomes are equally likely.

Example 6   Suppose a single fair die is rolled, with the sample space $S = \{1, 2, 3, 4, 5, 6\}$. Give the probability of each of the following events.

(a) E: The die shows an even number.

Solution Here, $E = \{2, 4, 6\}$, a set with three elements. Because S contains six elements,

$$P(E) = \frac{3}{6} = \frac{1}{2}.$$

(b) F: The die shows a number less than 10.

Solution Event F is a certain event, with

$$F = \{1, 2, 3, 4, 5, 6\},$$

so that

$$P(F) = \frac{6}{6} = 1.$$

(c) *G*: The die shows an 8.

Solution This event is impossible, so

$$P(G) = \frac{0}{6} = 0. \quad \overset{6}{\checkmark}$$

✓ **Checkpoint 6**

A fair die is rolled. Find the probability of rolling

(a) an odd number;

(b) 2, 4, 5, or 6;

(c) a number greater than 5;

(d) the number 7.

Answers: See page 495.

A standard deck of 52 cards has four suits—hearts (♥), clubs (♣), diamonds (♦), and spades (♠)—with 13 cards in each suit. The hearts and diamonds are red, and the spades and clubs are black. Each suit has an ace (A), a king (K), a queen (Q), a jack (J), and cards numbered from 2 to 10. The jack, queen, and king are called face cards and for many purposes can be thought of as having values 11, 12, and 13, respectively. The ace can be thought of as the low card (value 1) or the high card (value 14). See Figure 8.20. We will refer to this standard deck of cards often in our discussion of probability.

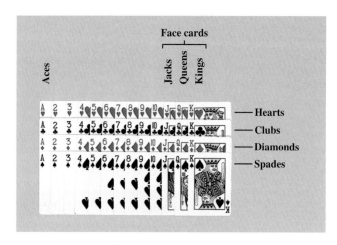

FIGURE 8.20

Example 7 If a single card is drawn at random from a standard, well-shuffled, 52-card deck, find the probability of each of the given events.

(a) Drawing an ace

Solution There are 4 aces in the deck. The event "drawing an ace" is

{heart ace, diamond ace, club ace, spade ace}.

Therefore,

$$P(\text{ace}) = \frac{4}{52} = \frac{1}{13}.$$

(b) Drawing a face card

Solution Since there are 12 face cards,

$$P(\text{face card}) = \frac{12}{52} = \frac{3}{13}.$$

(c) Drawing a spade

Solution The deck contains 13 spades, so

$$P(\text{spade}) = \frac{13}{52} = \frac{1}{4}.$$

(d) Drawing a spade or a heart

Solution Besides the 13 spades, the deck contains 13 hearts, so

$$P(\text{spade or heart}) = \frac{26}{52} = \frac{1}{2}. \checkmark$$

In the preceding examples, the probability of each event was a number between 0 and 1, inclusive. The same thing is true in general. Any event E is a subset of the sample space S, so $0 \leq n(E) \leq n(S)$. Since $P(E) = n(E)/n(S)$, it follows that $0 \leq P(E) \leq 1$.

For any event E,

$$0 \leq P(E) \leq 1.$$

RELATIVE FREQUENCY PROBABILITY

In many real-life problems, it is not possible to establish exact probabilities for events. Instead, useful estimates are often found by drawing on past experience. This approach is called **relative frequency probability**. We calculate our estimate of the probability by determining the percentage of the responses with the characteristic of interest. Estimates based on relative frequency probability are sometimes called *empirical probabilities*. The next example shows one approach to finding such relative frequency probabilities.

Example 8 **Business** The table gives the frequency of households having an average monthly electric bill in various dollar amounts from a portion of the respondents of the 2007 American Community Survey conducted by the U.S. Census Bureau.*

Monthly Electric Bill (Dollars)	Frequency
0–49.99	270
50.00–99.99	253
100.00–149.99	203
150.00–199.99	112
200.00–249.99	71
250.00–299.99	34
300.00 or higher	57

---
*Based on data available at www.census.gov/acs.

✓ Checkpoint 7

A single playing card is drawn at random from an ordinary 52-card deck. Find the probability of drawing

(a) a queen;

(b) a diamond;

(c) a red card.

Answers: See page 495.

(a) Find the relative frequency probability of having a monthly electric bill between $0 and $49.99.

Solution Let us define event A to be the event that a household has an average electric bill between $0 and $49.99. To find the relative frequency probability, we first need to find the total number of respondents. This is $270 + 253 + 203 + 112 + 71 + 34 + 57 = 1000$. We then divide the frequency in the 0–49.99 category (in this case, 270) by 1000 to obtain

$$P(A) = \frac{270}{1000} = .270.$$

(b) Find the relative frequency probability for event B of having an average monthly electric bill $250 or higher.

Solution Here, we add together the number of respondents in the categories 250.00–299.99 and 300 or higher to obtain

$$P(B) = \frac{34 + 57}{1000} = \frac{91}{1000} = .091. \quad \text{8} \checkmark$$

✓**Checkpoint 8**

From the data given in Example 8, find the probability that a household has an electric bill less than $200.

Answer: See page 495.

After conducting a study such as the American Community Survey, we can use the relative frequency probability estimates from the sample to make estimates for the entire population of the United States. We also usually use the term "probability" rather than "relative frequency probability." So we say the probability that a randomly chosen household in the United States has an average monthly electric bill of less than $50 is approximately .270.

A table of frequencies, as in Example 8, sets up a probability distribution; that is, for each possible outcome of an experiment, a number, called the probability of that outcome, is assigned. This assignment may be done in any reasonable way (on a relative frequency basis, as in Example 8, or by theoretical reasoning, as in Example 6), provided that it satisfies the following conditions.

> ### Properties of Probability
>
> Let S be a sample space consisting of n distinct outcomes $s_1, s_2, \ldots, s_n$. An acceptable probability assignment consists of assigning to each outcome s_i a number p_i (the probability of s_i) according to the following rules:
>
> **1.** The probability of each outcome is a number between 0 and 1:
>
> $$0 \leq p_1 \leq 1, \quad 0 \leq p_2 \leq 1, \ldots, \quad 0 \leq p_n \leq 1.$$
>
> **2.** The sum of the probabilities of all possible outcomes is 1:
>
> $$p_1 + p_2 + p_3 + \cdots + p_n = 1.$$

8.3 ▶ Exercises

 1. What is meant by a "fair" coin or die?

2. What is the sample space for a random experiment?

Write sample spaces for the random experiments in Exercises 3–9. (See Example 1.)

3. A month of the year is chosen for a wedding.

4. A day in April is selected for a bicycle race.

5. A student is asked how many points she earned on a recent 80-point test.

6. A person is asked the number of hours (to the nearest hour) he watched television yesterday.

7. The management of an oil company must decide whether to go ahead with a new oil shale plant or to cancel it.

8. A coin is tossed and a die is rolled.

9. The quarter of the year in which a company's profits were highest.

10. Define an event.

11. Define disjoint events in your own words.

Decide whether the events in Exercises 12–17 are disjoint.

12. Owning an SUV and owning a Hummer

13. Wearing a hat and wearing glasses

14. Being married and being under 30 years old

15. Being a doctor and being under 5 years old

16. Being male and being a nurse

17. Being female and being a pilot

For the random experiments in Exercises 18–20, write out an equally likely sample space, and then write the indicated events in set notation. (See Examples 2 and 3.)

18. A marble is drawn at random from a bowl containing 3 yellow, 4 white, and 8 blue marbles.
  (a) A yellow marble is drawn.
  (b) A blue marble is drawn.
  (c) A white marble is drawn.
  (d) A black marble is drawn.

19. Six people live in a dorm suite. Two are to be selected to go to the campus café to pick up a pizza. Of course, no one wants to go, so the six names (Connie, Kate, Lindsey, Jackie, Taisa, and Nicole) are placed in a hat. After the hat is shaken, two names are selected.
  (a) Taisa is selected.
  (b) The two names selected have the same number of letters.

20. An unprepared student takes a three-question true-or-false quiz in which he flips a coin to guess the answers. If the coin is heads, he guesses true, and if the coin is tails, he guesses false.

  (a) The student guesses true twice and guesses false once.
  (b) The student guesses all false.
  (c) The student guesses true once and guesses false twice.

In Exercises 21–23, write out the sample space and assume each outcome is equally likely. Then give the probability of the requested outcomes.

21. In deciding what color and style to paint a room, Greg has narrowed his choices to three colors—forest sage, evergreen whisper, and opaque emerald—and two styles—rag painting and colorwash.
  (a) Greg picks a combination with colorwash.
  (b) Greg picks a combination with opaque emerald or rag painting.

22. Tami goes shopping and sees three kinds of shoes: flats, 2″ heels, and 3″ heels. They come in two shades of beige (light and dark) and black.
  (a) The shoe selected has a heel and is black.
  (b) The shoe selected has no heel and is beige.
  (c) The shoe selected has a heel and is beige.

23. Doug Hall is shopping for a new patio umbrella. There is a 10-foot and a 12-foot model, and each is available in beige, forest green, and rust.
  (a) Doug buys a 12-foot forest green umbrella.
  (b) Doug buys a 10-foot umbrella.
  (c) Doug buys a rust-colored umbrella.

A single fair die is rolled. Find the probabilities of the given events. (See Example 6.)

24. Getting a 5

25. Getting a number less than 4

26. Getting a number greater than 4

27. Getting a 2 or a 5

28. Getting a multiple of 3

29. Getting any number except 3

David Klein wants to adopt a puppy from an animal shelter. At the shelter, he finds eight puppies that he likes: a male and female puppy from each of the four breeds of beagle, boxer, collie, and Labrador. The puppies are each so cute that Dave cannot make up his mind, so he decides to pick the dog randomly.

30. Write the sample space for the outcomes, assuming each outcome is equally likely.

Find the probability that Dave chooses the given puppy.

31. A male dog

32. A collie

33. A female Labrador

34. A beagle or a boxer

35. Anything except a Labrador

Business   *The following table gives the number of fatal work injuries categorized by cause from 2007.**

Cause	Number of Fatalities
Transportation accidents	2234
Assaults and violent acts	839
Contacts with objects and equipment	916
Falls	835
Exposure to harmful substances or environments	488
Fires and explosions	159

Find the probability that a randomly chosen work fatality had the given cause. (See Example 8.)

36. A fall   **37.** Fires and explosions

38. Social Science   Respondents for the 2006 General Social Survey (GSS) indicated the following categorizations pertaining to attendance at religious services:†

Attendance	Number of Respondents
Never	1020
Less than once a year	302
Once a year	571
Several times a year	502
Once a month	308
2–3 times a month	380
Nearly every week	240
Every week	839
More than once a week	329
Don't know/no answer	19
Total	4510

Find the probability that a randomly chosen person in the United States attends religious services
(a) several times a year;
(b) 2–3 times a month;
(c) nearly every week or more frequently.

39. Social Science   Married respondents to the 2006 General Social Survey indicated the age at which they were first married.† The table gives the results:

Age (Years)	Number of Respondents
Less than 18	80
18–19	215
20–21	250
22–23	178
24–25	143
26–30	187
31–40	90
Over 40	25

Find the probability that a person in the United States was
(a) 18 or 19 when he or she was married;
(b) less than 22 when he or she was married;
(c) over 25 when he or she was married.

40. Health   For a medical experiment, people are classified as to whether they smoke, have a family history of heart disease, or are overweight. Define events E, F, and G as follows:

E: person smokes;

F: person has a family history of heart disease;

G: person is overweight.

Describe each of the following events in words.
(a) G'
(b) $F \cap G$
(c) $E \cup G'$

41. Health   Refer to Exercise 40. Describe each of the events that follow in words.
(a) $E \cup F$
(b) $E' \cap F$
(c) $F' \cup G'$

42. Health   The National Health and Nutrition Examination Study (NHANES) is conducted every several years by the U.S. Centers for Disease Control and Prevention. In the 2005–2006 survey of 2683 American women ages 18 to 85, we have the following classifications of height (in inches).*

Height (Inches)	Females
Less than 60	301
60–62.9	846
63–65.9	1040
66–68.9	437
69–71.9	56
72 or more	3

*U.S. Bureau of Labor Statistics.

†Based on data available at www.norc.org/GSS+Website.

*Based on data available at www.cdc.gov/nchs/nhanes.htm.

Find the probability that an American woman is
(a) six feet tall or taller;
(b) less than 63 inches tall;
(c) between 63 and 65.9 inches tall.

An experiment is conducted for which the sample space is $S = \{s_1, s_2, s_3, s_4, s_5\}$. *Which of the probability assignments in Exercises 43–48 is possible for this experiment? If an assignment is not possible, tell why.*

43.

Outcomes	s_1	s_2	s_3	s_4	s_5
Probabilities	.09	.32	.21	.25	.13

44.

Outcomes	s_1	s_2	s_3	s_4	s_5
Probabilities	.92	.03	0	.02	.03

45.

Outcomes	s_1	s_2	s_3	s_4	s_5
Probabilities	1/3	1/4	1/6	1/8	1/10

46.

Outcomes	s_1	s_2	s_3	s_4	s_5
Probabilities	1/5	1/3	1/4	1/5	1/10

47.

Outcomes	s_1	s_2	s_3	s_4	s_5
Probabilities	.64	−.08	.30	.12	.02

48.

Outcomes	s_1	s_2	s_3	s_4	s_5
Probabilities	.05	.35	.5	.2	−.3

✓ **Checkpoint Answers**

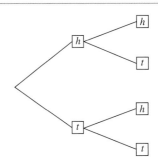

1. $\{hh, ht, th, tt\}$
2. (a) $\{1, 2\}$ (b) $\{5\}$ (c) $\varnothing$
3. (a) None (b) Part (c)
4. (a) $\{3\}$ (b) $\{1, 2, 3, 4, 5\}$ (c) $\{2, 4, 5, 6\}$
5. (a) Yes (b) No
6. (a) 1/2 (b) 2/3 (c) 1/6 (d) 0
7. (a) 1/13 (b) 1/4 (c) 1/2
8. .838

8.4 ▶ Basic Concepts of Probability

We determine the probability of more complex events in this section.

To find the probability of the union of two sets E and F in a sample space S, we use the union rule for counting given in Section 8.2:

$$n(E \cup F) = n(E) + n(F) - n(E \cap F).$$

Dividing both sides by $n(S)$ yields

$$\frac{n(E \cup F)}{n(S)} = \frac{n(E)}{n(S)} + \frac{n(F)}{n(S)} - \frac{n(E \cap F)}{n(S)}$$

$$P(E \cup F) = P(E) + P(F) - P(E \cap F).$$

This discussion is summarized in the next rule.

Addition Rule for Probability

For any events E and F from a sample space S,

$$P(E \cup F) = P(E) + P(F) - P(E \cap F).$$

In words, we have

$$P(E \text{ or } F) = P(E) + P(F) - P(E \text{ and } F).$$

(Although the addition rule applies to any events E and F from any sample space, the derivation we have given is valid only for sample spaces with equally likely simple events.)

Example 1   When playing American roulette, the croupier (attendant) spins a marble that lands in one of the 38 slots in a revolving turntable. The slots are numbered 1 to 36, with two additional slots labeled 0 and 00 that are painted green. Half the remaining slots are colored red, and half are black. (See Figure 8.21)

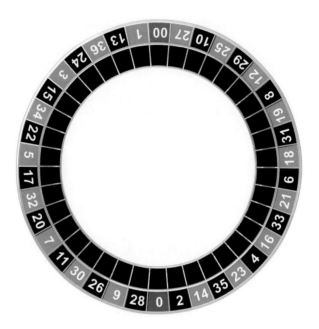

FIGURE 8.21

If we consider the numbers 0 and 00 as neither even nor odd, find the probability that the marble will land in a red or even number.

Solution Let R represent the event of the marble landing in a red slot and E the event of the marble landing in an even-numbered slot. There are 18 slots that are colored red, so $P(R) = 18/38$. There are also 18 even numbers between 1 and 36, so $P(E) = 18/38$. In order to use the addition rule, we also need to know the number of slots that are red and even numbered. Looking at Figure 8.21, we can see there are 8 such slots, which implies that $P(R \cap E) = 8/38$. Using the addition rule, we find the probability that the marble will land in a slot that is red or even numbered is

$$P(R \cup E) = P(R) + P(E) - P(R \cap E)$$
$$= \frac{18}{38} + \frac{18}{38} - \frac{8}{38} = \frac{28}{38} = \frac{14}{19}. \quad ✓$$

✓Checkpoint 1

If an American roulette wheel is spun, find the probability of the marble landing in a black slot or a slot whose number is divisible by 3.

Answer: See page 506.

ⓘ **CAUTION** Recall from Section 8.1 that the word "or" always indicates use of the addition rule.

Example 2 Suppose two fair dice (plural of *die*) are rolled. Find each of the given probabilities.

(a) The first die shows a 2 or the sum of the results is 6 or 7.

Solution The sample space for the throw of two dice is shown in Figure 8.22, where 1-1 represents the event "the first die shows a 1 and the second die shows a 1," 1-2 represents the event "the first die shows a 1 and the second die shows a 2," and so on. Let A represent the event "the first die shows a 2" and B represent the event "the sum of the results is 6 or 7." These events are indicated in color in Figure 8.22. From the diagram, event A has 6 elements, B has 11 elements, and the sample space has 36 elements. Thus,

$$P(A) = \frac{6}{36}, \quad P(B) = \frac{11}{36}, \quad \text{and} \quad P(A \cap B) = \frac{2}{36}.$$

By the addition rule,

$$P(A \cup B) = P(A) + P(B) - P(A \cap B),$$

$$P(A \cup B) = \frac{6}{36} + \frac{11}{36} - \frac{2}{36} = \frac{15}{36} = \frac{5}{12}.$$

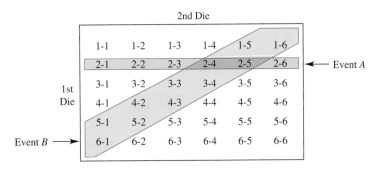

FIGURE 8.22

(b) The sum is 11 or the second die shows a 5.

Solution $P(\text{sum is } 11) = 2/36$, $P(\text{second die shows } 5) = 6/36$, and $P(\text{sum is 11 and second die shows } 5) = 1/36$, so

$$P(\text{sum is 11 or second die shows 5}) = \frac{2}{36} + \frac{6}{36} - \frac{1}{36} = \frac{7}{36}. \quad \boxed{2} \checkmark$$

If events E and F are disjoint, then $E \cap F = \varnothing$ by definition; hence, $P(E \cap F) = 0$. Applying the addition rule yields the useful fact that follows.

Addition Rule for Disjoint Events

For disjoint events E and F,

$$P(E \cup F) = P(E) + P(F).$$

✔**Checkpoint 2**

In the random experiment of Example 2, find the given probabilities.

(a) The sum is 5 or the second die shows a 3.

(b) Both dice show the same number, or the sum is at least 11.

Answers: See page 506.

Example 3 Assume that the probability of a couple having a baby boy is the same as the probability of the couple having a baby girl. If the couple has 3 children, find the probability that at least 2 of them are girls.

Solution The event of having at least 2 girls is the union of the disjoint events $E = $ "the family has exactly 2 girls" and $F = $ "the family has exactly 3 girls." Using the equally likely sample space

$$\{ggg, ggb, gbg, bgg, gbb, bgb, bbg, bbb\},$$

where b represents a boy and g represents a girl, we see that $P(\text{2 girls}) = 3/8$ and $P(\text{3 girls}) = 1/8$. Therefore,

$$P(\text{at least 2 girls}) = P(\text{2 girls}) + P(\text{3 girls})$$
$$= \frac{3}{8} + \frac{1}{8} = \frac{1}{2}. \quad \boxed{3} \checkmark$$

✓ **Checkpoint 3**

In Example 3, find the probability of having no more than 2 girls.

Answer: See page 506.

By definition of E', for any event E from a sample space S,

$$E \cup E' = S \quad \text{and} \quad E \cap E' = \varnothing.$$

Because $E \cap E' = \varnothing$, events E and E' are disjoint, so that

$$P(E \cup E') = P(E) + P(E').$$

However, $E \cup E' = S$, the sample space, and $P(S) = 1$. Thus,

$$P(E \cup E') = P(E) + P(E') = 1.$$

Rearranging these terms gives the following useful rule.

Complement Rule

For any event E,

$$P(E') = 1 - P(E) \quad \text{and} \quad P(E) = 1 - P(E').$$

Example 4 If a fair die is rolled, what is the probability that any number but 5 will come up?

Solution If E is the event that 5 comes up, then E' is the event that any number but 5 comes up. $P(E) = 1/6$, so we have $P(E') = 1 - 1/6 = 5/6$. $\quad \boxed{4} \checkmark$

✓ **Checkpoint 4**

(a) Let $P(K) = 2/3$. Find $P(K')$.

(b) If $P(X') = 3/4$, find $P(X)$.

Answers: See page 506.

Example 5 If two fair dice are rolled, find the probability that the sum of the numbers showing is greater than 3.

Solution To calculate this probability directly, we must find each of the probabilities that the sum is 4, 5, 6, 7, 8, 9, 10, 11, and 12 and then add them. It is much simpler to first find the probability of the complement, the event that the sum is less than or equal to 3:

$$P(\text{sum} \leq 3) = P(\text{sum is } 2) + P(\text{sum is } 3)$$

$$= \frac{1}{36} + \frac{2}{36} = \frac{3}{36} = \frac{1}{12}.$$

Now use the fact that $P(E) = 1 - P(E')$ to get

$$P(\text{sum} > 3) = 1 - P(\text{sum} \leq 3) = 1 - \frac{1}{12} = \frac{11}{12}. \; \overset{5}{\checkmark}$$

✓**Checkpoint 5**

In Example 5, find the probability that the sum of the numbers rolled is at least 5.

Answer: See page 506.

ODDS

Sometimes probability statements are given in terms of **odds**: a comparison of $P(E)$ with $P(E')$. For example, suppose $P(E) = \frac{4}{5}$. Then $P(E') = 1 - \frac{4}{5} = \frac{1}{5}$. These probabilities predict that E will occur 4 out of 5 times and E' will occur 1 out of 5 times. Then we say that the **odds in favor** of E are 4 to 1, or 4:1.

> ### Odds
>
> The **odds in favor** of an event E are defined as the ratio of $P(E)$ to $P(E')$, or
>
> $$\frac{P(E)}{P(E')}, \qquad P(E') \neq 0.$$

Example 6 Suppose the weather forecaster says that the probability of rain tomorrow is $1/3$. Find the odds in favor of rain tomorrow.

Solution Let E be the event "rain tomorrow." Then E' is the event "no rain tomorrow." Since $P(E) = 1/3$, $P(E') = 2/3$. By the definition of odds, the odds in favor of rain are

$$\frac{1/3}{2/3} = \frac{1}{2}, \quad \text{written 1 to 2 or 1:2.}$$

On the other hand, the odds that it will *not* rain, or the odds *against* rain, are

$$\frac{2/3}{1/3} = \frac{2}{1}, \quad \text{written 2 to 1.}$$

If the odds in favor of an event are, say, 3 to 5, then the probability of the event is $3/8$, while the probability of the complement of the event is $5/8$. (Odds of 3 to 5 indicate 3 outcomes in favor of the event out of a total of 8 outcomes.) The above example suggests the following generalization:

If the odds favoring event E are m to n, then

$$P(E) = \frac{m}{m + n} \quad \text{and} \quad P(E') = \frac{n}{m + n}.$$

Example 7 Often, weather forecasters give probability in terms of percentage. Suppose the weather forecaster says that there is a 40% chance that it will snow tomorrow. Find the odds of snow tomorrow.

Solution In this case, we can let E be the event "snow tomorrow." Then E' is the event "no snow tomorrow." Now, we have $P(E) = .4 = 4/10$ and $P(E') = .6 = 6/10$. By the definition of odds in favor, the odds in favor of snow are

$$\frac{4/10}{6/10} = \frac{4}{6} = \frac{2}{3}, \qquad \text{written 2 to 3 or 2:3.}$$

It is important to put the final fraction into lowest terms in order to communicate the odds. ✓ 6

Example 8 The odds that a particular bid will be the low bid are 4 to 5.

(a) Find the probability that the bid will be the low bid.

Solution Odds of 4 to 5 show 4 favorable chances out of $4 + 5 = 9$ chances altogether, so

$$P(\text{bid will be low bid}) = \frac{4}{4 + 5} = \frac{4}{9}.$$

(b) Find the odds against that bid being the low bid.

Solution There is a 5/9 chance that the bid will not be the low bid, so the odds against a low bid are

$$\frac{P(\text{bid will not be low})}{P(\text{bid will be low})} = \frac{5/9}{4/9} = \frac{5}{4},$$

or 5:4. ✓ 7

APPLICATIONS

Example 9 **Business** Let A represent living in a two-bedroom dwelling and B represent paying less than $100 a month for the average electric bill. From the 2007 American Community Survey,* we have the following probabilities:

$$P(A) = .267, \quad P(B) = .510, \quad \text{and} \quad P(A \cap B) = .173.$$

(a) Find the probability that an American does *not* live in a two-bedroom dwelling and pays *$100 or more* a month in electricity.

Solution Place the given information on a Venn diagram, starting with .173 in the intersection of the regions A and B. (See Figure 8.23.) As stated earlier, event A has probability .267. Since .173 has already been placed inside the intersection of A and B,

$$.267 - .173 = .094$$

goes inside region A, but outside the intersection of A and B. In the same way,

$$.510 - .173 = .337$$

goes inside region B, but outside the overlap.

*www.census.gov/acs.

✓ Checkpoint 6

In Example 7, suppose $P(E) = 9/10$. Find the odds

(a) in favor of E;

(b) against E.

Suppose the chance of snow is 80%. Find the odds

(c) in favor of snow;

(d) against snow.

Answers: See page 506.

✓ Checkpoint 7

If the odds in favor of event E are 1 to 5, find

(a) $P(E)$;

(b) $P(E')$.

Answers: See page 506.

The event we want is $A' \cap B'$. From the Venn diagram in Figure 8.23, the labeled regions have a total probability of

$$.094 + .173 + .337 = .604.$$

Since the entire region of the Venn diagram must have probability 1, the region outside A and B, namely $A' \cap B'$, has probability

$$1 - .604 = .396.$$

So the probability that an American does not live in a two-bedroom dwelling and pays $100 or more a month for electricity is .396.

(b) Find the probability that an American does not live in a two-bedroom dwelling *or* pays $100 or more a month for electricity.

Solution The corresponding region $A' \cup B'$, from Figure 8.23, has probability

$$.396 + .094 + .337 = .827. \quad 8✓$$

✓ **Checkpoint 8**

Using the data from Example 9, find the probability that an American

(a) pays $100 or more a month for electricity;

(b) does not live in a two-bedroom dwelling and pays less than $100 a month for electricity.

Answers: See page 506.

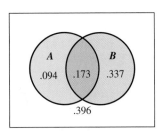

FIGURE 8.23

Example 10 **Business** Data from the 2008 *Forbes* magazine survey of the 100 highest paid chief executive officers (CEOs) is cross-classified by the CEO's age in years and the CEO's annual compensation (in millions of dollars), as shown in the table:

		Annual Compensation (Millions of dollars)			
		Less than 25	25–49	50 or more	Total
Age (Years)	**40s**	2	5	2	9
	50s	27	18	10	55
	60s	8	16	7	31
	70s or older	1	2	2	5
	Total	38	41	21	100

Let E be the event "the CEO earns less than $25 million" and F be the event "the CEO's age is in the 60s."

(a) Find $P(E)$.

Solution We need to find the total number of CEOs for whom the pay is less than $25 million for all of the different age groups, as shown in the shaded column in the following table:

		Annual Compensation (Millions of dollars)			
		Less than 25	25–49	50 or more	Total
Age (Years)	40s	2	5	2	9
	50s	27	18	10	55
	60s	8	16	7	31
	70s or older	1	2	2	5
	Total	38	41	21	100

Thus $2 + 27 + 8 + 1 = 38$ is the total number of CEOs who earned less than \$25 million dollars and

$$P(E) = 38/100 = .38.$$

(b) Find $P(E \cap F)$.

Solution We look to find the number that satisfy both conditions. We see there are 8 responses in the column for less than \$25 million and the row for age in the 60s, as shown in the shaded area in the following table:

		Annual Compensation (Millions of dollars)			
		Less than 25	25–49	50 or more	Total
Age (Years)	40s	2	5	2	9
	50s	27	18	10	55
	60s	8	16	7	31
	70s or older	1	2	2	5
	Total	38	41	21	100

Thus, $P(E \cap F) = 8/100 = .08$.

(c) Find $P(E \cup F)$.

Solution We can use the additive rule for probability to find $P(E \cup F)$. We know from part (a) that $P(E) = .38$. In a similar manner to part (a), we can find $P(F)$. There are $8 + 16 + 7 = 31$ CEOs whose age is in the 60s, so $P(F) = 31/100 = .31$. With the answer to (b), using the additive rule yields

$$P(E \cup F) = P(E) + P(F) - P(E \cap F) = .38 + .31 - .08 = .61.$$ ✔

✔**Checkpoint 9**

Let G be the event "the CEO earns \$50 million or more" and H be the event "the CEO's age is in the 40s." Find

(a) $P(G)$;

(b) $P(G \cap H)$;

(c) $P(G \cup H)$.

Answers: See page 506.

8.4 ▶ Exercises

Assume a single spin of the roulette wheel is made. (See Example 1.) Find the probability for the given events.

1. The marble lands on a green or black slot.

2. The marble lands on a green or even slot.

3. The marble lands on an odd or black slot.

Also with a single spin of the roulette wheel, find the probability of winning with the given bets.

4. The marble will land in a slot numbered 13–18.

5. The marble will land in a slots 0, 00, 1, 2, or 3.

6. The marble will land in a slot that is a multiple of 3.

7. The marble will land in a slot numbered 25–36.

Two dice are rolled. Find the probabilities of rolling the given sums. (See Examples 2, 4, and 5.)

8. **(a)** 2   **(b)** 4
    (c) 5   **(d)** 6

9. **(a)** 8   **(b)** 9
    (c) 10   **(d)** 13

10. **(a)** 9 or more
    (b) Less than 7
    (c) Between 5 and 8 (exclusive)

11. **(a)** Not more than 5
    (b) Not less than 8
    (c) Between 3 and 7 (exclusive)

Tami goes shopping and sees three kinds of shoes: flats, 2″ heels, and 3″ heels. The shoes come in two shades of beige (light and dark) and black. If each option has an equal chance of being selected, find the probabilities of the given events.

12. The shoes Tami buys have a heel.

13. The shoes Tami buys are black.

14. The shoes Tami buys have a 2″ heel and are beige.

Ms. Elliott invites 10 relatives to a party: her mother, 3 aunts, 2 uncles, 2 sisters, 1 male cousin, and 1 female cousin. If the chances of any one guest arriving first are equally likely, find the probabilities that the given guests will arrive first.

15. **(a)** A sister or an aunt
    (b) A sister or a cousin
    (c) A sister or her mother

16. **(a)** An aunt or a cousin
    (b) A male or an uncle
    (c) A female or a cousin

Use Venn diagrams to work Exercises 17–21. See Example 9.

17. Suppose $P(E) = .30$, $P(F) = .51$, and $P(E \cap F) = .19$. Find each of the given probabilities.
    (a) $P(E \cup F)$ **(b)** $P(E' \cap F)$
    (c) $P(E \cap F')$ **(d)** $P(E' \cup F')$

18. Let $P(Z) = .40$, $P(Y) = .30$, and $P(Z \cup Y) = .58$. Find each of the given probabilities.
    (a) $P(Z' \cap Y')$ **(b)** $P(Z' \cup Y')$
    (c) $P(Z' \cup Y)$ **(d)** $P(Z \cap Y')$

19. **Health** In 2007, in the state of North Carolina, the probability that a woman giving birth was under age 20 (event A) was .116. The probability that the child weighed 2500 grams or less—a common cutoff for classification as having low birth weight (event B)—was .093. The probability that

the mother was under age 20 and the child had a low birth weight was .013.* Find the probability of the given event.
    (a) $A \cup B$ **(b)** $A' \cap B$
    (c) $A' \cap B'$ **(d)** $A' \cup B'$

20. **Business** Data from a portion of the 2007 American Community Survey indicated that the probability a household earned $100,000 or more (event E) was 0.192. The probability a household owned three or more cars (event F) was .609. The probability a household earned $100,000 or more and owned three or more cars was .163. Find the probability of the given event.
    (a) $E' \cup F'$ **(b)** $E' \cap F$
    (c) $E \cup F'$

21. **Social Science** Data from the 2006 General Social Survey indicated the probability of being married is .473, the probability of being generally "very happy" is .308, and the probability of being both married and generally "very happy" is .201.† Find the probability of the given event.
    (a) Not being married and not being happy
    (b) Being married or not being happy
    (c) Not being married and being happy

22. Define what is meant by odds.

A single fair die is rolled. Find the odds in favor of getting the results in Exercises 23–26. (See Examples 6 and 7.)

23. 2

24. 2, 3, 4

25. 2, 3, 5, or 6

26. Some number greater than 5

27. A marble is drawn from a box containing 3 yellow, 4 white, and 8 blue marbles. Find the odds in favor of drawing the given marbles.
    (a) A yellow marble
    (b) A blue marble
    (c) A white marble

28. Find the odds of *not* drawing a white marble in Exercise 27.

29. Two dice are rolled. Find the odds of rolling a 7 or an 11.

30. In the "Ask Marilyn" column of *Parade* magazine, a reader wrote about the following game: "You and I each roll a die. If your die is higher than mine, you win. Otherwise, I win." The reader thought that the probability that each player wins is 1/2. Is this correct? If not, what is the probability that each player wins?*

---

*Based on data available at http://arc.irss.unc.edu/dvn.

†Based on data available at www.norc.edu/GSS+Website.

each player wins is 1/2. Is this correct? If not, what is the probability that each player wins?*

Social Science *For Exercises 31–33, find the odds of the event occurring from the given probability that a bachelor's degree recipient in 2006 majored in the given discipline.†*

31. Business; probability 21/100.

32. Biological or biomedical sciences; probability 1/20.

33. Education; probability 7/100.

Social Science *For Exercises 34–37, convert the given odds to the probability that the event will occur.‡*

34. The odds that an American adult is a high school graduate are 6:1.

35. The odds that an American adult is a college graduate are 2:5.

36. The odds that an American adult earned a bachelor's degree (and not a higher degree) are 1:4.

37. The odds that an American adult earned an advanced degree are 1:9.

Business *For Exercises 38–39, find the odds of the event occurring from the given probability.§*

38. In December 2008, the probability of being unemployed in the United States was 9/125.

39. In December 2008, the probability of being unemployed in Rhode Island was 1/10.

*One way to solve a probability problem is to repeat the experiment many times, keeping track of the results. Then the probability can be approximated by using the basic definition of the probability of an event E, which is $P(E) = n(E)/n(S)$, where E occurs $n(E)$ times out of $n(S)$ trials of an experiment. This is called the **Monte Carlo method** of finding probabilities. If physically repeating the experiment is too tedious, it may be simulated with the use of a random-number generator, available on most computers and scientific or graphing calculators. To simulate a coin toss or the roll of a die on a graphing calculator, change the setting to fixed decimal mode with 0 digits displayed. To simulate multiple tosses of a coin, press RAND (or RANDOM or RND#) in the PROB submenu of the MATH (or OPTN) menu, and then press ENTER repeatedly. Interpret 0 as a head and 1 as a tail. To simulate multiple rolls of a die, press RAND × 6 + .5, and then press ENTER repeatedly.*

40. Suppose two dice are rolled. Use the Monte Carlo method with at least 50 repetitions to approximate the given probabilities. Compare them with the results of Exercise 10.
 (a) P(the sum is 9 or more)
 (b) P(the sum is less than 7)

41. Suppose two dice are rolled. Use the Monte Carlo method with at least 50 repetitions to approximate the given probabilities. Compare them with the results of Exercise 11.
 (a) P(the sum is not more than 5)
 (b) P(the sum is not less than 8)

42. Suppose three dice are rolled. Use the Monte Carlo method with at least 100 repetitions to approximate the given probabilities.
 (a) P(the sum is 5 or less)
 (b) P(neither a 1 nor a 6 is rolled)

43. Suppose a coin is tossed 5 times. Use the Monte Carlo method with at least 50 repetitions to approximate the given probabilities.
 (a) P(exactly 4 heads)
 (b) P(2 heads and 3 tails)

44. **Business** Suppose that 8% of a certain batch of calculators have a defective case and that 11% have defective batteries. Also, 3% have both a defective case and defective batteries. A calculator is selected from the batch at random. Find the probability that the calculator has a good case and good batteries.

Health *Using the categories defined by the Centers for Disease Control and Prevention for weight status, the table cross-classifies adults by age and weight status.*

Age (Years)	Underweight	Healthy Weight	Overweight	Obese	Total
18–39	81	872	735	712	2400
40–64	48	421	601	739	1809
65 or Higher	49	264	355	309	977
Total	178	1557	1691	1760	5186

Define A as the event of being ages 18–39, B as the event of being ages 40–64, and C as the event of being age 65 or older. Let D be the event of being underweight, E be the event of having a healthy weight, F be the event of being overweight, and G be the event of being obese. Use the table for Exercises 45–50 to find the probability of the given event.

45. The event of being of a healthy weight

46. The event of being overweight or obese

47. The event of not being underweight

48. The event of being 65 or higher and being obese

49. The event of being 18–39 or of a healthy weight

50. The event of being 18–39 and overweight

Business *The table gives the number of vehicles owned cross-classified by income level for households from the 2007 American Community Survey:*

Parade Magazine, November 6, 1994, p. 10. Reprinted by permission of the William Morris Agency, Inc., on behalf of the author. Copyright © 1994 by Marilyn vos Savant.

†Digest of Educational Statistics.

‡www.census.gov.

§U.S. Bureau of Labor Statistics.

*Based on data available at www.cdc.gov/nchs/nhanes.htm.

	Number of Vehicles						
Income	**0**	**1**	**2**	**3**	**4**	**5**	**Total**
Less than $100,000	13	95	234	305	100	16	763
$100,000 or more	0	4	23	64	65	25	181
Total	13	99	257	369	165	41	944

Let A indicate the event "the household earns less than $100,000," let B indicate the event "the number of vehicles is 1," and let C indicate "the number of vehicles is 2." Use the table to find the requested probabilities in Exercises 51–56.

51. $P(A)$

52. $P(C)$

53. $P(B \cup C)$

54. $P(A' \cap B)$

55. $P(A \cup C)$

56. $P(A' \cup B)$

Business *Data from the 2006 General Social Survey can allow us to estimate how much part-time and full-time employees work per week. Use the following table to find the probabilities of the events in Exercises 57–60:*

	Hours Worked per Week						
Labor Force Status	**0–19**	**20–29**	**30–39**	**40–49**	**50–59**	**60 or more**	**Total**
Working Full Time	22	43	251	1251	401	354	2322
Working Part Time	143	165	103	16	1	12	440
Total	165	208	354	1267	402	366	2762

57. Working full time

58. Working part time and 0–19 hours

59. Working full time and 40–49 hours

60. Working part time or working less than 30 hours

61. **Natural Science** Color blindness is an inherited characteristic that is more common in males than in females. If M represents male and C represents red–green color blindness, we use the relative frequencies of the inci-

dences of males and red–green color blindness as probabilities to get

$$P(C) = .039, \quad P(M \cap C) = .035, \text{ and } P(M \cup C) = .495.*$$

Find the given probabilities.

(a) $P(C')$ **(b)** $P(M)$

(c) $P(M')$ **(d)** $P(M' \cap C')$

(e) $P(C \cap M')$ **(f)** $P(C \cup M')$

62. **Natural Science** Gregor Mendel, an Austrian monk, was the first to use probability in the study of genetics. In an effort to understand the mechanism of characteristic transmittal from one generation to the next in plants, he counted the number of occurrences of various characteristics. Mendel found that the flower color in certain pea plants obeyed this scheme:

Pure red crossed with pure white produces red.

From its parents, the red offspring received genes for both red (R) and white (W), but in this case red is *dominant* and white *recessive*, so the offspring exhibits the color red. However, the offspring still carries both genes, and when two such offspring are crossed, several things can happen in the third generation. The following table, called a *Punnett square*, shows the equally likely outcomes:

			Second Parent	
			R	**W**
First Parent		**R**	RR	RW
		W	WR	WW

Use the fact that red is dominant over white to find each of the given probabilities. Assume that there are an equal number of red and white genes in the population.

(a) P(a flower is red)   **(b)** P(a flower is white)

63. **Natural Science** Mendel (see Exercise 62) found no dominance in snapdragons, with one red gene and one white gene producing pink-flowered offspring. These second-generation pinks, however, still carry one red and one white gene, and when they are crossed, the next generation still yields the Punnett square in Exercise 62. Find each of the given probabilities.

(a) P(red)   **(b)** P(pink)   **(c)** P(white)

(Mendel verified these probability ratios experimentally and did the same for many characteristics other than flower color. His work, published in 1866, was not recognized until 1890.)

*The probabilities of a person being male or female are from *The World Almanac and Book of Facts*, 2002. The probabilities of a male and female being color blind are from *Parsons' Diseases of the Eye* (18th ed.), by Stephen J. H. Miller (Churchill Livingston, 1990), p. 269. This reference gives a range of 3 to 4% for the probability of gross color blindness in men; we used the midpoint of that range.

64. Social Science Answers to a question on the legalization of marijuana in the 2006 General Social Survey indicated that there were 1044 females who answered the question, 336 females who favored making marijuana legal, and 672 men and women together who favored making marijuana legal. With the entire number of males and females who answered the question being 1828, find the probability that a person is

(a) female and not in favor of legalization;

(b) not in favor of legalization;

(c) female or in favor of legalization;

(d) male and not in favor of legalization.

(*Hint:* Draw two circles respectively denoting females and favoring legalization that overlap in the middle.)

65. Social Science Answers to a question on the existence of an afterlife in the 2006 General Social Survey indicated that there were 1124 men who responded to the question, 891 men who said they believed in an afterlife, and 2177 men and women who believed in an afterlife. With a total of 2629 men and women who answered the question, find the probability that a person

(a) believes in an afterlife;

(b) is male and believes in an afterlife;

(c) is female and does not believe in an afterlife.

(*Hint:* Draw two circles respectively denoting males and believing in an afterlife that overlap in the middle.)

Finance *The National Association of College and University Business Officers researched the change in university and college endowments from 2007 to 2008. The table below shows findings for 203 colleges and universities with 2008 endowment levels above $300 million dollars. It indicates how many schools with a particular endowment level had their endowment increase in value, how many had their endowment decrease by between 0 and 5%, and how many had their endowment decrease by more than 5%. Among these 203 colleges and universities, find the probabilities of the events in Exercises 66–70.*

Endowment Value (Dollars)	Change in Value			
	Positive Increase	Between 0 and 5% Decrease	More than 5% Decrease	Total
300–499 Million	19	27	16	62
500–999 Million	24	26	14	64
1–1.999 Billion	22	17	6	45
2 Billion or More	20	8	4	32
Total	85	78	40	203

66. The endowment had a positive increase in value.

67. The endowment was valued at $2 billion or more and lost more than 5%.

68. The endowment did not decrease by 5% or more.

69. The endowment had between a 0 and 5% reduction or had a value of $300–499 million.

70. The endowment was less than $2 billion and had a positive increase.

✓**Checkpoint Answers**

1. 13/19			**2. (a)** 1/4	**(b)** 2/9
3. 7/8			**4. (a)** 1/3	**(b)** 1/4
5. 5/6				
6. (a) 9 to 1	**(b)** 1 to 9	**(c)** 4 to 1	**(d)** 1 to 4	
7. (a) 1/6	**(b)** 5/6			
8. (a) .490	**(b)** .337			
9. (a) .21	**(b)** .02	**(c)** .28		

8.5 ▶ Conditional Probability and Independent Events

Did you ever wonder what salary the president of your college or university earns per year? The *Chronicle of Higher Education* conducted a survey in November 2008 to examine that question. The following table examines whether presidents of public universities and community colleges earned less than $250,000 or $250,000 or more in compensation.*

---

*The figures in the table do not include house, car, and supplemental compensation. From http://chronicle.com/stats/990/public.htm.

	Earned less than $250,000	Earned $250,000 or more	Total
University President	53	101	154
Community College President	21	14	35
Total	74	115	189

Let A be the event "earned $250,000 or more," and let B be the event "community college president." We can find $P(A), P(A'), P(B),$ and $P(B')$. For example, the table shows that a total of 115 presidents earned $250,000 or more, so

✔**Checkpoint 1**

Use the data in the table to find

(a) $P(B)$;
(b) $P(A')$;
(c) $P(B')$.

Answers: See page 519.

$$P(A) = \frac{115}{189} \approx .608. \quad ✔$$

Suppose we want to know the probability that a community college president earns $250,000 or more. From the table, of 35 community college presidents, 14 earned $250,000 or more, so

$$P(\text{community college president earns \$250,000 or more}) = \frac{14}{35} = .4.$$

This is a different number from the probability of making $250,000 or more, .608, because *we have additional information* (the president is the president of a community college) *that has reduced the sample space.* In other words, we found the probability of earning $250,000 or more, A, given the additional information that the president is a community college president, B. This probability is called the *conditional probability* of event A, given that event B has occurred, written $P(A|B)$ and often read as "the probability of A given B."

In the preceding example,

$$P(A|B) = \frac{14}{35} = .4.$$

If we divide the numerator and denominator by 189 (the size of the sample space), this quantity can be written as

$$P(A|B) = \frac{\dfrac{14}{189}}{\dfrac{35}{189}} = \frac{P(A \cap B)}{P(B)},$$

where $P(A \cap B)$ represents, as usual, the probability that both A and B will occur.

To generalize this result, assume that E and F are two events for a particular experiment. Assume also that the sample space S for the experiment has n possible equally likely outcomes. Suppose event F has m elements and $E \cap F$ has k elements ($k \leq m$). Then, using the fundamental principle of probability yields

$$P(F) = \frac{m}{n} \quad \text{and} \quad P(E \cap F) = \frac{k}{n}.$$

We now want to find $P(E|F)$: the probability that E occurs, given that F has occurred. Since we assume that F has occurred, we reduce the sample space to F;

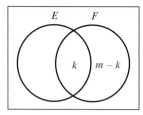

Event *F* has a total of *m* elements.

FIGURE 8.24

that is, we look only at the *m* elements inside *F*. (See Figure 8.24.) Of these *m* elements, there are *k* elements for which *E* also occurs, because $E \cap F$ has *k* elements. This yields

$$P(E|F) = \frac{k}{m}.$$

Divide numerator and denominator by *n* to get

$$P(E|F) = \frac{k/n}{m/n} = \frac{P(E \cap F)}{P(F)}.$$

The last result motivates the following definition of conditional probability. The **conditional probability** of an event *E*, given event *F*, written $P(E|F)$, is

$$P(E|F) = \frac{P(E \cap F)}{P(F)} = \frac{P(E \text{ and } F)}{P(F)}, P(F) \neq 0.$$

This definition tells us that, for equally likely outcomes, conditional probability is found by *reducing the sample space to event F* and then finding the number of outcomes in *F* that are also in event *E*. Thus,

$$P(E|F) = \frac{n(E \cap F)}{n(F)}.$$

Although the definition of conditional probability was motivated by an example with equally likely outcomes, it is valid in all cases. For an intuitive explanation, think of the formula as giving the probability that both *E* and *F* occur, compared with the entire probability of *F* occuring.

✓**Checkpoint 2**

The table shows the results of the 2006 General Social Survey regarding happiness for married and never married respondents.

	Very Happy	Partially Happy or Not Happy	Total
Married	600	813	1413
Never Married	144	586	730
Total	744	1399	2143

Let *M* represent married respondents and *V* represent very happy respondents. Find each of the given probabilities.

(a) $P(V|M)$

(b) $P(V|M')$

(c) $P(M|V)$

(d) $P(M'|V')$

(e) State the probability of part (d) in words.

Answers: See page 519.

Example 1   **Business** Use the information from the table on the salary of university and community college presidents (page 507) to find the given probabilities.

(a) $P(A|B')$

    Solution In words, this is the probability of earning \$250,000 or more, given that the president is a university president, or

$$P(A|B') = \frac{n(A \cap B')}{n(B')} = \frac{101}{154} \approx .656.$$

(b) $P(B|A)$

    Solution This represents the probability that the president is a community college president, given that he or she makes \$250,000 or more. Reduce the sample space to *A*. Then find $n(A \cap B)$ and $n(A)$. The result is

$$P(B|A) = \frac{n(A \cap B)}{n(A)} = \frac{14}{115} \approx .122.$$

So if a president earns \$250,000 or more, then the probability is .122 that the president is a community college president.

(c) $P(B'|A')$

Solution Here, we want the probability the president is a university president, given that he or she earns less than \$250,000:

$$P(B'|A') = \frac{n(B' \cap A')}{n(A')} = \frac{53}{74} \approx .716.$$

Venn diagrams can be used to illustrate problems in conditional probability. A Venn diagram for Example 1, in which the probabilities are used to indicate the number in the set defined by each region, is shown in Figure 8.25. In the diagram, $P(B|A)$ is found by *reducing the sample space to just set A*. Then $P(B|A)$ is the ratio of the number in that part of set B which is also in A to the number in set A, or $.074/(.074 + .534) = .074/.608 \approx .122$.

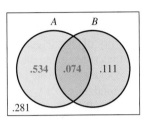

FIGURE 8.25

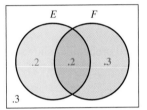

FIGURE 8.26

Example 2   Given $P(E) = .4$, $P(F) = .5$, and $P(E \cup F) = .7$, find $P(E|F)$.

Solution Find $P(E \cap F)$ first. Then use a Venn diagram to find $P(E|F)$. By the addition rule,

$$P(E \cup F) = P(E) + P(F) - P(E \cap F)$$
$$.7 = .4 + .5 - P(E \cap F)$$
$$P(E \cap F) = .2.$$

Now use the probabilities to indicate the number in each region of the Venn diagram in Figure 8.26. $P(E|F)$ is the ratio of the probability of that part of E which is in F to the probability of F, or

$$P(E|F) = \frac{P(E \cap F)}{P(F)} = \frac{.2}{.5} = \frac{2}{5} = .4.$$

✓ **Checkpoint 3**

Find $P(F|E)$ if $P(E) = .3$, $P(F) = .4$, and $P(E \cup F) = .6$.

Answer: See page 519.

Example 3   Two fair coins were tossed, and it is known that at least one was a head. Find the probability that both were heads.

Solution The sample space has four equally likely outcomes: $S = \{hh, ht, th, tt.\}$ Define two events

$$E_1 = \text{at least 1 head} = \{hh, ht, th\}$$

and

$$E_2 = 2 \text{ heads} = \{hh\}.$$

Because there are four equally likely outcomes, $P(E_1) = 3/4$. Also, $P(E_1 \cap E_2) = 1/4$. We want the probability that both were heads, given that at least one was a head; that is, we want to find $P(E_2|E_1)$. Because of the condition that at least one coin was a head, the reduced sample space is

$$\{hh, ht, th\}.$$

Since only one outcome in this reduced sample space is two heads,

$$P(E_2|E_1) = \frac{1}{3}.$$

Alternatively, use the definition given earlier:

$$P(E_2|E_1) = \frac{P(E_2 \cap E_1)}{P(E_1)} = \frac{1/4}{3/4} = \frac{1}{3}. \quad \text{✓} \textbf{4}$$

✔ **Checkpoint 4**

In Example 3, find the probability that exactly one coin showed a head, given that at least one was a head.

Answer: See page 519.

It is important not to confuse $P(A|B)$ with $P(B|A)$. For example, in a criminal trial, a prosecutor may point out to the jury that the probability of the defendant's DNA profile matching that of a sample taken at the scene of the crime, given that the defendant is innocent, is very small. What the jury must decide, however, is the probability that the defendant is innocent, given that the defendant's DNA profile matches the sample. Confusing the two is an error sometimes called "the prosecutor's fallacy," and the 1990 conviction of a rape suspect in England was overturned by a panel of judges who ordered a retrial, because the fallacy made the original trial unfair.* This mistake is often called "confusion of the inverse."

In the next section, we will see how to compute $P(A|B)$ when we know $P(B|A)$.

PRODUCT RULE

If $P(E) \neq 0$ and $P(F) \neq 0$, then the definition of conditional probability shows that

$$P(E|F) = \frac{P(E \cap F)}{P(F)} \quad \text{and} \quad P(F|E) = \frac{P(F \cap E)}{P(E)}.$$

Using the fact that $P(E \cap F) = P(F \cap E)$, and solving each of these equations for $P(E \cap F)$, we obtain the following rule.

> ### Product Rule of Probability
>
> If E and F are events, then $P(E \cap F)$ may be found by either of these formulas:
>
> $$P(E \cap F) = P(F) \cdot P(E|F) \quad \text{or} \quad P(E \cap F) = P(E) \cdot P(F|E).$$

The **product rule** gives a method for finding the probability that events E and F both occur. Here is a simple way to remember the ordering of E and F in the probability rule:

$$P(E \cap F) = P(F) \cdot P(E|F) \quad \text{or} \quad P(E \cap F) = P(E) \cdot P(F|E).$$

Example 4 **Business** According to data from the U.S. Census Bureau, we can estimate the probability that a business is female owned as .282. We can also estimate the probability that a female-owned business has one to four employees as .504. What is the probability that a business is female owned *and* has one to four employees?

*David Pringle, "Who's the DNA Fingerprinting Pointing At?", *New Scientist*, January 29, 1994, pp. 51–52.

Solution Let F represent the event of "having a female-owned business" and E represent the event of "having one to four employees." We want to find $P(F \cap E)$. By the product rule,

$$P(F \cap E) = P(F)P(E|F).$$

From the given information, $P(F) = .282$, and the probability that a female-owned business has one to four employees is $P(E|F) = .504$. Thus,

$$P(F \cap E) = .282(.504) \approx .142. \quad \text{5} \checkmark$$

✔**Checkpoint 5**

In a litter of puppies, 3 were female and 4 were male. Half the males were black. Find the probability that a puppy chosen at random from the litter would be a black male.

Answer: See page 519.

In Section 8.1, we used a tree diagram to find the number of subsets of a given set. By including the probabilities for each branch of a tree diagram, we convert it to a **probability tree**. The following examples show how a probability tree is used with the product rule to find the probability of a sequences of events.

Example 5 A company needs to hire a new director of advertising. It has decided to try to hire either person A or person B, both of whom are assistant advertising directors for its major competitor. To decide between A and B, the company does research on the campaigns managed by A or B (none are managed by both) and finds that A is in charge of twice as many advertising campaigns as B. Also, A's campaigns have yielded satisfactory results three out of four times, while B's campaigns have yielded satisfactory results only two out of five times. Suppose one of the competitor's advertising campaigns (managed by A or B) is selected randomly.

We can represent this situation schematically as follows: Let A denote the event "Person A does the job" and B the event "Person B does the job." Let S be the event "satisfactory results" and U the event "unsatisfactory results." Then the given information can be summarized in the probability tree in Figure 8.27. Since A does twice as many jobs as B, $P(A) = 2/3$ and $P(B) = 1/3$, as noted on the first-stage branches of the tree. When A does a job, the probability of satisfactory results is $3/4$ and of unsatisfactory results $1/4$, as noted on the second-stage branches. Similarly, the probabilities when B does the job are noted on the remaining second-stage branches. The composite branches labeled 1–4 represent the four disjoint possibilities for the running and outcome of the campaign.

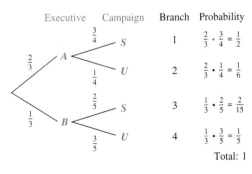

FIGURE 8.27

(a) Find the probability that A is in charge of a campaign that produces satisfactory results.

Solution We are asked to find $P(A \cap S)$. We know that when A does the job, the probability of success is 3/4; that is, $P(S|A) = 3/4$. Hence, by the product rule,

$$P(A \cap S) = P(A) \cdot P(S|A) = \frac{2}{3} \cdot \frac{3}{4} = \frac{1}{2}.$$

The event $(A \cap S)$ is represented by branch 1 of the tree, and as we have just seen, its probability is the product of the probabilities that make up that branch.

(b) Find the probability that B runs a campaign that produces satisfactory results.

Solution We must find $P(B \cap S)$. This event is represented by branch 3 of the tree, and as before, its probability is the product of the probabilities of the pieces of that branch:

$$P(B \cap S) = P(B) \cdot P(S|B) = \frac{1}{3} \cdot \frac{2}{5} = \frac{2}{15}.$$

(c) What is the probability that the selected campaign is satisfactory?

Solution The event S is the union of the disjoint events $A \cap S$ and $B \cap S$, which are represented by branches 1 and 3 of the tree diagram. By the addition rule,

$$P(S) = P(A \cap S) + P(B \cap S) = \frac{1}{2} + \frac{2}{15} = \frac{19}{30}.$$

Thus, the probability of an event that appears on several branches is the sum of the probabilities of each of these branches.

(d) What is the probability that the selected campaign is unsatisfactory?

Solution $P(U)$ can be read from branches 2 and 4 of the tree:

$$P(U) = \frac{1}{6} + \frac{1}{5} = \frac{11}{30}.$$

Alternatively, because U is the complement of S,

$$P(U) = 1 - P(S) = 1 - \frac{19}{30} = \frac{11}{30}.$$

(e) Find the probability that either A runs the campaign or the results are satisfactory (or possibly both).

Solution Event A combines branches 1 and 2, while event S combines branches 1 and 3, so use branches 1, 2, and 3:

$$P(A \cup S) = \frac{1}{2} + \frac{1}{6} + \frac{2}{15} = \frac{4}{5}. \quad \boxed{6} ✓$$

✓ **Checkpoint 6**

Find each of the given probabilities for the Scenario in Example 5.

(a) $P(U|A)$

(b) $P(U|B)$

Answers: See page 519.

Example 6 Suppose 6 potential jurors remain in a jury pool and 2 are to be selected to sit on the jury for the trial. The races of the 6 potential jurors are 1 Hispanic, 3 Caucasian, and 2 African-American. If we select one juror at a time, find the probability that one Caucasian and one African-American are drawn.

Solution A probability tree showing the various possible outcomes is given in Figure 8.28. In this diagram, C represents the event "selecting a Caucasian juror" and A represents "selecting an African-American juror." On the first draw, $P(C$ on the 1st$) = 3/6 = 1/2$ because three of the six jurors are Caucasian. On the second draw, $P(A$ on the 2nd$|C$ on the 1st$) = 2/5$. One Caucasian juror has been removed, leaving 5, of which 2 are African-American.

We want to find the probability of selecting exactly one Caucasian and exactly one African-American. Two events satisfy this condition: selecting a Caucasian first and then selecting an African-American (branch 2 of the tree) and drawing an African-American juror first and then selecting a Caucasian juror (branch 4). For branch 2,

$$P(C \text{ on 1st}) \cdot P(A \text{ on 2nd}|C \text{ on 1st}) = \frac{1}{2}\cdot\frac{2}{5} = \frac{1}{5}. \;✓$$

For branch 4, on which the African-American juror is selected first,

$$P(A \text{ first}) \cdot P(C \text{ second}|A \text{ first}) = \frac{1}{3}\cdot\frac{3}{5} = \frac{1}{5}.$$

Since these two events are disjoint, the final probability is the sum of the two probabilities.

$$P(\text{one } C, \text{ one } A) = P(C \text{ on 1st}) \cdot P(A \text{ on 2nd}|C \text{ on 1st})$$
$$+ P(A \text{ on 1st}) \cdot P(C \text{ on 2nd}|A \text{ on 1st}) = \frac{2}{5}. \;✓$$

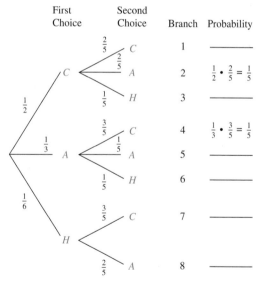

FIGURE 8.28

The product rule is often used in dealing with *stochastic processes*, which are mathematical models that evolve over time in a probabilistic manner. For example, selecting different jurors is such a process, because the probabilities change with each successive selection. (Particular stochastic processes are studied further in Section 9.5.)

✓**Checkpoint 7**

In Example 6, find the probability of selecting an African-American juror and then a Caucasian juror.

Answer: See page 519.

✓**Checkpoint 8**

In Example 6, find the probability of selecting a Caucasian juror and then a Hispanic juror.

Answer: See page 519.

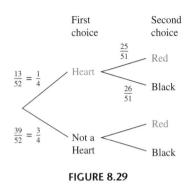

First choice   Second choice

FIGURE 8.29

✓**Checkpoint 9**

Find the probability of drawing a heart on the first draw and a black card on the second if two cards are drawn without replacement.

Answer: See page 519.

Example 7   Two cards are drawn without replacement from an ordinary deck (52 cards). Find the probability that the first card is a heart and the second card is red.

Solution Start with the probability tree of Figure 8.29. (You may wish to refer to the deck of cards shown on page 490.) On the first draw, since there are 13 hearts in the 52 cards, the probability of drawing a heart first is $13/52 = 1/4$. On the second draw, since a (red) heart has been drawn already, there are 25 red cards in the remaining 51 cards. Thus, the probability of drawing a red card on the second draw, given that the first is a heart, is $25/51$. By the product rule of probability,

$$P(\text{heart on 1st and red on 2nd})$$
$$= P(\text{heart on 1st}) \cdot P(\text{red on 2nd} \mid \text{heart on 1st})$$
$$= \frac{1}{4} \cdot \frac{25}{51} = \frac{25}{204} \approx .123. \quad \mathbf{9}✓$$

Example 8   Three cards are drawn, without replacement, from an ordinary deck. Find the probability that exactly 2 of the cards are red.

Solution Here, we need a probability tree with three stages, as shown in Figure 8.30. The three branches indicated with arrows produce exactly 2 red cards from the draws. Multiply the probabilities along each of these branches and then add:

$$P(\text{exactly 2 red cards}) = \frac{26}{52} \cdot \frac{25}{51} \cdot \frac{26}{50} + \frac{26}{52} \cdot \frac{26}{51} \cdot \frac{25}{50} + \frac{26}{52} \cdot \frac{26}{51} \cdot \frac{25}{50}$$

$$= \frac{50,700}{132,600} = \frac{13}{34} \approx .382. \quad \mathbf{10}✓$$

✓**Checkpoint 10**

Use the tree in Example 8 to find the probability that exactly one of the cards is red.

Answer: See page 519.

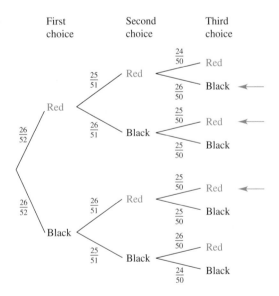

First choice   Second choice   Third choice

FIGURE 8.30

INDEPENDENT EVENTS

Suppose in Example 7 that we draw the two cards *with* replacement rather than without replacement. (That is, we put the first card back, shuffle them and then draw the second card.) If the first card is a heart, then the probability of drawing a red card on the second draw is 26/52, rather than 25/51, because there are still 52 cards in the deck, 26 of them red. In this case, P(red second|heart first) is the same as P(red second). The value of the second card is not affected by the value of the first card. We say that the event that the second card is red is *independent* of the event that the first card is a heart, since knowledge of the first card does not influence what happens to the second card. On the other hand, when we draw *without* replacement, the events that the first card is a heart and the second is red are *dependent* events. The fact that the first card is a heart means that there is one fewer red card in the deck, influencing the probability that the second card is red.

As another example, consider tossing a fair coin twice. If the first toss shows heads, the probability that the next toss is heads is still 1/2. Coin tosses are independent events, since the outcome of one toss does not influence the outcome of the next toss. Similarly, rolls of a fair die are independent events. On the other hand, the events "the milk is old" and "the milk is sour" are dependent events: If the milk is old, there is an increased chance that it is sour. Also, in the example at the beginning of this section, the events A (the president earned \$250,000 or more) and B (the president was the head of a community college) are dependent events, because information about the institution type affects the probability of salary level. That is, $P(A|B)$ is different from $P(A)$.

If events E and F are independent, then the knowledge that E has occurred gives no (probability) information about the occurrence or nonoccurrence of event F. That is, $P(F)$ is exactly the same as $P(F|E)$, or

$$P(F|E) = P(F).$$

This, in fact, is the formal definition of independent events.

E and F are **independent events** if

$$P(F|E) = P(F) \quad \text{or} \quad P(E|F) = P(E).$$

If the events are not independent, they are **dependent events**.

When E and F are independent events, $P(F|E) = P(F)$, and the product rule becomes

$$P(E \cap F) = P(E) \cdot P(F|E) = P(E) \cdot P(F).$$

Conversely, if this equation holds, it follows that $P(F) = P(F|E)$. Consequently, we have the useful rule that follows.

Product Rule for Independent Events

E and F are independent events if and only if

$$P(E \cap F) = P(E) \cdot P(F).$$

Example 9 A calculator requires a keystroke assembly and a logic circuit. Assume that 99% of the keystroke assemblies are satisfactory and 97% of the logic circuits are satisfactory. Find the probability that a finished calculator will be satisfactory.

Solution If the failure of a keystroke assembly and the failure of a logic circuit are independent events, then

P(satisfactory calculator)

$= P$(satisfactory keystroke assembly) $\cdot P$(satisfactory logic circuit)

$= (.99)(.97) \approx .96.$ ✓

✓**Checkpoint 11**

Find the probability of getting 4 successive heads on 4 tosses of a fair coin.

Answer: See page 519.

CAUTION It is common for students to confuse the ideas of *disjoint* events and *independent* events. Events E and F are disjoint if $E \cap F = \emptyset$. For example, if a family has exactly one child, the only possible outcomes are $B = \{$boy$\}$ and $G = \{$girl$\}$. These two events are disjoint. However, the events are *not* independent, since $P(G|B) = 0$ (if a family with only one child has a boy, the probability that it has a girl is then 0). Since $P(G|B) \neq P(G)$, the events are not independent. Of all the families with exactly *two* children, the events $G_1 = \{$first child is a girl$\}$ and $G_2 = \{$second child is a girl$\}$ are independent, because $P(G_2|G_1)$ equals $P(G_2)$. However, G_1 and G_2 are not disjoint, since $G_1 \cap G_2 = \{$both children are girls$\} \neq \emptyset$.

To show that two events E and F are independent, we can show that $P(F|E) = P(F)$, that $P(E|F) = P(E)$, or that $P(E \cap F) = P(E) \cdot P(F)$. Another way is to observe that knowledge of one outcome does not influence the probability of the other outcome, as we did for coin tosses.

NOTE In some cases, it may not be apparent from the physical description of the problem whether two events are independent or not. For example, it is not obvious whether the event that a baseball player gets a hit tomorrow is independent of the event that he got a hit today. In such cases, it is necessary to use the definition and calculate whether $P(F|E) = P(F)$, or, equivalently, whether $P(E \cap F) = P(E) \cdot P(F)$.

Example 10 The probability that someone living in the United States lives in Massachusetts is .02, the probability that someone living in the United States speaks English at home is .83, and the probability that someone living in the United States lives in Massachusetts or speaks English at home is .8334.* Are the events "living in Massachusetts" and "speaking English at home" independent?

Solution Let M represent the event "living in Massachusetts" and E represent the event "speaking English at home." We must determine whether

$$P(E|M) = P(E) \quad \text{or} \quad P(M|E) = P(M).$$

---

*Data taken from U.S. Census population estimates and the 2007 American Community Survey. Some probabilities are rounded to the nearest hundredth.

✓**Checkpoint 12**

The probability of living in Texas is .08, the probability of speaking English at home is .83, and the probability of living in Texas or speaking English at home is .854. Are the events "speaking English at home" and "living in Texas" independent?

Answer: See page 519.

We know that $P(E) = .83$, $P(M) = .02$, and $P(E \cup M) = .8334$. We can use the addition rule (or a Venn diagram) to find that $P(E \cap M) = .0166$, $P(E|M) = .83$, and $P(M|E) = .02$. We have

$$P(E|M) = P(E) = .83 \quad \text{and} \quad P(M|E) = P(M) = .02,$$

so the events "living in Massachusetts" and "speaking English at home" are independent. **12**✓

Although we showed that $P(E|M) = P(M)$ and $P(M|E) = P(E)$ in Example 10, only one of these results is needed to establish independence. It is also important to note that independence of events does not necessarily follow our intuition; it is established from the mathematical definition of independence.

8.5 ▶ Exercises

If a single fair die is rolled, find the probability of rolling the given events. (See Examples 1 and 2.)

1. 3, given that the number rolled was odd

2. 5, given that the number rolled was even

3. An odd number, given that the number rolled was 3

If two fair dice are rolled (recall the 36-outcome sample space), find the probability of rolling the given events.

4. A sum of 8, given that the sum was greater than 7

5. A sum of 6, given that the roll was a "double" (two identical numbers)

6. A double, given that the sum was 9

If two cards are drawn without replacement from an ordinary deck, find the probabilities of the given event. (See Example 7.)

7. The second is a heart, given that the first is a heart

8. The second is black, given that the first is a spade

9. A jack and a 10 are drawn.

10. An ace and a 4 are drawn.

11. In your own words, explain how to find the conditional probability $P(E|F)$.

12. Your friend asks you to explain how the product rule for independent events differs from the product rule for dependent events. How would you respond?

13. Another friend asks you to explain how to tell whether two events are dependent or independent. How would you reply? (Use your own words.)

Decide whether the two events listed are independent.

14. S is the event that it snows tomorrow and L is the event that the instructor is late for class.

15. R is the event that four semesters of theology are required to graduate from a certain college and A is the event that the college is a religiously affiliated school.

16. R is the event that it rains in the Amazon jungle and H is the event that an instructor in New York City writes a difficult exam.

17. T is the event that Tom Cruise's next movie grosses over $200 million and R is the event that the Republicans have a majority in Congress in 2016.

18. A student reasons that the probability in Example 3 of both coins being heads is just the probability that the other coin is a head—that is, $1/2$. Explain why this reasoning is wrong.

19. In a two-child family, if we assume that the probabilities of a child being male and a child being female are each .5, are the events "the children are the same sex" and "at most one child is male" independent? Are they independent for a three-child family?

20. Let A and B be independent events with $P(A) = \dfrac{1}{4}$ and $P(B) = \dfrac{1}{5}$. Find $P(A \cap B)$ and $P(A \cup B)$.

Business *Use a probability tree or Venn diagram in Exercises 21 and 22. (See Examples 2 and 5–9.) A shop that produces custom kitchen cabinets has two employees: Sitlington and Čapek. 95% of Čapek's work is satisfactory, and 10% of Sitlington's work is unsatisfactory. 60% of the shop's cabinets are made by Čapek, and the rest are made by Sitlington. Find the given probabilities.*

21. An unsatisfactory cabinet was made by Čapek. (*Hint:* Consider which event came first.)

22. A finished cabinet is unsatisfactory.

23. **Business** According to the Bureau of Labor Statistics, for 2008, 48.4% of the civilian population 16 years or older was male, 34% was not in the labor force, and 69.3% was male or not in the labor force. Find the probability of not being in the labor force, given that the person is male.

24. Business Using the information from Exercise 23 and the fact that 20.9% of the population is female and not in the labor force, find the probability of not being in the labor force, given that the person is female.

25. Health The table cross-classifies gender and height status for 5186 American adults.*

	Under 6 Feet	6 Feet or Taller	Total
Male	2108	395	2503
Female	2680	3	2683
Total	4788	398	5186

Find the probability of the given event.
(a) Being 6 feet or taller, given the person is male
(b) Being 6 feet or taller, given the person is female
(c) Being female, given the person is 6 feet or taller
(d) Being male, given the person is under 6 feet

Health *Using the categories defined by the Centers for Disease Control and Prevention for weight status, the table cross-classifies sex and weight status for the same adults in Exercise 25.*

	Underweight	Healthy Weight	Overweight	Obese	Total
Male	85	709	952	757	2503
Female	93	848	739	1003	2683
Total	178	1557	1691	1760	5186

Find the probability of the given event.

26. Being obese, given the person is male

27. Being obese, given the person is female

28. Being male, given the person is of a healthy weight

29. Being female, given the person is underweight

Natural Science *In a letter to the journal* Nature, *Robert A. J. Matthews gives the following table of outcomes of forecast and actual weather over 1000 1-hour walks, based on the United Kingdom's Meteorological Office's 83% accuracy in 24-hour forecasts.†*

	Rain	No Rain	Sum
Forecast of Rain	66	156	222
Forecast of No Rain	14	764	778
Sum	80	920	1000

---

30. Verify that the probability that the forecast called for rain, given that there was rain, is indeed 83%. Also, verify that the probability that the forecast called for no rain, given that there was no rain, is 83%.

31. Calculate the probability that there was rain, given that the forecast called for rain.

32. Calculate the probability that there was no rain, given that the forecast called for no rain.

33. Observe that your answer to Exercise 32 is higher than 83% and that your answer to Exercise 31 is much lower. Discuss which figure best describes the accuracy of the weather forecast in recommending whether you should carry an umbrella.

Natural Science *The following table shows frequencies for red–green color blindness, where M represents that a person is male and C represents that a person is color blind.*

	M	M'	Totals
C	.042	.007	.049
C'	.485	.466	.951
Totals	.527	.473	1.000

Use the table to find the given probabilities.

34. $P(M)$

35. $P(C)$

36. $P(M \cap C)$

37. $P(M \cup C)$

38. $P(M|C)$

39. $P(M'|C)$

40. Are the events C and M dependent? Recall that two events E and F are dependent if $P(E|F) \neq P(E)$. (See Example 10.)

41. Are the events M' and C dependent?

42. Natural Science A scientist wishes to determine whether there is any dependence between color blindness (C) and deafness (D). Given the probabilities listed in the table, what should his findings be (see Example 10)?

	D	D'	Totals
C	.0004	.0796	.0800
C'	.0046	.9154	.9200
Totals	.0050	.9950	1.0000

Social Science *The Motor Vehicle Department in a certain state has found that the probability of a person passing the test for a driver's license on the first try is .75. The probability that an individual who fails on the first test will pass on the second try is .80, and the probability that an individual who fails the first and second tests will pass the third time is .70. Find the probability of the given event.*

43. A person fails both the first and second tests

44. A person will fail three times in a row

45. A person will require at least two tries to pass the test

---

*Based on data available at www.cdc.gov/nchs/nhanes.htm.

†Robert A. J. Matthews, *Nature,* 382, August 29, 1996: p. 3.

Business   *The table shows results from a subset of the 2007 American Community Survey.*

Number of Vehicles	Household Income				
	$0–49,999	**$50,000– 99,999**	**$100,000– 149,999**	**$150,000 or more**	**Total**
0–2	504	199	64	46	813
3 or more	36	80	36	35	187
Total	540	279	100	81	1000

Find the probability of the given event.

46. Earning $150,000 or more, given that a household has 3 or more cars

47. Having 0–2 cars, given that a household earns $0–49,999

48. Having 3 or more cars, given that a household earns between $100,000–149,999

49. Earning $50,000–99,999, given that the household has 0–2 cars

Transportation   *The numbers of domestic and international flights for American Airlines, Continental Air Lines, and United Air Lines for 2007 are given in the table.**

Airline	Domestic	International	Total
American	618,615	147,768	766,383
Continental	321,818	87,656	409,474
United	479,660	64,161	543,821
Total	1,420,093	299,585	1,719,678

Find the probability of the given event.

50. A Continental flight was domestic

51. An international flight was American

52. A United flight was international

53. A non-American flight was international

Suppose the probability that the first record by a singing group will be a hit is .32. If the first record is a hit, so are all the group's subsequent records. If the first record is not a hit, the probability of the group's second record and all subsequent ones being hits is .16. If the first two records are not hits, the probability that the third is a hit is .08. The probability that a record is hit continues to decrease by half with each successive nonhit record. Find the probability of the given event.

54. The group will have at least one hit in its first four records

55. The group will have exactly one hit in its first three records

56. The group will have a hit in its first six records if the first three are not hits

---

*www.transtats.bts.gov.

Work the given problems on independent events. (See Examples 9 and 10.)

57. **Business**   Corporations such as banks, where a computer is essential to day-to-day operations, often have a second, backup computer in case of failure by the main computer. Suppose that there is a .003 chance that the main computer will fail in a given period and a .005 chance that the backup computer will fail while the main computer is being repaired. Suppose these failures represent independent events, and find the fraction of the time the corporation can assume that it will have computer service. How realistic is our assumption of independence?

58. **Transportation**   According to data from the U.S. Department of Transportation, Delta Airlines was on time approximately 76% of the time in 2008. Use this information, and assume that the event that a given flight takes place on time is independent of the event that another flight is on time to answer the following questions
   (a) Elisabeta Gueyara plans to visit her company's branch offices; her journey requires 3 separate flights on Delta Airlines. What is the probability that all of these flights will be on time?
   (b) How reasonable do you believe it is to suppose the independence of being on time from flight to flight?

59. **Natural Science**   The probability that a key component of a space rocket will fail is .03.
   (a) How many such components must be used as backups to ensure that the probability that at least one of the components will work is .999999?
   (b) Is it reasonable to assume independence here?

60. **Natural Science**   A medical experiment showed that the probability that a new medicine is effective is .75, the probability that a patient will have a certain side effect is .4, and the probability that both events will occur is .3. Decide whether these events are dependent or independent.

61. **Social Science**   A teacher has found that the probability that a student studies for a test is .6, the probability that a student gets a good grade on a test is .7, and the probability that both events occur is .52. Are these events independent?

62. **Business**   Refer to Exercises 46–49. Are the events of a household having 3 or more cars and a household earning $150,000 or more independent?

✓ Checkpoint Answers

1. **(a)** .185   **(b)** .392   **(c)** .815
2. **(a)** .425   **(b)** .197   **(c)** .806   **(d)** .419
   (e) The probability of never being married, given that the person is partially or not happy
3. 1/3   **4.** 2/3   **5.** 2/7
6. **(a)** 1/4   **(b)** 3/5
7. 1/5   **8.** 1/10   **9.** $13/102 \approx .1275$
10. $13/34 \approx .382$ **11.** 1/16   **12.** No

8.6 ▶ Bayes' Formula

Suppose the probability that a person gets lung cancer, given that the person smokes a pack or more of cigarettes daily, is known. For a research project, it might be necessary to know the probability that a person smokes a pack or more of cigarettes daily, given that the person has lung cancer. More generally, if $P(E|F)$ is known for two events E and F, can $P(F|E)$ be found? The answer is yes, we can find $P(F|E)$ by using the formula to be developed in this section. To develop this formula, we can use a probability tree to find $P(F|E)$. Since $P(E|F)$ is known, the first outcome is either F or F'. Then, for each of these outcomes, either E or E' occurs, as shown in Figure 8.31.

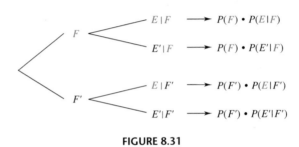

FIGURE 8.31

The four cases have the probabilities shown on the right. By the definition of conditional probability and the product rule,

$$P(E) = P(F \cap E) + P(F' \cap E),$$

$$P(F \cap E) = P(F) \cdot P(E|F), \quad \text{and} \quad P(F' \cap E) = P(F') \cdot P(E|F').$$

By substitution,

$$P(E) = P(F) \cdot P(E|F) + P(F') \cdot P(E|F')$$

and

$$P(F|E) = \frac{P(F \cap E)}{P(E)} = \frac{P(F) \cdot P(E|F)}{P(F) \cdot P(E|F) + P(F') \cdot P(E|F')}.$$

We have proved a special case of Bayes' formula, which is generalized later in this section. ✓

✓ Checkpoint 1

Use the special case of Bayes' formula to find $P(F|E)$ if $P(F) = .2$, $P(E|F) = .1$, and $P(E|F') = .3$.
[*Hint:* $P(F') = 1 - P(F)$.]

Answer: See page 526.

Bayes' Formula (Special Case)

$$P(F|E) = \frac{P(F) \cdot P(E|F)}{P(F) \cdot P(E|F) + P(F') \cdot P(E|F')}.$$

Example 1 **Business** For a fixed length of time, the probability of worker error on a certain production line is .1, the probability that an accident will occur when there is a worker error is .3, and the probability that an accident will occur when there is no worker error is .2. Find the probability of a worker error if there is an accident.

Solution Let E represent the event of an accident, and let F represent the event of a worker error. From the given information,

$$P(F) = .1, \quad P(F') = 1 - .1 = .9 \quad P(E|F) = .3, \quad \text{and} \quad P(E|F') = .2.$$

These probabilities are shown on the probability tree in Figure 8.32.

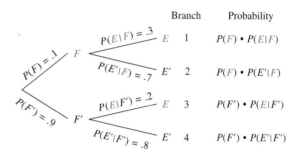

	Branch	Probability
$P(E\backslash F) = .3$ E	1	$P(F) \cdot P(E|F)$
$P(E'|F) = .7$ E'	2	$P(F) \cdot P(E'|F)$
$P(E\backslash F') = .2$ E	3	$P(F') \cdot P(E|F')$
$P(E'|F') = .8$ E'	4	$P(F') \cdot P(E'|F')$

FIGURE 8.32

Applying Bayes' Formula, we find that

$$P(F|E) = \frac{P(F) \cdot P(E|F)}{P(F) \cdot P(E|F) + P(F') \cdot P(E|F')}$$

$$= \frac{(.1)(.3)}{(.1)(.3) + (.9)(.2)} \approx .143. \quad \text{✓}$$

 **Checkpoint 2**

In Example 1, find $P(F'|E)$.

Answer: See page 526.

If we rewrite the special case of Bayes' Formula, replacing F by F_1 and F' by F_2, then it says:

$$P(F_1|E) = \frac{P(F_1) \cdot P(E|F_1)}{P(F_1) \cdot P(E|F_1) + P(F_2) \cdot P(E|F_2)}.$$

Since $F_1 = F$ and $F_2 = F'$ we see that F_1 and F_2 are disjoint and that their union is the entire sample space. The generalization of Bayes' Formula to more than two possibilities follows this same pattern.

Bayes' Formula

Suppose $F_1, F_2, \ldots F_n$ are pairwise disjoint events (meaning that any two of them are disjoint) whose union is the sample space. Then for an event E and for each i with $1 \le i \le n$,

$$P(F_i|E) = \frac{P(F_i) \cdot P(E|F_i)}{P(F_1) \cdot P(E|F_1) + \cdots + P(F_n) \cdot P(E|F_n)}.$$

This result is known as Bayes' formula, after the Reverend Thomas Bayes (1702–61), whose paper on probability was published about 245 years ago.

The statement of Bayes' formula can be daunting. It may be easier to remember the formula by thinking of the probability tree that produced it. Go through the following steps.

Using Bayes' Formula

Step 1   Start a probability tree with branches representing events $F_1, F_2, \ldots, F_n$. Label each branch with its corresponding probability.

Step 2   From the end of each of these branches, draw a branch for event E. Label this branch with the probability of getting to it, or $P(E|F_i)$.

Step 3   There are now n different paths that result in event E. Next to each path, put its probability: the product of the probabilities that the first branch occurs, $P(F_i)$, and that the second branch occurs, $P(E|F_i)$: that is, $P(F_i) \cdot P(E|F_i)$.

Step 4 $P(F_i|E)$ is found by dividing the probability of the branch for F_i by the sum of the probabilities of all the branches producing event E.

Example 2 illustrates this process.

Example 2   **Social Science**   The 2006 General Social Survey of women who are age 18 or older indicated that 86% of married women have one or more children, 31% of never married women have one or more children, and 86% of women who are divorced, separated, or widowed have one or more children. The survey also indicated that 48% of women age 18 or older were currently married, 24% had never been married, and 28% were divorced, separated, or widowed (labeled "other"). Find the probability that a woman who has one or more children is married.

Solution   Let E represent the event "having one or more children," with F_1 representing "married women," F_2 representing "never married women," and F_3 "other". Then

$$P(F_1) = .48; \quad P(E|F_1) = .86;$$
$$P(F_2) = .24; \quad P(E|F_2) = .31;$$
$$P(F_3) = .28; \quad P(E|F_3) = .86.$$

We need to find $P(F_1|E)$, the probability that a woman is married, given that she has one or more children. First, draw a probability tree using the given information, as in Figure 8.33. The steps leading to event E are shown.

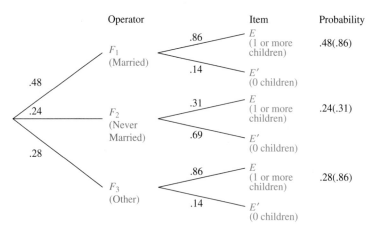

FIGURE 8.33

Find $P(F_1|E)$, using the top branch of the tree shown in Figure 8.35, by dividing the probability of this branch by the sum of the probabilities of all the branches leading to E:

$$P(F_1|E) = \frac{.48(.86)}{.48(.86) + .24(.31) + .28(.86)} = \frac{.4128}{.7280} \approx .567. \; ✔^{3}$$

✔**Checkpoint 3**

In Example 2, find

(a) $P(F_2|E)$;

(b) $P(F_3|E)$.

Answers: See page 526.

Example 3 **Business** A manufacturer buys items from six different suppliers. The fraction of the total number of items obtained from each supplier, along with the probability that an item purchased from that supplier is defective, is shown in the following table:

Supplier	Fraction of Total Supplied	Probability of Being Defective
1	.05	.04
2	.12	.02
3	.16	.07
4	.23	.01
5	.35	.03
6	.09	.05

Find the probability that a defective item came from supplier 5.

Solution Let F_1 be the event that an item came from supplier 1, with F_2, F_3, F_4, F_5, and F_6 defined in a similar manner. Let E be the event that an item is defective. We want to find $P(F_5|E)$. By Bayes' formula,

$$P(F_5|E) = \frac{(.35)(.03)}{(.05)(.04)+(.12)(.02)+(.16)(.07)+(.23)(.01)+(.35)(.03)+(.09)(.05)}$$

$$= \frac{.0105}{.0329} \approx .319.$$

✓**Checkpoint 4**

In Example 3, find the probability that the defective item came from

(a) supplier 3;

(b) supplier 6.

_____

Answers: See page 526.

There is about a 32% chance that a defective item came from supplier 5. Even though supplier 5 has only 3% defectives, his probability of being "guilty" is relatively high, about 32%, because of the large fraction of items he supplies. ✓

8.6 ▶ Exercises

For two events M and N, $P(M) = .4, P(N|M) = .3$, and $P(N|M') = .4$. Find each of the given probabilities. (See Example 1.)

1. $P(M|N)$

2. $P(M'|N)$

For disjoint events R_1, R_2, and R_3, $P(R_1) = .05$, $P(R_2) = .6$, and $P(R_3) = .35$. In addition, $P(Q|R_1) = .40$, $P(Q|R_2) = .30$, and $P(Q|R_3) = .60$. Find each of the given probabilities. (See Examples 2 and 3.)

3. $P(R_1|Q)$

4. $P(R_2|Q)$

5. $P(R_3|Q)$

6. $P(R_1'|Q)$

Suppose three jars have the following contents: 2 black balls and 1 white ball in the first; 1 black ball and 2 white balls in the second; 1 black ball and 1 white ball in the third. If the probability of selecting one of the three jars is 1/2, 1/3, and 1/6, respectively, find the probability that if a white ball is drawn, it came from the given jar.

7. The second jar

8. The third jar

Business *According to Forbes's list of the 100 top-earning chief executive officers (CEOs) of 2008, the probability of a CEO on the list being under 60 years old was .64. The probability of earning $50 million or more for those under age 60 was .1875. The probability of earning $50 million or more for those age 60 or older was .25. Find the probability of the given event.*

9. A CEO who was earning $50 million or more was under age 60.

10. A CEO who was earning less than $50 million was age 60 or older.

Business *Data from the Bureau of Labor Statistics indicates that for December 2008, 38.2% of the labor force had a high school diploma or fewer years of education, 27.9% had some college or an associate's degree, and 33.9% had a bachelor's degree or more education. Of those with a high school diploma or fewer years of education, 8.4% were unemployed. Of those with some college or an associate's degree, 5.6% were unemployed, and of those with a bachelor's degree or more education, 3.7% were unemployed. Find the probability that a randomly chosen labor force participant has the given characteristics.*

11. Some college or an associate's degree, given that he or she is unemployed

12. A bachelors degree or more education, given that he or she is unemployed

13. A high school diploma or less education, given that he or she is employed

14. A bachelor's degree or more education, given that he or she is employed

Transportation *In 2007, the probability was .179 that in a traffic fatality, the victim was age 20 or younger. The probability that a fatal accident for someone age 20 or younger involved an alcohol-impaired driver was .25. The probability that a fatal accident for someone older than age 20 involved an alcohol-impaired driver was .326.* Suppose we know a fatality involved an alcohol-impaired driver. Find the probability that the victim was in the given age group.*

15. Age 20 or younger

16. Older than age 20

Social Science *According to data from the U.S. Census Bureau and the 2006 General Social Survey, the probability of being male in the United States was .493. The probability a male considered himself "very happy" was .303, "pretty happy" was .570, and "not too happy" was .126. The probability a female considered herself "very happy" was .31, "pretty happy" was .555, and "not too happy" was .134. Find the probability that a person selected at random had the given characteristics.*

17. Male, given that he was "not too happy"

18. Female, given that she was "very happy"

19. **Management** The following information pertains to three shipping terminals operated by Krag Corp.†

Terminal	Percentage of Cargo Handled	Percent Error
Land	50	2
Air	40	4
Sea	10	14

_____

*www-nrd.nhtsa.dot.gov/Pubs/811016.PDF.

†Uniform CPA Examination, November 1989.

Krag's internal auditor randomly selects one set of shipping documents and ascertains that the set selected contains an error. Which of the following gives the probability that the error occurred in the Land Terminal?

(a) .02

(b) .10

(c) .25

(d) .50

Health *In a test for toxemia, a disease that affects pregnant women, a woman lies on her left side and then rolls over on her back. The test is considered positive if there is a 20-mm rise in her blood pressure within 1 minute. The results have produced the following probabilities, where T represents having toxemia at some time during the pregnancy and N represents a negative test:*

$$P(T'|N) = .90 \quad and \quad P(T|N') = .75.$$

Assume that $P(N') = .11$, and find each of the given probabilities.

20. $P(N|T)$ 21. $P(N'|T)$

Health *In 2007, 9.5% of the population was ages 18–24. Of these people, 28.1% did not have health insurance. Among all others in the United States, 13.9% did not have health insurance.* Find the probability of each event.*

22. A person without health insurance is age 18–24.

23. A person with health insurance is not age 18–24.

24. **Health** The probability that a person with certain symptoms has hepatitis is .8. The blood test used to confirm this diagnosis gives positive results for 90% of people with the disease and 5% of those without the disease. What is the probability that an individual who has the symptoms and who reacts positively to the test actually has hepatitis?

Health *The 2005–2006 National Health and Nutrition Examination Survey (NHANES) collected data on age and cholesterol level. If we define high cholesterol as having a total cholesterol level of 200 or higher, the following table gives percentages and probabilities of having high cholesterol for three age categories.†*

Age Group	Percentage in Sample	Probability of High Cholesterol
18–39	46.3	.315
40–64	34.9	.504
65 and older	18.8	.405

Find the probability of the given event.

25. Being 18–39, given that the person has high cholesterol.

26. Being 65 and older, given that the person does not have high cholesterol.

27. **Social Science** A recent study by the Harvard School of Public Health reported that 78.9% of college students living in a fraternity or sorority house are binge drinkers. For students living in a regular dormitory, the rate of binge drinking is 44.5%, and for students living off campus, the rate is 43.7%.* Suppose that 10% of U.S. students live in a fraternity or sorority house, 20% live in regular dormitories, and 70% live off campus.

(a) What is the probability that a randomly selected student is a binge drinker?

(b) If a randomly selected student is a binge drinker, what is the probability that he or she lives in a fraternity or sorority house?

Finance *In 2008, credit unions whose deposits were insured by the National Credit Union Association (NCUA) were classified into three categories: those with fewer than 25,000 members, those with between 25,000 and 49,999 members, and those with 50,000 members or more. Of interest is whether the credit unions' total deposits had decreased from 2007 levels. The table summarizes the percentages of the three sizes of credit unions and the probability of decreasing deposits from 2007 to 2008.†*

Credit Union Size (Number of Members)	Percentage of Credit Unions	Probability of Decreasing Deposits
Fewer than 25,000	91%	.479
25,000–49,999	4.7%	.213
50,000 or more	4.3%	.117

Find the probability that a credit union selected at random had the given characteristics.

28. Fewer than 25,000 members, given that the total deposits decreased

29. 50,000 or more members, given that the total deposits decreased

30. Between 25,000–49,999 members, given that the total deposits did not decrease

*U.S. Census Bureau.

†Based on data from www.cdc.gov/nchs/nhanes.htm.

*Wechsler, H., Lee, J., Kuo, M., and Lee, H., "College Binge Drinking in the 1990s: A Continuing Problem, Results of the Harvard School of Public Health 1999 College Alcohol Study," online at http://www.hsph.harvard.edu/cas/rpt2000/CAS2000rpt.shtml.

†Based on data from www.ncua.gov.

Social Science   *The table gives proportions of people over age 15 in the U.S. population, and proportions of people that live alone, in a recent year.* * *Use this table for Exercises 31–35.*

Age	Proportion in Population Age 15 or Higher	Proportion Living Alone
15–24	.177	.038
25–34	.169	.097
35–44	.179	.086
45–64	.318	.144
65 and higher	.157	.287

31. Find the probability that a randomly selected person age 15 or older who lives alone is between the ages of 45 and 64.

Statistical Abstract of the United States: 2009.

32. Find the probability that a randomly selected person age 15 or older who lives alone is age 65 or older.

33. Find the probability of not living alone for any person age 15 or higher.

34. Find the probability of not living alone for one person age 15–24.

35. Find the probability of not living alone for any adult age 65 or older.

✓ Checkpoint Answers

1. $1/13 \approx .077$ **2.** $6/7 \approx .857$
3. (a) .102   (b) .331
4. (a) .340   (b) .137

CHAPTER 8 ▶ Summary

KEY TERMS AND SYMBOLS

{ }	set braces
$\in$	is an element of
$\notin$	is not an element of
$\varnothing$	empty set
$\subseteq$	is a subset of
$\not\subseteq$	is not a subset of
$\subset$	is a proper subset of
A'	complement of set A
$\cap$	set intersection
$\cup$	set union
$P(E)$	probability of event E
$P(F|E)$	probability of event F, given that event E has occurred

8.1 ▶ set
element (member)
empty set

set-builder notation
universal set
subset
set operations
tree diagram
Venn diagram
complement
intersection
disjoint sets
union

8.2 ▶ addition rule for counting

8.3 ▶ experiment
trial
outcome
sample space
event
certain event

impossible event
disjoint events
basic probability principle
relative frequency probability
probability distribution

8.4 ▶ addition rule for probability
complement rule
odds

8.5 ▶ conditional probability
product rule of probability
probability tree
independent events
dependent events

8.6 ▶ Bayes' formula

CHAPTER 8 KEY CONCEPTS

Sets ▶ Set A is a **subset** of set B if every element of A is also an element of B.

A set of n elements has 2^n subsets.

Let A and B be any sets with universal set U.

The **complement** of A is $A' = \{x | x \notin A \text{ and } x \in U\}$.
The **intersection** of A and B is $A \cap B = \{x | x \in A \text{ and } x \in B\}$.
The **union** of A and B is $A \cup B = \{x | x \in A \text{ or } x \in B \text{ or both}\}$.

$n(A \cup B) = n(A) + n(B) - n(A \cap B)$, where $n(X)$ is the number of elements in set X.

Probability Summary ▶

Basic Probability Principle Let S be a sample space of equally likely outcomes, and let event E be a subset of S. Then the probability that event E occurs is

$$P(E) = \frac{n(E)}{n(S)}.$$

Addition Rule For any events E and F from a sample space S,

$$P(E \cup F) = P(E) + P(F) - P(E \cap F).$$

For disjoint events E and F,

$$P(E \cup F) = P(E) + P(F).$$

Complement Rule $P(E) = 1 - P(E')$ and $P(E') = 1 - P(E)$.

Odds The odds in favor of event E are $\dfrac{P(E)}{P(E')}, P(E') \neq 0$.

Properties of Probability **1.** For any event E in sample space S, $0 \leq P(E) \leq 1$.

2. The sum of the probabilities of all possible distinct outcomes is 1.

Conditional Probability The conditional probability of event E, given that event F has occurred, is

$$P(E|F) = \frac{P(E \cap F)}{P(F)}, \quad \text{where} \quad P(F) \neq 0.$$

For equally likely outcomes, conditional probability is found by reducing the sample space to event F; then

$$P(E|F) = \frac{n(E \cap F)}{n(F)}.$$

Product Rule of Probability If E and F are events, then $P(E \cap F)$ may be found by either of these formulas:

$$P(E \cap F) = P(F) \cdot P(E|F) \quad \text{or} \quad P(E \cap F) = P(E) \cdot P(F|E).$$

If E and F are independent events, then $P(E \cap F) = P(E) \cdot P(F)$.

Bayes' Formula $$P(F_i|E) = \frac{P(F_i) \cdot P(E|F_i)}{P(F_1) \cdot P(E|F_1) + P(F_2) \cdot P(E|F_2) + \cdots + P(F_n) \cdot P(E|F_n)}.$$

CHAPTER 8 REVIEW EXERCISES

Write true or false for each of the given statements.

1. $9 \in \{8, 4, -3, -9, 6\}$

2. $4 \in \{3, 9, 7\}$

3. $2 \notin \{0, 1, 2, 3, 4\}$

4. $0 \notin \{0, 1, 2, 3, 4\}$

5. $\{3, 4, 5\} \subseteq \{2, 3, 4, 5, 6\}$

6. $\{1, 2, 5, 8\} \subseteq \{1, 2, 5, 10, 11\}$

7. $\{1, 5, 9\} \subset \{1, 5, 6, 9, 10\}$

8. $0 \subseteq \emptyset$

List the elements in the given sets.

9. $\{x | x \text{ is a national holiday}\}$

10. $\{x | x \text{ is an integer}, -3 \leq x < 1\}$

11. {all counting numbers less than 5}

12. {$x|x$ is a leap year between 1989 and 2006}

Let U = {Vitamins A, B$_1$, B$_2$, B$_3$, B$_6$, B$_{12}$, C, D, E}, M = {Vitamins A, C, D, E}, and N = {Vitamins A, B$_1$, B$_2$, C, E}. Find the given sets.

13. M'

14. N'

15. $M \cap N$

16. $M \cup N$

17. $M \cup N'$

18. $M' \cap N$

Consider these sets:

U = {Students taking Intermediate Accounting};
A = {Females};
B = {Finance majors};
C = {Students older than 22};
D = {Students with a GPA > 3.5}.

Describe each of the following in words.

19. $A \cap C$

20. $B \cap D$

21. $A \cup D$

22. $A' \cap D$

23. $B' \cap C'$

Draw a Venn diagram and shade the given set in it.

24. $B \cup A'$

25. $A' \cap B$

26. $A' \cap (B' \cap C)$

27. $(A \cup B)' \cap C$

Business *In early 2009, reporters for* The Big Money *and* Slate *collected data on every major motion picture that grossed $75 million or more domestically for 2004–2008.* They found the following regarding the 161 movies:*

 56 were action movies;
 87 were rated PG-13;
 44 were 2 hours or longer;
 43 were action and PG-13;
 27 were action and 2 hours or longer;
 28 were rated PG-13 and 2 hours or longer;
 20 were action, rated PG-13, and 2 hours or longer.

28. How many movies were action movies and were *not* 2 hours or longer?

29. How many movies were action or rated PG-13?

30. How many movies were neither action, PG-13, nor 2 hours or longer?

Write sample spaces for the given scenarios.

31. A die is rolled and the number of points showing is noted.

32. A card is drawn from a deck containing only 4 aces.

33. A color is selected from the set {red, blue, green}, and then a number is chosen from the set {10, 20, 30}.

Business *A student purchases a digital music player and installs 10 songs on the device to see how it works. The genres of the songs are rock (3 songs), pop (4 songs), and alternative (3 songs). She listens to the first two songs on shuffle mode.*

34. Write the sample space for the genre if shuffle mode picks songs at random. (*Note:* Shuffle mode is allowed to play the same song twice in a row.)

35. Are the outcomes in the sample space for Exercise 34 equally likely?

Business *A customer wants to purchase a computer and printer. She has narrowed her selection among 2 Dell models, 1 Gateway model, and 2 HP models for the computer and 2 Epson models and 3 HP models for the printer.*

36. Write the sample space for the brands among which she can choose for the computer and printer.

37. Are the outcomes in the sample space for Exercise 36 equally likely?

Business *A company sells computers and copiers. Let E be the event "a customer buys a computer," and let F be the event "a customer buys a copier." In Exercises 38 and 39, write each of the given scenarios, using* ∩, ∪, *or* ′ *as necessary.*

38. A customer buys neither a computer nor a copier.

39. A customer buys at least one computer or copier.

40. A student gives the answer to a probability problem as 6/5. Explain why this answer must be incorrect.

41. Describe what is meant by disjoint sets, and give an example.

42. Describe what is meant by mutually exclusive events, and give an example.

43. How are disjoint sets and mutually exclusive events related?

Finance *The Standard and Poor's 500 index had the following allocations, as of December 31, 2008.**

Sector	Percentage
Consumer Discretionary	8.40
Consumer Staples	12.88
Energy	13.34
Financials	13.29
Health Care	14.79
Industrials	11.08
Information Technology	15.27
Materials	2.93
Telecommunication Services	3.83
Utilities	4.19

Find the probability that a company chosen at random from the S&P 500 was from the given sectors.

44. Consumer Discretionary or Consumer Staples

45. Information Technology or Telecommunication Services

---

*www.thebigmoney.com.

*www.standardandpoors.com.

Finance *The table gives the number of institutions insured by the Federal Deposit Insurance Corporation (FDIC), cross-classified by asset size and institution type as of June 30, 2008:**

Asset Size	Commercial Banks	Saving Institutions	Total
Less than $25 million	422	55	477
$25 million–$50 million	960	115	1075
$50 million–$100 million	1557	178	1735
$100 million–$300 million	2517	393	2910
$300 million–$500 million	691	163	854
$500 million–$1 billion	548	159	707
$1 billion–$3 billion	310	100	410
$3 billion–$10 billion	114	32	146
$10 billion or greater	84	32	116
Total	7203	1227	8430

(Note: Asset-size categories have the left endpoint included in the count. For example, asset size $50 million–$100 million includes institutions with at least $50 million and less than $100 million.)

If an FDIC-insured institution is chosen at random, find the probability of the given event.

46. $3 billion or greater in assets

47. $25 million–$50 million in assets and is a savings institution

48. $1 billion–$3 billion in assets and is a commercial bank

49. Less than $25 million in assets or is a savings institution

50. $10 billion or greater in assets or is a commercial bank

51. $500 million–$1 billion in assets, given that it is a savings institution

52. $500 million–$1 billion in assets, given that it is a commercial bank

53. Given that an institution has $10 billion or greater in assets, what is the probability it is a savings institution?

54. Given that an institution has less than $25 million in assets, what is the probability it is a commercial bank?

Health *The partial table shows the four possible (equally likely) combinations when both parents are carriers of the sickle-cell anemia trait. Each carrier parent has normal cells (N) and trait cells (T).*

		2nd Parent	
		N_2	T_2
1st Parent	N_1		N_1T_2
	T_1		

*www.fdic.gov/sod.

55. Complete the table.

56. If the disease occurs only when two trait cells combine, find the probability that a child born to these parents will have sickle-cell anemia.

57. Find the probability that the child will carry the trait, but not have the disease, if a normal cell combines with a trait cell.

58. Find the probability that the child neither is a carrier nor has the disease.

Find the probabilities for the given sums when two fair dice are rolled.

59. 8

60. No more than 4

61. At least 9

62. Odd and greater than 8

63. 2, given that the sum is less than 4

64. 7, given that at least one die shows a 4

Suppose $P(E) = .62$, $P(F) = .45$, and $P(E \cap F) = .28$. Find each of the given probabilities.

65. $P(E \cup F)$

66. $P(E \cap F')$

67. $P(E' \cup F)$

68. $P(E' \cap F')$

69. For the events E and F, $P(E) = .2$, $P(E|F) = .3$, and $P(F) = .4$. Find each of the given probabilities.
(a) $P(E'|F)$ (b) $P(E|F')$

70. Define independent events, and give an example of one.

71. Are independent events always disjoint? Are they ever disjoint? Give examples.

Business *Of the appliance repair shops listed in the phone book, 80% are competent and 20% are not. A competent shop can repair an appliance correctly 95% of the time; an incompetent shop can repair an appliance correctly 60% of the time. Suppose an appliance was repaired correctly. Find the probability that it was repaired by the given type of shop.*

72. A competent shop

73. An incompetent shop

Suppose an appliance was repaired incorrectly. Find the probability that it was repaired by the given type of shop.

74. A competent shop

75. An incompetent shop

76. **Business** A manufacturer buys items from four different suppliers. The fraction of the total number of items that is obtained from each supplier, along with the probability that an item purchased from that supplier is defective, is shown in the following table:

Supplier	Fraction of Total Supplied	Probability of Defective
1	.17	.04
2	.39	.02
3	.35	.07
4	.09	.03

(a) Find the probability that a defective item came from supplier 4.

(b) Find the probability that a defective item came from supplier 2.

77. Social Science   The following tables list the number of passengers who were on the Titanic and the number of passengers who survived, according to class of ticket:*

	CHILDREN		WOMEN	
	On	Survived	On	Survived
First Class	6	6	144	140
Second Class	24	24	165	76
Third Class	79	27	93	80
Total	109	57	402	296

	MEN		TOTALS	
	On	Survived	On	Survived
First Class	175	57	325	203
Second Class	168	14	357	114
Third Class	462	75	634	182
Total	805	146	1316	499

Use this information to determine the given probabilities. (Round answers to two decimal places.)

(a) What is the probability that a randomly selected passenger was in second class?

(b) What is the overall probability of surviving?

(c) What is the probability of a first-class passenger surviving?

(d) What is the probability of a child who was in third class surviving?

(e) Given that a survivor is from first class, what is the probability that she was a woman?

(f) Given that a male has survived, what is the probability that he was in third class?

(g) Are the events "third-class survival" and "male survival" independent events? What does this imply?

78. Social Science   The following partial table gives results of the 2006 General Social Survey question, "Are federal income taxes too high, about right, or too low?", categorized by sex:

Sex	Too High	About Right	Too Low	Total
Male	479		8	
Female		428	15	1098
Total	1134	792		

(a) Complete the table.

(b) How many were surveyed?

(c) How many men think taxes are about right?

(d) How many women think taxes are too high?

(e) How many women are in the survey?

(f) How many who think taxes are too high are male?

(g) Rewrite the event stated in part (f), using the expression "given that."

(h) Find the probability of the outcome in parts (f) and (g).

(i) Find the probability that a woman thinks that taxes are about right.

Additional Probability Review Exercises

Use these exercises for practice, deciding which rule, principle, or formula to apply.

1. Suppose $P(E) = .4$, $P(F) = .22$, and $P(E \cup F) = .52$. Find

(a) $P(E \cup F')$;   **(b)** $P(E \cap F')$;   **(c)** $P(E' \cup F)$.

2. A jar contains 2 white, 3 orange, 5 yellow, and 8 black marbles. If a marble is drawn at random, find the probability that it is

(a) white;   **(b)** orange;

(c) not black;   **(d)** orange or yellow.

3. Finance   The sector weightings for the investments in the American Century Growth Fund as of March 17, 2009 are given in the table.*

Sector	Percent
Information Technology	27.36
Health Care	18.32
Consumer Staples	12.50
Industrials	10.78
Consumer Discretionary	9.62
Energy	8.71
Financials	4.71
Materials	3.23
Utilities	2.72
Telecommunication Services	2.05

Find the probability that an investment selected at random from this fund has the given characteristics.

(a) Is in the Consumer Discretionary Sector

(b) Is in the Materials or Utilities Sector

(c) Is not in the Health Care Sector

4. Finance   The American Century Growth Fund described in Exercise 3 is invested in the following geographical regions:

---

*www.americancentury.com.

Country	Percentage Invested
United States	95.35
Switzerland	2.36
Denmark	1.13
Bermuda	.86
Netherlands	.30

Find the probability that an investment selected at random from this fund has the given characteristics.
(a) Is in Bermuda or the United States
(b) Is in Europe
(c) Is not in the United States

5. A single fair die is rolled. Find the probability that the die shows
   (a) a 2, given that the number was odd;
   (b) a 4, given that the number was even;
   (c) an even number, given that the number was 6.

6. **Finance** In 2007, the United States Department of Education spent the following dollar amounts on elementary and secondary education programs (where the dollar amounts are given in millions—for example, 14,842.9 in the table signifies $14,842,900,000):*

Program	Amount
Grants for the disadvantaged	14,842.9
School improvement programs	7697.0
Indian education	120.9
Special education	11,543.0
Vocational and adult education	2091.6
Education reform: Goals 2000	16.5

Find the probability that funds for a particular project
(a) came from special education;
(b) came from special education, or vocational and adult education;
(c) did not come from grants for the disadvantaged.

Social Science *The projected population of the United States (in thousands) by age groups in 2015 and 2050 are given in the table:†*

Age Group	2015	2050
0–4	22,076	28,148
5–17	56,030	73,425
18–44	116,686	150,400
45–64	83,911	98,490
65–84	40,545	69,506
85 and older	6292	19,041

*U.S. National Center for Education Statistics.

†U.S. Census Bureau.

Find the probability that a randomly selected person is of the given age group in the given year.
7. Age 18–44 in 2015   8. Age 18–44 in 2050
9. Age 65 or older in 2015   10. Age 65 or older in 2050

11. **Social Science** In one area, 4% of the population drives luxury cars. However, 17% of the certified public accountants (CPAs) drive luxury cars. Are the events "person drives a luxury car" and "person is a CPA" independent?

12. Suppose $P(E) = .05$, $P(F) = .1$, and $P(E \cap F) = .02$. Find
    (a) $P(E' \cap F)$;   (b) $P(E' \cup F')$;   (c) $P(E \cap F')$.

13. One orange and four red slips of paper are placed in a box. Two red and three orange slips are placed in a second box. A box is chosen at random, and a slip of paper is selected from it. The probability of choosing the first box is 3/8. If the selected slip of paper is orange, what is the probability that it came from the first box?

14. Find the probability that the slip of paper in Exercise 13 came from the second box, given that it is red.

15. **Business** A manufacturing firm finds that 70% of its new hires turn out to be good workers and 30% poor workers. All current workers are given a reasoning test. Of the good workers, 80% pass it; 40% of the poor workers pass it. Assume that these figures will hold true in the future. If the company makes the test part of its hiring procedure and hires only people who meet the previous requirements and pass the test, what percentage of the new hires will turn out to be good workers?

Social Science *The 2006 General Social Survey estimates the percentage of women working full time at 42.6%. Of these women, 46.0% are married. It also estimates the percentage of women working part time as 11.7%, with 53.4% of these women married. The percentage of women not working full or part time, but who are married, is 40.9%. Find the probability that a woman has the given characteristics.*

16. Is married

17. Is married and works full time

18. Is not married and works part time

19. Is not married and is not working full or part time

Business *On a given weekend in the fall, a tire company can buy television advertising time for a college football game, a professional baseball game, or a professional football game. If the company sponsors the college football game, there is a 70% chance that the company will get a high rating. There is a 50% chance if the company sponsors a professional baseball game and a 60% chance if it sponsors a professional football game. The probability of the company sponsoring these various games is .5, .2, and .3, respectively. Suppose the company does get a high rating; find the probability that it sponsored the given type of game.*

20. A college football game

21. A professional football game

22. Transportation As reported by the National Highway Traffic Safety Administration (NHSTA), in 2006, the state of Washington had the highest rate of seat belt compliance; the odds that a driver was using a seat belt were 26:1. What is the probability that a driver in Washington in 2006 was *not* using a seat belt?

23. Transportation The same report as cited in Exercise 22 stated that Wyoming and New Hampshire had the lowest rates of seat belt compliance. The probability of using the seat belt in those states was .635. What are the odds that a driver in either of those two states in 2006 was using a seat belt?

Health *The table cross-classifies gender and height with data collected from the 2005–2006 National Health and Nutrition Examination Survey (NHANES).**

*Table compiled by the author from data available at www.cdc.gov/nchs/nhanes.htm.

Gender	Less than 60 Inches	Between 61 and 66 Inches	Between 67 and 72 Inches	Greater than 72 Inches	Total
Male	38	441	1645	379	2503
Female	316	1897	467	3	2683
Total	354	2338	2112	382	5186

Find the probability that a person selected at random had the given characteristics.

24. Male and between 67 and 72 inches tall

25. Female or less than 60 inches tall

26. 72 inches tall or shorter

27. Between 61 and 66 inches tall, given that the person is a male

28. Female, given that the person is between 67 and 72 inches tall

CASE 8

Medical Diagnosis

When patients undergo medical testing, a positive test result for a disease or condition can be emotionally devastating. In many cases, however, testing positive does not necessarily imply that the patient actually has the disease. Bayes' formula can be very helpful in determining the probability of actually having the disease when a patient tests positive.

Let us label the event of having the disease as D and not having the disease as D'. We will denote testing positive for the disease as T and testing negative as T'. Suppose a medical test is calibrated on patients so that we know that among patients with the disease, the test is positive 99.95% of the time. (This quantity is often called the **sensitivity** of the test.) Among patients known not to have the disease, 99.90% of the time the test gave a negative result. (This quantity is often called the **specificity** of the test.) In summary, we have

Sensitivity $= P(T|D) = .9995$ and Specificity $= P(T'|D') = .9990$.

Using the complement rule, we find that the probability the test will give a negative result when a patient has the disease is

$$P(T'|D) = 1 - P(T|D) = 1 - .9995 = .0005.$$

Similarly, for those patients without the disease, the probability of testing positive is .0010, calculated by

$$P(T|D') = 1 - P(T'|D') = 1 - .9990 = .0010.$$

These results do not yet answer the question of interest: If a patient tests positive for the disease, what is the probability the patient actually has the disease? Using our notation, we want to know $P(D|T)$. There are two steps to finding this probability. The first is that we need an estimate of the prevalence of the disease in the general population. Let us assume that one person in a thousand has the disease. We can then calculate that

$$P(D) = \frac{1}{1000} = .001 \quad \text{and} \quad P(D') = 1 - .001 = .999.$$

With this information, and the previous results from testing, we can now use Bayes' formula to find $P(D|T)$:

$$P(D|T) = \frac{P(D)P(T|D)}{P(D)P(T|D) + P(D')P(T|D')}.$$

Using $P(D) = .001$, $P(D') = .999$, the sensitivity $P(T|D) = .9995$ and the complement to the specificity $P(T|D') = .0010$, we have

$$P(D|T) = \frac{(.001)(.9995)}{(.001)(.9995) + (.999)(.0010)} = \frac{.0009995}{.0019985} \approx .5001.$$

Hence, the probability the patient actually has the disease after testing positive for the disease is only .5. This is approximately the same probability as guessing "heads" when flipping a coin. It seems paradoxical that a test which has such high sensitivity (in this case, .9995) and specificity (in this case, .999) could lead to a probability of merely .5 that a person who tests positive for the disease actually has the disease. This is why it is imperative to have confirmatory tests run after testing positive.

The other factor in the calculation is the prevalence of the disease among the general population. In our example, we used $P(D) = .001$. Often, it is very difficult to know how prevalent a disease is among the general population. If the disease is more prevalent, such as 1 in 100, or $P(D) = .01$, we find the proba-bility of a patient's having the disease, given that the patient tests positive, as

$$P(D|T) = \frac{(.01)(.9995)}{(.01)(.9995) + (.99)(.0010)} = \frac{.009995}{.010985} \approx .9099.$$

So when the disease has higher prevalence, then the probability of having the disease after testing positive is also higher. If the disease has a lower prevalence (as in the case of our first example), then the probability of having the disease after testing positive could be much lower than one might otherwise think.

EXERCISES

1. Suppose the specificity of a test is 0.999. Find $P(T|D')$.

2. If the sensitivity of a test for a disease is .99 and the prevalence of the disease is .005, use your answer to Exercise 1 to find the probability of a patient's having the disease, given that the patient tested positive, or $P(D|T)$.

3. Recalculate your answer to Exercise 2 using a prevalence of disease of .0005.

Counting, Probability Distributions, and Further Topics in Probability

Probability has applications to quality control in manufacturing and to decision making in business. It plays a role in testing new medications, in evaluating DNA evidence in criminal trials, and in a host of other situations. See Exercises 1 and 2 on page 565, and Exercises 41–43 on page 545. Sophisticated counting techniques are often necessary for determining the probabilities used in these applications. See Exercises 33–35 on pages 566–567.

CASE 9: Quick Draw® from the New York State Lottery

Probability distributions enable us to compute the "average value" or "expected outcome" when an experiment or process is repeated a number of times. These distributions are introduced in Section 9.1 and used in Sections 9.4 and 9.6. The other focus of this chapter is the development of effective ways to count the possible outcomes of an experiment without actually listing them all (which can be *very* tedious when large numbers are involved). These counting techniques are introduced in Section 9.2 and are used to find probabilities throughout the rest of the chapter.

9.1 ▶ Probability Distributions and Expected Value

Probability distributions were introduced briefly in Section 8.4. Now we take a more complete look at them. In this section, we shall see that the *expected value* of a probability distribution is a type of average. A probability distribution depends on the idea of a *random variable*, so we begin with that.

RANDOM VARIABLES

One of the questions asked in the 2006 National Health and Nutrition Examination Study (NHANES) had to do with respondents' daily hours of TV or video use.* The answer to that question, which we will label x, is one of the numbers 0 through 6 (corresponding to the numbers of hours of use). Since the value of x is random, x is called a random variable.

◤ Random Variable

A **random variable** is a function that assigns a real number to each outcome of an experiment.

The following table gives each possible outcome of the study question on TV and video use together with the probability $P(x)$ of each outcome x.

x	0	1	2	3	4	5	6
$P(x)$	.13	.19	.27	.16	.10	.13	.02

A table that lists all the outcomes with the corresponding probabilities is called a **probability distribution**. The sum of the probabilities in a probability distribution must always equal 1. (The sum in some distributions may vary slightly from 1 because of rounding.)

Instead of writing the probability distribution as a table, we could write the same information as a set of ordered pairs:

$$\{(0, .13), (1, .19), (2, .27), (3, .16), (4, .10), (5, .13), (6, .02)\}.$$

There is just one probability for each value of the random variable.

---

*National Health and Nutrition Examination Study, www.cdc.gov/nchs/nhanes.htm.

The information in a probability distribution is often displayed graphically as a special kind of bar graph called a **histogram**. The bars of a histogram all have the same width, usually 1 unit. The heights of the bars are determined by the probabilities. A histogram for the data in the probability distribution on the previous page is given in Figure 9.1. A histogram shows important characteristics of a distribution that may not be readily apparent in tabular form, such as the relative sizes of the probabilities and any symmetry in the distribution.

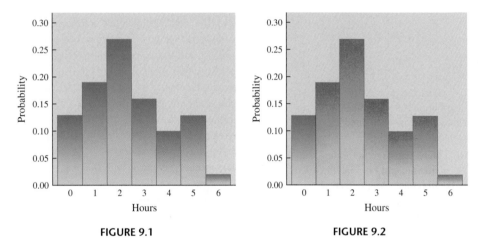

FIGURE 9.1   FIGURE 9.2

The area of the bar above $x = 0$ in Figure 9.1 is the product of 1 and .13, or $1 \cdot .13 = .13$. Since each bar has a width of 1, its area is equal to the probability that corresponds to its x-value. The probability that a particular value will occur is thus given by the area of the appropriate bar of the graph. For example, the probability that one or more hours are spent watching TV or a video is the sum of the areas for $x = 1, x = 2, x = 3, x = 4, x = 5$, and $x = 6$. This area, shown in red in Figure 9.2, corresponds to .87 of the total area, since

$$P(x \geq 1) = P(x = 1) + P(x = 2) + P(x = 3) + P(x = 4)$$
$$+ P(x = 5) + P(x = 6)$$
$$= .19 + .27 + .16 + .10 + .13 + .02$$
$$= .87.$$

Example 1

(a) Give the probability distribution for the number of heads showing when two coins are tossed.

Solution Let x represent the random variable "number of heads." Then x can take on the value 0, 1, or 2. Now find the probability of each outcome. When two coins are tossed, the sample space is {TT, TH, HT, HH}. So the probability of getting one head is $2/4 = 1/2$. Similar analysis of the other cases produces this table.

x	0	1	2
$P(x)$	1/4	1/2	1/4

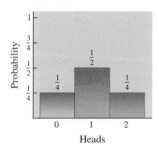

FIGURE 9.3

✓**Checkpoint 1**

(a) Give the probability distribution for the number of heads showing when three coins are tossed.

(b) Draw a histogram for the distribution in part (a). Find the probability that no more than one coin comes up heads.

Answers: See page 546.

(b) Draw a histogram for the distribution in the table. Find the probability that at least one coin comes up heads.

Solution The histogram is shown in Figure 9.3. The portion in red represents

$$P(x \geq 1) = P(x = 1) + P(x = 2)$$
$$= \frac{3}{4}. \checkmark$$

TECHNOLOGY TIP Virtually all graphing calculators can produce histograms. The procedures differ on various calculators, but you usually are required to enter the outcomes in one list and the corresponding frequencies in a second list. For specific details, check your instruction manual under "statistics graphs" or "statistical plotting." To get the histogram in Figure 9.3 with a TI-84+ calculator, we entered the outcomes 0, 1, and 2 in the first list and entered the probabilities .25, .5, and .25 in a second list. Two versions of the histogram are shown in Figure 9.4. They differ slightly because different viewing windows were used. With some calculators, the probabilities must be entered as integers, so make the entries in the second list 1, 2, and 1 (corresponding to 1/4, 2/4, and 1/4, respectively), and use a window with $0 \leq y \leq 4$.

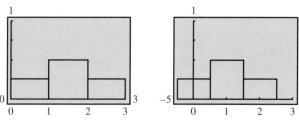

FIGURE 9.4

EXPECTED VALUE

In working with probability distributions, it is useful to have a concept of the typical or average value that the random variable takes on. In Example 1, for instance, it seems reasonable that, on the average, one head shows when two coins are tossed. This does not tell what will happen the next time we toss two coins; we may get two heads, or we may get none. If we tossed two coins many times, however, we would expect that, in the long run, we would average about one head for each toss of two coins.

A way to solve such problems in general is to imagine flipping two coins 4 times. Based on the probability distribution in Example 1, we would expect that 1 of the 4 times we would get 0 heads, 2 of the 4 times we would get 1 head, and 1 of the 4 times we would get 2 heads. The total number of heads we would get, then, is

$$0 \cdot 1 + 1 \cdot 2 + 2 \cdot 1 = 4.$$

The expected number of heads per toss is found by dividing the total number of heads by the total number of tosses:

$$\frac{0 \cdot 1 + 1 \cdot 2 + 2 \cdot 1}{4} = 0 \cdot \frac{1}{4} + 1 \cdot \frac{1}{2} + 2 \cdot \frac{1}{4} = 1.$$

Notice that the expected number of heads turns out to be the sum of the three values of the random variable x, multiplied by their corresponding probabilities. We can use this idea to define the *expected value* of a random variable as follows.

Expected Value

Suppose that the random variable x can take on the n values $x_1, x_2, x_3, \ldots, x_n$. Suppose also that the probabilities that these values occur are, respectively, $p_1, p_2, p_3, \ldots, p_n$. Then the **expected value** of the random variable is

$$E(x) = x_1 p_1 + x_2 p_2 + x_3 p_3 + \cdots + x_n p_n.$$

Example 2 **Social Science** In the example with the TV and video usage on page 536, find the expected number of hours per day of viewing.

Solution Multiply each outcome in the table on page 536 by its probability, and sum the products:

$$E(x) = 0 \cdot .13 + 1 \cdot .19 + 2 \cdot .27 + 3 \cdot .16 + 4 \cdot .10 + 5 \cdot .13 + 6 \cdot .02$$
$$= 2.38.$$

On the average, a respondent of the survey will indicate 2.38 hours of TV or video usage. ✔2️⃣

✔ **Checkpoint 2**

Find the expected value of the number of heads showing when four coins are tossed.

Answer: See page 546.

Physically, the expected value of a probability distribution represents a balance point. If we think of the histogram in Figure 9.1 as a series of weights with magnitudes represented by the heights of the bars, then the system would balance if supported at the point corresponding to the expected value.

Example 3 **Business** Suppose a local symphony decides to raise money by raffling off a microwave oven worth $400, a dinner for two worth $80, and two books worth $20 each. A total of 2000 tickets are sold at $1 each. Find the expected value of winning for a person who buys one ticket in the raffle.

Solution Here, the random variable represents the possible amounts of net winnings, where net winnings = amount won − cost of ticket. For example, the net winnings of the person winning the oven are $400 (amount won) − $1 (cost of ticket) = $399, and the net winnings for each losing ticket are $0 − $1 = −$1.

The net winnings of the various prizes, as well as their respective probabilities, are shown in the table below. The probability of winning $19 is 2/2000, because there are 2 prizes worth $20. (We have not reduced the fractions in order to keep all the denominators equal.) Because there are 4 winning tickets, there are 1996 losing tickets, so the probability of winning −$1 is 1996/2000.

x	$399	$79	$19	−$1
$P(x)$	1/2000	1/2000	2/2000	1996/2000

The expected winnings for a person buying one ticket are

$$399\left(\frac{1}{2000}\right) + 79\left(\frac{1}{2000}\right) + 19\left(\frac{2}{2000}\right) + (-1)\left(\frac{1996}{2000}\right) = -\frac{1480}{2000}$$
$$= -.74.$$

On the average, a person buying one ticket in the raffle will lose $.74, or 74¢.

It is not possible to lose 74¢ in this raffle: Either you lose $1, or you win a prize worth $400, $80, or $20, minus the $1 you paid to play. But if you bought tickets in many such raffles over a long time, you would lose 74¢ per ticket, on the average. It is important to note that the expected value of a random variable may be a number that can never occur in any one trial of the experiment. ✓3

NOTE An alternative way to compute expected value in this and other such examples is to calculate the expected amount won and then subtract the cost of the ticket afterward. The amount won is either $400 (with probability 1/2000), $80 (with probability 1/2000), $20 (with probability 2/2000), or $0 (with probability 1996/2000). The expected winnings for a person buying one ticket are then

$$400\left(\frac{1}{2000}\right) + 80\left(\frac{1}{2000}\right) + 20\left(\frac{2}{2000}\right) + 0\left(\frac{1996}{2000}\right) - 1 = -\frac{1480}{2000}$$

$$= -.74.$$

✓ **Checkpoint 3**

Suppose you buy 1 of 10,000 tickets at $1 each in a lottery where the prize is $5,000. What are your expected net winnings? What does this answer mean?

Answer: See page 546.

Example 4   Each day, Lynette and Tanisha toss a coin to see who buys coffee (at $1.75 a cup). One tosses, while the other calls the outcome. If the person who calls the outcome is correct, the other buys the coffee; otherwise the caller pays. Find Lynette's expected winnings.

Solution Assume that an honest coin is used, that Tanisha tosses the coin, and that Lynette calls the outcome. The possible results and corresponding probabilities are shown in the following table:

	Possible Results			
Result of Toss	Heads	Heads	Tails	Tails
Call	Heads	Tails	Heads	Tails
Caller Wins?	Yes	No	No	Yes
Probability	1/4	1/4	1/4	1/4

Lynette wins a $1.75 cup of coffee whenever the results and calls match, and she loses $1.75 when there is no match. Her expected winnings are

$$1.75\left(\frac{1}{4}\right) + (-1.75)\left(\frac{1}{4}\right) + (-1.75)\left(\frac{1}{4}\right) + 1.75\left(\frac{1}{4}\right) = 0.$$

On the average, over the long run, Lynette breaks even. ✓4

✓ **Checkpoint 4**

Find Tanisha's expected winnings.

Answer: See page 546.

A game with an expected value of 0 (such as the one in Example 4) is called a **fair game**. Casinos do not offer fair games. If they did, they would win (on the average) $0 and have a hard time paying the help! Casino games have expected winnings for the house that vary from 1.5 cents per dollar to 60 cents per dollar. The next example examines the popular game of roulette.

Example 5 **Business** As we saw in Chapter 8, an American roulette wheel has 38 slots. Two of the slots are marked 0 and 00 and are colored green. The remaining slots are numbered 1–36 and are colored red and black (18 red and 18 black). One simple wager is to bet $1 on the color red. If the marble lands in a red slot, the player gets his or her dollar back, plus a $1 of winnings. Find the expected winnings for a $1 bet on red.

Solution For this bet, there are only two possible outcomes: winning or losing. The random variable has outcomes +1 if the marble lands in a red slot and −1 if it does not. We need to find the probability for these two outcomes. Since there are 38 total slots, 18 of which are colored red, the probability of winning a dollar is 18/38. The player will lose if the marble lands in any of the remaining 20 slots, so the probability of losing the dollar is 20/38. Thus, the probability distribution is

x	-1	$+1$
$P(x)$	$\dfrac{20}{38}$	$\dfrac{18}{38}$

The expected winnings are

$$E(x) = -1\left(\frac{20}{38}\right) + 1\left(\frac{18}{38}\right) = -\frac{2}{38} \approx -.053.$$

The winnings on a dollar bet for red average out to losing about a nickel on every spin of the roulette wheel. In other words, a casino earns on average 5.3 cents on every dollar bet on red. **5** ✓

Exercises 17–20 at the end of the section ask you to find the expected winnings for other bets on games of chance. The idea of expected value can be very useful in decision making, as shown by the next example.

✓Checkpoint 5

A gambling game requires a $1 bet. If the player wins, she gets $100, but if she loses, she loses her $1. The probability of winning is .005. What are the expected winnings of this game?

Answer: See page 546.

✓Checkpoint 6

After college, a person is offered two jobs. With job A, after five years, there is a 50% chance of making $60,000 per year and a 50% chance of making $45,000. With job B, after five years, there is a 30% chance of making $80,000 per year and a 70% chance of making $35,000. Based strictly on expected value, which job should be taken?

Answer: See page 546.

Example 6 **Finance** Suppose that, at age 50, you receive a letter from Mutual of Mauritania Insurance Company. According to the letter, you must tell the company immediately which of the following two options you will choose: Take $50,000 at age 60 (if you are alive, and $0 otherwise), or take $65,000 at age 70 (again, if you are alive, and $0 otherwise). Based *only* on the idea of expected value, which should you choose?

Solution Life insurance companies have constructed elaborate tables showing the probability of a person living a given number of years into the future. From a recent such table, the probability of living from age 50 to age 60 is .88, while the probability of living from age 50 to 70 is .64. The expected values of the two options are as follows.

First Option: $(50,000)(.88) + (0)(.12) = 44,000;$

Second Option: $(65,000)(.64) + (0)(.36) = 41,600.$

Strictly on the basis of expected value, choose the first option. **6** ✓

Example 7   **Social Science**   The table gives the probability distribution for the number of children of respondents to the 2006 General Social Survey,* for those with 7 or fewer children.

x	0	1	2	3	4	5	6	7
$P(x)$	.273	.159	.257	.165	.087	.031	.019	.010

Find the expected value for the number of children.

Solution   Using the formula for the expected value, we have

$$E(x) = 0(.273) + 1(.159) + 2(.257) + 3(.165)$$
$$+ 4(.087) + 5(.031) + 6(.019) + 7(.010)$$
$$= 1.855.$$

For those respondents with 7 or fewer children, the number of children, on average, is 1.855.

———————————
*www.norc.org/GSS+Website.

9.1 ▶ **Exercises**

For each of the experiments described, let x determine a random variable and use your knowledge of probability to prepare a probability distribution. (Hint: Use a tree diagram.)

1. Four children are born, and the number of boys is noted. (Assume an equal chance of a boy or a girl for each birth.)

2. Two dice are rolled, and the total number of points is recorded.

3. Three cards are drawn from a deck. The number of queens is counted.

4. Two names are drawn from a hat, signifying who should go pick up pizza. Three of the names are on the swim team and two are not. The number of swimmers selected is counted.

Draw a histogram for each of the given exercises, and shade the region that gives the indicated probability. (See Example 1.)

5. Exercise 1; $P(x \leq 2)$

6. Exercise 2; $P(x \geq 11)$

7. Exercise 3; $P(\text{at least one queen})$

8. Exercise 4; $P(\text{fewer than two swimmers})$

Find the expected value for each random variable. (See Example 2.)

9.

x	1	3	5	7
$P(x)$	.1	.5	.2	.2

10.

y	0	15	30	40
$P(y)$	.15	.20	.40	.25

11.

z	0	2	4	8	16
$P(z)$	.21	.24	.21	.17	.17

12.

x	5	10	15	20	25
$P(x)$	.40	.30	.15	.10	.05

Find the expected values for the random variables x whose probability functions are graphed.

13.
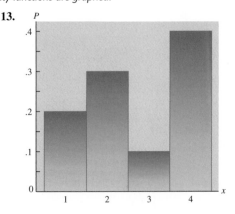

14.

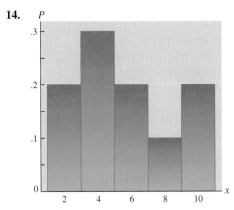

15.

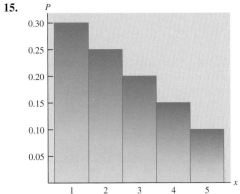

16.

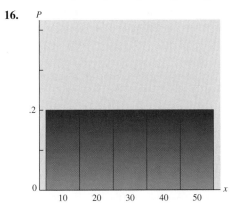

Find the expected winnings for the games of chance described in Exercises 17–20. (See Example 5.)

17. In one form of roulette, you bet $1 on "even." If one of the 18 even numbers comes up, you get your dollar back, plus another one. If one of the 20 noneven (18 odd, 0, and 00) numbers comes up, you lose your dollar.

18. Repeat Exercise 17 if there are only 19 noneven numbers (no 00).

19. *Numbers* is a game in which you bet $1 on any three-digit number from 000 to 999. If your number comes up, you get $500.

20. In one form of the game Keno, the house has a pot containing 80 balls, each marked with a different number

from 1 to 80. You buy a ticket for $1 and mark one of the 80 numbers on it. The house then selects 20 numbers at random. If your number is among the 20, you get $3.20 (for a net winning of $2.20).

21. **Business** An online gambling site offers a first prize of $50,000 and two second prizes of $10,000 each for registered users when they place a bet. A random bet will be selected over a 24-hour period. Two million bets are received in the contest. Find the expected winnings if you can place one registered bet of $1 in the given period.

Business *A contest at a fast-food restaurant offered the following cash prizes and probabilities of winning when one buys a large order of French fries for $1.89:*

Prize	Probability
$100,000	1/8,504,860
$50,000	1/302,500
$10,000	1/282,735
$1000	1/153,560
$100	1/104,560
$25	1/9,540

22. Find the expected winnings if the player buys one large order of French fries.

23. Find the expected winnings if the player buys 25 large orders of French fries in multiple visits.

24. **Business** According to the Web site of Mars, the makers of M&M's Plain Chocolate Candies, 21% of the candies produced are green.* If we select 4 candies from a bag at random and record the number of green candies, the probability distribution is as follows:

x	0	1	2	3	4
$P(x)$	.3895	.4141	.1651	.0293	.0019

Find the expected value for the number of green candies.

25. **Social Science** Recently, it has been estimated that 85.7% of the U.S. population has achieved a high school degree or higher.† If four adults are selected at random, the probability distribution for the number with a high school degree or higher is given in the table:

x	0	1	2	3	4
$P(x)$	.0004	.0100	.0901	.3600	.5394

Find the expected value.

26. **Social Science** Recently, it has been estimated that 28.7% of the population has earned a college degree or

*http://us.mms.com/us/.

†www.census.gov.

higher.* If four people are chosen at random, the following table gives the probability distribution for the number with a college degree or higher:

x	0	1	2	3	4
$P(x)$	.258	.416	.251	.067	.007

Find $E(x)$.

For Exercises 27–30, determine whether the probability distributions are valid or not. If not, explain why.

27.

x	5	10	15	20	25	30	35
$P(x)$	.01	.09	.25	.45	.05	.20	−.05

28.

x	−2	−1	0	1	2	3	4
$P(x)$	.05	.10	.75	.02	.03	.04	.01

29.

x	1	3	5	7	9	11
$P(x)$	.01	.02	.03	.04	.05	.85

30.

x	−10	−5	0	5	10
$P(x)$	.50	.10	−.20	.30	.30

For Exercises 31–35, fill in the missing value(s) to make a valid probability distribution.

31.

x	5	10	15	20	25	30
$P(x)$	.01	.09	.25	.45	.05	

32.

x	−3	−2	−1	0	1	2	3
$P(x)$		.15	.15	.15	.15	.15	.15

33.

x	10	20	30	40
$P(x)$	.20		.25	.30

34.

x	−50	−40	−30	−20	−10	0	10
$P(x)$	.05	.25	.10	.10	.05		

35.

x	1	2	3	6	12	24	48
$P(x)$	.10	.10	.20	.25	.05		

36. Business During the month of July, a home improvement store sold a great many air-conditioning units, but some were returned. The following table shows the probability distribution for the daily number of returns of air-conditioning units sold in July:

x	0	1	2	3	4	5
$P(x)$	.55	.31	.08	.04	.01	.01

Find the expected number of returns per day.

37. Finance An insurance company has written 100 policies of $15,000, 250 of $10,000, and 500 of $5000 for people age 20. If experience shows that the probability that a person will die in the next year at age 20 is .0007, how much can the company expect to pay out during the year after the policies were written?

38. Social Science According to a recent study, 62% of teenagers have television sets in their bedrooms.* If 6 teens are selected at random, the probability distribution for the number of teens with televisions in their bedrooms is as follows.

x	0	1	2	3	4	5	6
$P(x)$	.003	.029	.120	.262	.320	.209	.057

Find the expected number of teens with televisions in their bedrooms in a random sample of 6 teens.

39. Business In 2008, Toyota captured 15.9% of auto sales in the United States.† If 3 cars are selected at random, the probability distribution for the number that were manufactured by Toyota is given in the following table:

x	0	1	2	3
$P(x)$	.595	.337	.064	.004

Find $E(x)$.

40. Natural Science According to the U.S. Fish and Wildlife service, 16.7% of the endangered species in the United States are birds. If we select 5 endangered species at random, the probability distribution for the number of bird species is given in the following table:

x	0	1	2	3	4	5
$P(x)$	.4011	.4020	.1612	.0323	.0032	.0001

Find $E(x)$.

---

*http://health.usnews.com/blogs/on-parenting/2008/4/7/tv-in-the-bedroom-bad-idea.htm.

†http://online.wsj.com.

41. Business Levi Strauss and Company uses expected value to help its salespeople rate their accounts.* For each account, a salesperson estimates potential additional volume and the probability of getting it. The product of these figures gives the expected value of the potential, which is added to the existing volume. The totals are then classified as *A*, *B*, or *C* as follows: $40,000 or below, class *C*; above $40,000, up to and including $55,000, class *B*; above $55,000, class *A*. Complete the chart.

Account Number	Existing Volume	Potential Additional Volume	Probability of Additional Volume	Expected Value of Potential	Existing Volume + Expected Value of Potential	Class
1	$15,000	$10,000	.25	$2,500	$17,500	C
2	40,000	0	—	—	40,000	C
3	20,000	10,000	.20			
4	50,000	10,000	.10			
5	5,000	50,000	.50			
6	0	100,000	.60			
7	30,000	20,000	.80			

42. According to Len Pasquarelli, in the first 10 games of the 2004 professional football season in the United States, two-point conversions were successful 51.2% of the time.† We can compare this rate with the historical success rate of extra-point kicks of 94%.‡

(a) Calculate the expected value of each strategy.

(b) Over the long run, which strategy will maximize the number of points scored?

(c) From this information, should a team always use only one strategy? Explain.

43. Natural Science Otitis media, or middle-ear infection, is initially treated with an antibiotic. Researchers have compared two antibiotics—amoxicillin and cefaclor—for their cost effectiveness. Amoxicillin is inexpensive, safe, and effective. Cefaclor is also safe. However, it is considerably more expensive and is generally more effective. Use the given tree diagram (in which costs are estimated as the total cost of medication, an office visit, an ear check, and hours of lost work) to complete the following tasks:*

(a) Find the expected cost of using each antibiotic to treat a middle-ear infection.

(b) To minimize the total expected cost, which antibiotic should be chosen?

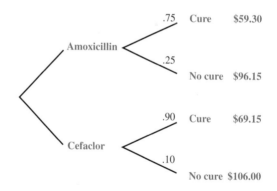

44. Physical Science One of the few methods that can be used in an attempt to cut the severity of a hurricane is to *seed* the storm. In this process, silver iodide crystals are dropped into the storm in order to decrease the wind speed. Unfortunately, silver iodide crystals sometimes cause the storm to *increase* its speed. Wind speeds may

---

*This example was supplied by James McDonald, Levi Strauss and Company, San Francisco.

†Len Pasquarelli, "Teams More Successful Going for Two," November 18, 2004,www.espn.com.

‡David Leonhardt, "In Football, 6 + 2 Often Equals 6," *New York Times*, January 16, 2000, p. 4-2.

*Jeffrey Weiss and Shoshana Melman, "Cost Effectiveness in the Choice of Antibiotics for the Initial Treatment of Otitis Media in Children: A Decision Analysis Approach." *Journal of Pediatric Infectious Disease*, vol. 7, no. 1 (1998): 23–26.

also increase or decrease even with no seeding. Use the given tree diagram to complete the following tasks.*

(a) Find the expected amount of damage under each of the options, "seed" and "do not seed."

(b) To minimize total expected damage, which option should be chosen?

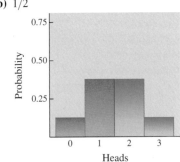

	Change in wind speed	Property damage (millions of dollars)
Seed		
0.038	+32%	335.8
0.143	+16%	191.1
0.392	0	100.0
0.255	−16%	46.7
0.172	−34%	16.3
Do not seed		
0.054	+32%	335.8
0.206	+16%	191.1
0.480	0	100.0
0.206	−16%	46.7
0.054	−34%	16.3

45. In the 2008 Wimbledon Championships, Roger Federer and Rafeal Nadal played in the finals. The prize money for the winner was £750,000 (British pounds sterling), and the prize money for the runner-up was £350,000. Find the expected winnings for Rafeal Nadal if

(a) we assume both players had an equal chance of winning;

(b) we use the players' prior head-to-head match record, whereby Nadal had a .67 probability of winning.

*Data from "The Decision to Seed Hurricanes," by R. A. Howard from *Science*, Vol. 176, pp. 1191–1202, Copyright 1972 by the American Association for the Advancement of Science.

46. Bryan Miller has two cats and a dog. Each pet has a 35% probability of climbing into the chair in which Bryan is sitting, independently of how many pets are already in the chair with Bryan.

(a) Find the probability distribution for the number of pets in the chair with Bryan. (*Hint*: List the sample space.)

(b) Use the probability distribution in part (a) to find the expected number of pets in the chair with Bryan.

✓ Checkpoint Answers

1. **(a)**

x	$P(x)$
0	1/8
1	3/8
2	3/8
3	1/8

(b) 1/2

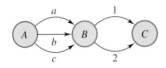

2. 2

3. −$ .50. On the average, you lose $ .50 per ticket purchased.

4. 0   **5.** −$.495

6. Job A has an expected salary of $52,500, and job B has an expected salary of $48,500. Take job A.

9.2 ▶ The Multiplication Principle, Permutations, and Combinations

We begin with a simple example. If there are three roads from town A to town B and two roads from town B to town C, in how many ways can someone travel from A to C by way of B? We can solve this simple problem with the help of Figure 9.5, which lists all the possible ways to go from A to C.

FIGURE 9.5

The possible ways to go from A through B to C are a1, a2, b1, b2, c1, and c2. So there are 6 possible ways. Note that 6 is the product of $3 \cdot 2$, 3 is the number of ways to go from A to B, and 2 is the number of ways to go from B to C.

Another way to solve this problem is to use a tree diagram, as shown in Figure 9.6. This diagram shows that, for each of the 3 roads from A, there are 2 different routes leading from B to C, making $3 \cdot 2 = 6$ different ways.

This example is an illustration of the *multiplication principle*.

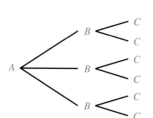

FIGURE 9.6

Multiplication Principle

Suppose n choices must be made, with

$$m_1 \text{ ways to make choice 1,}$$
$$m_2 \text{ ways to make choice 2,}$$
$$\vdots$$
$$m_n \text{ ways to make choice } n.$$

Then there are

$$m_1 \cdot m_2 \cdots \cdot m_n$$

different ways to make the entire sequence of choices.

Example 1   Suppose Angela has 9 skirts, 8 blouses, and 13 different pairs of shoes. If she is willing to wear any combination, how many different skirt–blouse–shoe choices does she have?

Solution By the multiplication principle, there are 9 skirt choices, 8 blouse choices, and 13 shoe choices, for a total of $9 \cdot 8 \cdot 13 = 936$ skirt–blouse–shoe outfits.

Example 2   **Business** In March 2009, there were 881 sink faucets, 314 bath vanities, and 87 medicine cabinets available to order at the Home Depot® Web site. How many different ways could you buy one sink faucet, bath vanity, and medicine cabinet?

Solution A tree (or other diagram) would be far too complicated to use here, but the multiplication principle easily answers the question. There are

$$881 \cdot 314 \cdot 87 = 24,067,158$$

ways.

Example 3   A combination lock can be set to open to any 3-letter sequence.

(a) How many sequences are possible?

Solution Since there are 26 letters of the alphabet, there are 26 choices for each of the 3 letters, and, by the multiplication principle, $26 \cdot 26 \cdot 26 = 17,576$ different sequences.

(b) How many sequences are possible if no letter is repeated?

Solution There are 26 choices for the first letter. It cannot be used again, so there are 25 choices for the second letter and then 24 choices for the third letter. Consequently, the number of such sequences is $26 \cdot 25 \cdot 24 = 15,600$. ✓

FACTORIAL NOTATION

The use of the multiplication principle often leads to products such as $5 \cdot 4 \cdot 3 \cdot 2 \cdot 1$, the product of all the natural numbers from 5 down to 1. If n is a natural number, the symbol $n!$ (read "n *factorial*") denotes the product of all the natural numbers from n down to 1. The factorial is an algebraic shorthand. For example, instead of writing $5 \cdot 4 \cdot 3 \cdot 2 \cdot 1$, we simply write $5!$. If $n = 1$, this formula is understood to give $1! = 1$.

✓ **Checkpoint 1**

(a) In how many ways can 6 business tycoons line up their golf carts at the country club?

(b) How many ways can 4 pupils be seated in a row with 4 seats?

Answers: See page 560.

> ### *n*-Factorial
>
> For any natural number n,
>
> $$n! = n(n-1)(n-2) \ldots (3)(2)(1).$$
>
> By definition, $0! = 1$.

Note that $6! = 6 \cdot 5 \cdot 4 \cdot 3 \cdot 2 \cdot 1 = 6 \cdot (5 \cdot 4 \cdot 3 \cdot 2 \cdot 1) = 6 \cdot 5!$. Similarly, the definition of $n!$ shows that

$$n! = n \cdot (n-1)!.$$

One reason that $0!$ is defined to be 1 is to make the preceding formula valid when $n = 1$, for when $n = 1$, we have $1! = 1$ and $1 \cdot (1-1)! = 1 \cdot 0! = 1 \cdot 1 = 1$, so $n! = n \cdot (n-1)!$. ✓

Almost all calculators have an $n!$ key. A calculator with a 10-digit display and scientific-notation capability will usually give the exact value of $n!$ for $n \leq 13$ and approximate values of $n!$ for $14 \leq n \leq 69$. The value of $70!$ is approximately $1.198 \cdot 10^{100}$, which is too large for most calculators. So how would you simplify $\dfrac{100!}{98!}$? Depending on the type of calculator, there may be an overflow problem. The next two examples show how to avoid this problem.

✓ **Checkpoint 2**

Evaluate:

(a) 4!

(b) 6!

(c) 1!

(d) 6!/4!

Answers: See page 560.

TECHNOLOGY TIP The factorial key on a graphing calculator is usually located in the PRB or PROB submenu of the MATH or OPTN menu.

Example 4 Evaluate $\dfrac{100!}{98!}$.

Solution We use the fact that $n! = n \cdot (n-1)!$ several times:

$$\frac{100!}{98!} = \frac{100 \cdot 99!}{98!} = \frac{100 \cdot 99 \cdot 98!}{98!} = 100 \cdot 99 = 9900.$$

Example 5 Evaluate $\dfrac{5!}{2!\,3!}$.

Solution $\dfrac{5!}{2!\,3!} = \dfrac{5 \cdot 4!}{2!\,3!} = \dfrac{5 \cdot 4 \cdot 3!}{2!\,3!} = \dfrac{5 \cdot 4}{2 \cdot 1} = 10.$

Example 6 Morse code uses a sequence of dots and dashes to represent letters and words. How many sequences are possible with at most 3 symbols?

Solution "At most 3" means "1 or 2 or 3." Each symbol may be either a dot or a dash. Thus, the following numbers of sequences are possible in each case:

Number of Symbols	Number of Sequences
1	2
2	$2 \cdot 2 = 4$
3	$2 \cdot 2 \cdot 2 = 8$

Altogether, $2 + 4 + 8 = 14$ different sequences of at most 3 symbols are possible. Because there are 26 letters in the alphabet, some letters must be represented by sequences of 4 symbols in Morse code. ✓ ³

✓**Checkpoint 3**

How many Morse code sequences are possible with at most 4 symbols?

Answer: See page 560.

PERMUTATIONS

A **permutation** of a set of elements is an ordering of the elements. For instance, there are six permutations (orderings) of the letters *A*, *B*, and *C*, namely,

$$ABC, ACB, BAC, BCA, CAB, \text{ and } CBA,$$

as you can easily verify. As this listing shows, order counts when determining the number of permutations of a set of elements. By saying "order counts," we mean that the event *ABC* is indeed distinct from *CBA* or any other ordering of the three letters. We can use the multiplication principle to determine the number of possible permutations of any set.

Example 7 How many batting orders are possible for a 9-person baseball team?

Solution There are 9 possible choices for the first batter, 8 possible choices for the second batter, 7 for the third batter, and so on, down to the eighth batter (2 possible choices) and the ninth batter (1 possibility). So the total number of batting orders is

$$9 \cdot 8 \cdot 7 \cdot 6 \cdot 5 \cdot 4 \cdot 3 \cdot 2 \cdot 1 = 362,880.$$

In other words, the number of permutations of a 9-person set is 9!.

The argument in Example 7 applies to any set, leading to the conclusion that follows.

> The number of permutations of an *n* element set is *n*!.

Sometimes we want to order only some of the elements in a set, rather than all of them.

Example 8 A teacher has 5 books and wants to display 3 of them side by side on her desk. How many arrangements of 3 books are possible?

Solution The teacher has 5 ways to fill the first space, 4 ways to fill the second space, and 3 ways to fill the third space. Because she wants only 3 books on the desk, there are only 3 spaces to fill, giving $5 \cdot 4 \cdot 3 = 60$ possible arrangements. ✓

✓**Checkpoint 4**

How many ways can a merchant with limited space display 4 fabric samples side by side from her collection of 8?

Answer: See page 560.

In Example 8, we say that the possible arrangements are *the permutations of 5 things taken 3 at a time*, and we denote the number of such permutations by $_5P_3$. In other words, $_5P_3 = 60$. More generally, an ordering of *r* elements from a set of *n* elements is called a **permutation of *n* things taken *r* at a time**, and the number of such permutations is denoted $_nP_r$.* To see how to compute this number, look at the answer in Example 8, which can be expressed like this:

$$_5P_3 = 5 \cdot 4 \cdot 3 = 5 \cdot 4 \cdot 3 \cdot \frac{2 \cdot 1}{2 \cdot 1} = \frac{5 \cdot 4 \cdot 3 \cdot 2 \cdot 1}{2 \cdot 1} = \frac{5!}{2!} = \frac{5!}{(5-3)!}.$$

A similar analysis in the general case leads to this useful fact:

> **Permutations**
>
> If $_nP_r$ (where $r \le n$) is the number of permutations of *n* elements taken *r* at a time, then
>
> $$_nP_r = \frac{n!}{(n-r)!}.$$

🖱 **TECHNOLOGY TIP** The permutation function on a graphing calculator is in the same menu as the factorial key. For large values of *n* and *r*, the calculator display for $_nP_r$ may be an approximation.

To find $_nP_r$, we can either use the preceding rule or apply the multiplication principle directly, as the next example shows.

---

*Another notation that is sometimes used is $P(n, r)$.

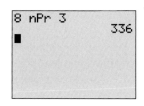

FIGURE 9.7

✓ **Checkpoint 5**

Find the number of permutations of

(a) 5 things taken 2 at a time;

(b) 9 things taken 3 at a time.

Find each of the following:

(c) $_3P_1$;

(d) $_7P_3$;

(e) $_{12}P_2$.

Answers: See page 560.

Example 9   Early in 2008, 8 candidates sought the Republican nomination for president at the Iowa caucus. In a poll, how many ways could voters rank their first, second, and third choices?

Solution   This is the same as finding the number of permutations of 8 elements taken 3 at a time. Since there are 3 choices to be made, the multiplication principle gives $_8P_3 = 8 \cdot 7 \cdot 6 = 336$. Alternatively, by the formula for $_nP_r$,

$$_8P_3 = \frac{8!}{(8-3)!} = \frac{8!}{5!} = \frac{8 \cdot 7 \cdot 6 \cdot 5 \cdot 4 \cdot 3 \cdot 2 \cdot 1}{5 \cdot 4 \cdot 3 \cdot 2 \cdot 1} = 8 \cdot 7 \cdot 6 = 336.$$

Figure 9.7 shows this result on a TI-84+ graphing calculator.

Example 10   In a college admissions forum, 5 female and 4 male sophomore panelists discuss their college experiences with high school seniors.

(a) In how many ways can the panelists be seated in a row of 9 chairs?

Solution   Find $_9P_9$, the total number of ways to seat 9 panelists in 9 chairs:

$$_9P_9 = \frac{9!}{(9-9)!} = \frac{9!}{0!} = \frac{9!}{1} = 9 \cdot 8 \cdot 7 \cdot 6 \cdot 5 \cdot 4 \cdot 3 \cdot 2 \cdot 1 = 362{,}880.$$

So, there are 362,880 ways to seat the 9 panelists.

(b) In how many ways can the panelists be seated if the males and females are to be alternated?

Solution   Use the multiplication principle. In order to alternate males and females, a female must be seated in the first chair (since there are 5 females and only 4 males), any of the males next, and so on. Thus, there are 5 ways to fill the first seat, 4 ways to fill the second seat, 4 ways to fill the third seat (with any of the 4 remaining females), and so on, or

$$5 \cdot 4 \cdot 4 \cdot 3 \cdot 3 \cdot 2 \cdot 2 \cdot 1 \cdot 1 = 2880.$$

So, there are 2880 ways to seat the panelists.

(c) In how many ways can the panelists be seated if the males must sit together and the females sit together?

Solution   Use the multiplication principle. We first must decide how to arrange the two groups (males and females). There are 2! ways of doing this. Next, there are 5! ways of arranging the females and 4! ways of arranging the men, for a total of

$$2! \, 5! \, 4! = 2 \cdot 120 \cdot 24 = 5760$$

ways. ⁶✓

✓ **Checkpoint 6**

A collection of 3 paintings by one artist and 2 by another is to be displayed. In how many ways can the paintings be shown

(a) in a row?

(b) if the works of the artists are to be alternated?

(c) if one painting by each artist is displayed?

Answers: See page 560.

COMBINATIONS

In Example 8, we found that there are 60 ways a teacher can arrange 3 of 5 different books on a desk. That is, there are 60 permutations of 5 things taken 3 at a time. Suppose now that the teacher does not wish to arrange the books on her desk, but rather wishes to choose, at random, any 3 of the 5 books to give to a book sale to raise money for her school. In how many ways can she do this?

At first glance, we might say 60 again, but that is incorrect. The number 60 counts all possible *arrangements* of 3 books chosen from 5. However, the following arrangements, for example, would all lead to the same set of 3 books being given to the book sale:

mystery–biography–textbook	biography–textbook–mystery
mystery–textbook–biography	textbook–biography–mystery
biography–mystery–textbook	textbook–mystery–biography

The foregoing list shows 6 different *arrangements* of 3 books, but only one *subset* of 3 books. A subset of items selected *without regard to order* is called a **combination**. The number of combinations of 5 things taken 3 at a time is written $_5C_3$. Since they are subsets, combinations are *not ordered*.

To evaluate $_5C_3$, start with the $5 \cdot 4 \cdot 3$ *permutations* of 5 things taken 3 at a time. Combinations are unordered; therefore, we find the number of combinations by dividing the number of permutations by the number of ways each group of 3 can be ordered—that is, by 3!:

$$_5C_3 = \frac{5 \cdot 4 \cdot 3}{3!} = \frac{5 \cdot 4 \cdot 3}{3 \cdot 2 \cdot 1} = 10.$$

There are 10 ways that the teacher can choose 3 books at random for the book sale.

Generalizing this discussion gives the formula for the number of combinations of n elements taken r at a time, written $_nC_r$.* In general, a set of r elements can be ordered in $r!$ ways, so we divide $_nP_r$ by $r!$ to get $_nC_r$:

$$_nC_r = \frac{_nP_r}{r!}$$

$$= {_nP_r} \frac{1}{r!}$$

$$= \frac{n!}{(n-r)!} \cdot \frac{1}{r!} \qquad \text{Definition of } _nP_r$$

$$= \frac{n!}{(n-r)!\, r!}.$$

This last form is the most useful for setting up the calculation. ✓

✓ **Checkpoint 7**

Evaluate $\dfrac{_nP_r}{r!}$ for the given values.

(a) $n = 6, r = 2$

(b) $n = 8, r = 4$

(c) $n = 7, r = 0$

Answers: See page 560.

> **Combinations**
>
> The number of combinations of n elements taken r at a time, where $r \le n$, is
>
> $$_nC_r = \frac{n!}{(n-r)!\, r!}.$$

---

*Another notation that is sometimes used in place of $_nC_r$ is $\binom{n}{r}$.

Example 11 From a group of 10 students, a committee is to be chosen to meet with the dean. How many different 3-person committees are possible?

Solution A committee is not ordered, so we compute

$$_{10}C_3 = \frac{10!}{(10-3)!\,3!} = \frac{10!}{7!\,3!} = \frac{10\cdot9\cdot8\cdot7!}{7!\,3!} = \frac{10\cdot9\cdot8}{3\cdot2\cdot1} = 120.$$

TECHNOLOGY TIP The key for obtaining $_nC_r$ on a graphing calculator is located in the same menu as the key for obtaining $_nP_r$.

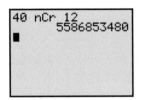

FIGURE 9.8

✔ Checkpoint 8

Use $\dfrac{n!}{(n-r)!\,r!}$ to evaluate $_nC_r$.

(a) $_6C_2$

(b) $_8C_4$

(c) $_7C_0$

Compare your answers with the answers to Checkpoint 7.

___

Answers: See page 560.

Example 12 In how many ways can a 12-person jury be chosen from a pool of 40 people?

Solution Since the order in which the jurors are chosen does not matter, we use combinations. The number of combinations of 40 things taken 12 at a time is

$$_{40}C_{12} = \frac{40!}{(40-12)!\,12!} = \frac{40!}{28!\,12!}.$$

Using a calculator to compute this number (Figure 9.8), we see that there are 5,586,853,480 possible ways to choose a jury. **8 ✔**

Example 13 Three managers are to be selected from a group of 30 to work on a special project.

(a) In how many different ways can the managers be selected?

Solution Here, we wish to know the number of 3-element combinations that can be formed from a set of 30 elements. (We want combinations, not permutations, since order within the group of 3 does not matter.) So, we calculate

$$_{30}C_3 = \frac{30!}{27!\,3!} = 4060.$$

There are 4060 ways to select the project group.

(b) In how many ways can the group of 3 be selected if a certain manager must work on the project?

Solution Since 1 manager has already been selected for the project, the problem is reduced to selecting 2 more from the remaining 29 managers:

$$_{29}C_2 = \frac{29!}{27!\,2!} = 406.$$

In this case, the project group can be selected in 406 ways.

(c) In how many ways can a nonempty group of at most 3 managers be selected from these 30 managers?

Solution The group is to be nonempty; therefore, "at most 3" means "1 or 2 or 3." Find the number of ways for each case:

Case	Number of Ways
1	$_{30}C_1 = \dfrac{30!}{29!\,1!} = \dfrac{30 \cdot 29!}{29!\,1!} = 30$
2	$_{30}C_2 = \dfrac{30!}{28!\,2!} = \dfrac{30 \cdot 29 \cdot 28!}{28! \cdot 2 \cdot 1} = 435$
3	$_{30}C_3 = \dfrac{30!}{27!\,3!} = \dfrac{30 \cdot 29 \cdot 28 \cdot 27!}{27! \cdot 3 \cdot 2 \cdot 1} = 4060$

The total number of ways to select at most 3 managers will be the sum

$$30 + 435 + 4060 = 4525. \quad \checkmark$$

✔**Checkpoint 9**

Five orchids from a collection of 20 are to be selected for a flower show.

(a) In how many ways can this be done?

(b) In how many different ways can the group of 5 be selected if 2 particular orchids must be included?

(c) In how many ways can at least 1 and at most 5 orchids be selected? (*Hint:* Use a calculator.)

Answers: See page 560.

CHOOSING A METHOD

The formulas for permutations and combinations given in this section will be very useful in solving probability problems in later sections. Any difficulty in using these formulas usually comes from being unable to differentiate among them. Both permutations and combinations give the number of ways to choose r objects from a set of n objects. The differences between permutations and combinations are outlined in the following summary.

Permutations	**Combinations**
Different orderings or arrangements of the r objects are different permutations.	Each choice or subset of r objects gives 1 combination. Order within the r objects does not matter.
$$_nP_r = \frac{n!}{(n-r)!}$$	$$_nC_r = \frac{n!}{(n-r)!\,r!}$$
Clue words: arrangement, schedule, order Order matters!	Clue words: group, committee, set, sample Order does not matter!

In the examples that follow, concentrate on recognizing which of the formulas should be applied.

Example 14 For each of the given problems, tell whether permutations or combinations should be used to solve the problem.

(a) How many 4-digit numbers are possible if no digits are repeated?

Solution Since changing the order of the 4 digits results in a different number, we use permutations.

(b) A sample of 3 lightbulbs is randomly selected from a batch of 15 bulbs. How many different samples are possible?

Solution The order in which the 3 lightbulbs are selected is not important. The sample is unchanged if the bulbs are rearranged, so combinations should be used.

(c) In a basketball conference with 8 teams, how many games must be played so that each team plays every other team exactly once?

Solution The selection of 2 teams for a game is an *unordered* subset of 2 from the set of 8 teams. Use combinations again.

(d) In how many ways can 4 patients be assigned to 6 hospital rooms so that each patient has a private room?

Solution The room assignments are an *ordered* selection of 4 rooms from the 6 rooms. Exchanging the rooms of any 2 patients within a selection of 4 rooms gives a different assignment, so permutations should be used. **10** ✓

✔Checkpoint 10

Solve the problems in Example 14.

Answers: See page 560.

Example 15 A manager must select 4 employees for promotion. Twelve employees are eligible.

(a) In how many ways can the 4 employees be chosen?

Solution Because there is no reason to consider the order in which the 4 are selected, we use combinations:

$$_{12}C_4 = \frac{12!}{4!\ 8!} = 495.$$

(b) In how many ways can 4 employees be chosen (from 12) to be placed in 4 different jobs?

Solution In this case, once a group of 4 is selected, its members can be assigned in many different ways (or arrangements) to the 4 jobs. Therefore, this problem requires permutations:

$$_{12}P_4 = \frac{12!}{8!} = 11,880.$$ **11** ✓

✔Checkpoint 11

A mailman has special-delivery mail for 7 customers.

(a) In how many ways can he arrange his schedule to deliver to all 7?

(b) In how many ways can he schedule deliveries if he can deliver to only 4 of the 7?

Answers: See page 560.

FIGURE 9.9

Example 16 Powerball is a lottery game played in 30 states (plus the District of Columbia and the U.S. Virgin Islands). For a $1 ticket, a player selects five different numbers from 1 to 59 and one powerball number from 1 to 39 (which may be the same as one of the first five chosen). A match of all six numbers wins the jackpot. How many different selections are possible?

Solution The order in which the first five numbers are chosen does not matter. So we use combinations to find the number of combinations of 59 things taken 5 at a time—that is, $_{59}C_5$. There are 39 ways to choose one powerball number from 1 to 39. So, by the multiplication principle, the number of different selections is

$$_{59}C_5 \cdot 39 = \frac{59!}{(59-5)!\ 5!} \cdot 39 = \frac{59! \cdot 39}{54!\ 5!} = 195,249,054,$$

as shown in two ways on a graphing calculator in Figure 9.9. **12** ✓

✔Checkpoint 12

Under earlier Powerball rules, you had to choose five different numbers from 1 to 53 and then choose one powerball number from 1 to 42. Under those rules, how many different selections were possible?

Answer: See page 560.

Example 17 A male student going on spring break at Daytona Beach has 8 tank tops and 12 pairs of shorts. He decides he will need 5 tank tops and 6 pairs of shorts for the trip. How many ways can he choose the tank tops and the shorts?

Solution We can break this problem into two parts: finding the number of ways to choose the tank tops, and finding the number of ways to choose the shorts. For the tank tops, the order is not important, so we use combinations to obtain

$$_8C_5 = \frac{8!}{3!\,5!} = 56.$$

Likewise, order is not important for the shorts, so we use combinations to obtain

$$_{12}C_6 = \frac{12!}{6!\,6!} = 924.$$

We now know there are 56 ways to choose the tank tops and 924 ways to choose the shorts. The total number of ways to choose the tank tops and shorts can be found using the multiplication principle to obtain $56 \cdot 924 = 51{,}744.$ **13**✓

As Examples 16 and 17 show, often both combinations and the multiplication principle must be used in the same problem.

> **✓Checkpoint 13**
>
> Lacy wants to pack 4 of her 10 blouses and 2 of her 4 pairs of jeans for her trip to Europe. How many ways can she choose the blouses and jeans?
>
> *Answer: See page 560.*

Example 18   To illustrate the differences between permutations and combinations in another way, suppose 2 cans of soup are to be selected from 4 cans on a shelf: noodle (N), bean (B), mushroom (M), and tomato (T). As shown in Figure 9.10(a), there are 12 ways to select 2 cans from the 4 cans if the order matters (if noodle first and bean second is considered different from bean and then noodle, for example). However, if order is unimportant, then there are 6 ways to choose 2 cans of soup from the 4, as illustrated in Figure 9.10(b).

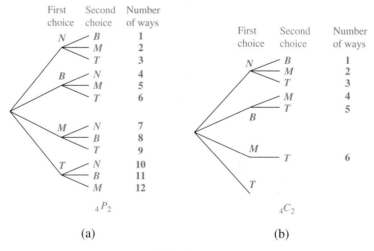

(a)   (b)

FIGURE 9.10

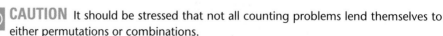

⊘ CAUTION It should be stressed that not all counting problems lend themselves to either permutations or combinations.

9.2 ▶ Exercises

Evaluate the given factorials, permutations, and combinations.

1. $_4P_2$ **2.** $3!$ **3.** $_8C_5$

4. $7!$ **5.** $_8P_1$ **6.** $_7C_2$

7. $4!$ **8.** $_4P_4$ **9.** $_9C_6$

10. $_8C_2$ **11.** $_{13}P_3$ **12.** $_9P_5$

Use a calculator to find values for Exercises 13–20.

13. $_{25}P_5$ **14.** $_{40}P_5$

15. $_{14}P_5$ **16.** $_{17}P_8$

17. $_{18}C_5$ **18.** $_{32}C_9$

19. $_{28}C_{14}$ **20.** $_{35}C_{30}$

21. Some students find it puzzling that $0! = 1$, and they think that $0!$ should equal 0. If this were true, what would be the value of $_4P_4$ according to the permutations formula?

22. If you already knew the value of $8!$, how could you find the value of $9!$ quickly?

Use the multiplication principle to solve the given problems. (See Examples 1–6.)

23. Social Science   An ancient Chinese philosophical work known as the *I Ching* (*Book of Changes*) is often used as an oracle from which people can seek and obtain advice. The philosophy describes the duality of the universe in terms of two primary forces: *yin* (passive, dark, receptive) and *yang* (active, light, creative). See the accompanying figure. The yin energy is represented by a broken line (– –) and the yang by a solid line (—). These lines are written on top of one another in groups of three, known as *trigrams*. For example, the trigram ☱ is called *Tui*, the Joyous, and has the image of a lake.

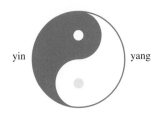

yin   yang

(a) How many trigrams are there altogether?

(b) The trigrams are grouped together, one on top of the other, in pairs known as hexagrams. Each hexagram represents one aspect of the *I Ching* philosophy. How many hexagrams are there?

24. Business   How many different heating–cooling units are possible if a home owner has 3 choices for the efficiency rating of the furnace, 3 options for the fan speed, and 6 options for the air condenser?

25. Business   An auto manufacturer produces 6 models, each available in 8 different colors, with 4 different upholstery fabrics and 3 interior colors. How many varieties of the auto are available?

26. Business   How many different 4-letter radio station call letters can be made
   (a) if the first letter must be K or W and no letter may be repeated?
   (b) if repeats are allowed (but the first letter still must be K or W)?
   (c) How many of the 4-letter call letters (starting with K or W) with no repeats end in R?

27. Social Science   A Social Security number has 9 digits. How many Social Security numbers are possible? The U.S. population in 2009 was approximately 307 million. Was it possible for every U.S. resident to have a unique Social Security number? (Assume no restrictions.)

28. Social Science   The United States Postal Service currently uses 5-digit zip codes in most areas. How many zip codes are possible if there are no restrictions on the digits used? How many would be possible if the first number could not be 0?

29. Social Science   The Postal Service is encouraging the use of 9-digit zip codes in some areas, adding 4 digits after the usual 5-digit code. How many such zip codes are possible with no restrictions?

30. Social Science   For many years, the state of California used 3 letters followed by 3 digits on its automobile license plates.
   (a) How many different license plates are possible with this arrangement?
   (b) When the state ran out of new numbers, the order was reversed to 3 digits followed by 3 letters. How many new license plate numbers were then possible?
   (c) Several years ago, the numbers described in part (b) were also used up. The state then issued plates with 1 letter followed by 3 digits and then 3 letters. How many new license plate numbers will this arrangement provide?

31. Business   A recent trip to the drug store revealed 12 different kinds of Pantene® shampoo and 10 different kinds of Pantene® conditioner. How many ways can Sherri buy 1 Pantene® shampoo and 1 Pantene® conditioner?

32. Business   A pharmaceutical salesperson has 6 doctors' offices to call on.
   (a) In how many ways can she arrange her schedule if she calls on all 6 offices?
   (b) In how many ways can she arrange her schedule if she decides to call on 4 of the 6 offices?

Social Science *The United States is rapidly running out of telephone numbers. In large cities, telephone companies have introduced new area codes as numbers are used up.*

33. (a) Until recently, all area codes had a 0 or a 1 as the middle digit and the first digit could not be 0 or 1. How many area codes were possible with this arrangement? How many telephone numbers does the current 7-digit sequence permit per area code? (The 3-digit sequence that follows the area code cannot start with 0 or 1. Assume that there are no other restrictions.)
    (b) The actual number of area codes under the previous system was 152. Explain the discrepancy between this number and your answer to part (a).

34. The shortage of area codes under the previous system was avoided by removing the restriction on the second digit. How many area codes are available under this new system?

35. A problem with the plan in Exercise 34 was that the second digit in the area code had been used to tell phone company equipment that a long-distance call was being made. To avoid changing all equipment, an alternative plan proposed a 4-digit area code and restricted the first and second digits as before. How many area codes would this plan have provided?

36. Still another solution to the area-code problem is to increase the local dialing sequence to 8 digits instead of 7. How many additional numbers would this plan create? (Assume the same restrictions.)

37. Define permutation in your own words.

Use permutations to solve each of the given problems. (See Examples 7–10.)

38. A baseball team has 15 players. How many 9-player batting orders are possible?

39. Tim is a huge fan of the latest album by country-music singer Kenny Chesney. If Tim has time to listen to only 5 of the 12 songs on the album, how many ways can he listen to the 5 songs?

40. **Business** From a cooler with 8 cans of different kinds of soda, 3 are selected for 3 people. In how many ways can this be done?

41. The Greek alphabet has 24 letters. How many ways can one name a fraternity using 3 Greek letters (with no repeats)?

42. **Finance** A customer speaks to his financial advisor about investment products. The advisor has 9 products available, but knows he will only have time to speak about 4. How many different ways can he give the details on 4 different investment products to the customer?

43. The student activity club at the college has 32 members. In how many different ways can the club select a president, a vice president, a treasurer, and a secretary?

44. A student can only take one class a semester, and she needs to take 4 more electives in any order. If there are 20 courses from which she can choose, how many ways can she take her 4 electives?

45. In a club with 17 members, how many ways can the club elect a president and a treasurer?

Use combinations to solve each of the given problems. (See Examples 11–13.)

46. **Business** Four items are to be randomly selected from the first 25 items on an assembly line in order to determine the defect rate. How many different samples of 4 items can be chosen?

47. **Social Science** A group of 4 students is to be selected from a group of 10 students to take part in a class in cell biology.
    (a) In how many ways can this be done?
    (b) In how many ways can the group that will *not* take part be chosen?

48. **Natural Science** From a group of 15 smokers and 21 nonsmokers, a researcher wants to randomly select 7 smokers and 6 nonsmokers for a study. In how many ways can the study group be selected?

49. The college football team has 11 seniors. The team needs to elect a group of 4 senior co-captains. How many different 4-person groups of co-captains are possible?

50. The drama department holds auditions for a play with a cast of 5 roles. If 33 students audition, how many casts of 5 people are possible?

51. Explain the difference between a permutation and a combination.

52. Padlocks with digit dials are often referred to as "combination locks." According to the mathematical definition of combination, is this an accurate description? Explain.

Exercises 53–70 are mixed problems that may require permutations, combinations, or the multiplication principle. (See Examples 14–18.)

53. Use a tree diagram to find the number of ways 2 letters can be chosen from the set $\{P, Q, R\}$ if order is important and
    (a) if repetition is allowed;
    (b) if no repeats are allowed.
    (c) Find the number of combinations of 3 elements taken 2 at a time. Does this answer differ from that to part (a) or (b)?

54. Repeat Exercise 53, using the set $\{P, Q, R, S\}$ and 4 in place of 3 in part (c).

55. **Social Science** The U.S. Senate Foreign Relations Committee in 2009 had 11 Democrats and 7 Republicans. A delegation of 5 people is to be selected to visit Iraq.
    (a) How many delegations are possible?
    (b) How many delegations would have all Republicans?

(c) How many delegations would have 3 Democrats and 2 Republicans?

(d) How many delegations would have at least one Democrat?

56. Natural Science   In an experiment on plant hardiness, a researcher gathers 6 wheat plants, 5 barley plants, and 3 rye plants. She wishes to select 4 plants at random.

(a) In how many ways can this be done?

(b) In how many ways can this be done if exactly 2 wheat plants must be included?

57. Business   According to the Baskin-Robbins® Web site, there are 21 "classic flavors" of ice cream.

(a) How many different double-scoop cones can be made if order does not matter (for example, putting chocolate on top of vanilla is equivalent to putting vanilla on top of chocolate)?

(b) How many different triple-scoop cones can be made if order does matter?

58. Finance   A financial advisor offers 8 mutual funds in the high-risk category, 7 in the moderate-risk category, and 10 in the low-risk category. An investor decides to invest in 3 high-risk funds, 4 moderate-risk funds and 3 low-risk funds. How many ways can the investor do this?

59. A lottery game requires that you pick 6 different numbers from 1 to 99. If you pick all 6 winning numbers, you win $4 million.

(a) How many ways are there to choose 6 numbers if order is not important?

(b) How many ways are there to choose 6 numbers if order matters?

60. In Exercise 59, if you pick 5 of the 6 numbers correctly, you win $5,000. In how many ways can you pick exactly 5 of the 6 winning numbers without regard to order?

61. The game of Sets* consists of a special deck of cards. Each card has on it either one, two, or three shapes. The shapes on each card are all the same color, either green, purple, or red. The shapes on each card are the same style, either solid, shaded, or outline. There are three possible shapes—squiggle, diamond, and oval—and only one type of shape appears on a card. The deck consists of all possible combinations of shape, color, style, and number. How many cards are in a deck?

62. Health   Over the course of the previous nursing shift, 16 new patients were admitted onto a hospital ward. If a nurse begins her shift by caring for 6 of the new patients, how many possible ways could the 6 patients be selected from the 16 new arrivals?

63. Natural Science   A biologist is attempting to classify 52,000 species of insects by assigning 3 initials to each

species. Is it possible to classify all the species in this way? If not, how many initials should be used?

64. One play in a state lottery consists of choosing 6 numbers from 1 to 44. If your 6 numbers are drawn (in any order), you win the jackpot.

(a) How many possible ways are there to draw the 6 numbers?

(b) If you get 2 plays for a dollar, how much would it cost to guarantee that one of your choices would be drawn?

(c) Assuming that you work alone and can fill out a betting ticket (for 2 plays) every second, and assuming that the lotto drawing will take place 3 days from now, can you place enough bets to guarantee that 1 of your choices will be drawn?

65. A cooler contains 5 cans of Pepsi®, 1 can of Diet Coke®, and 3 cans of 7UP®; you pick 3 cans at random. How many samples are possible in which the soda cans picked are

(a) only Pepsi;   **(b)** only Diet Coke;

(c) only 7UP;   **(d)** 2 Pepsi, 1 Diet Coke;

(e) 2 Pepsi, 1 7UP;   **(f)** 2 7UP, 1 Pepsi;

(g) 2 Diet Coke, 1 7UP?

66. A class has 9 male students and 8 female students. How many ways can the class select a committee of four people to petition the teacher not to make the final exam cumulative if the committee has to have 2 males and 2 females?

67. Health   A hospital wants to test the viability of a new medication for attention deficit disorder. It has 35 adults volunteer for the study, but can only enroll 20 in the study. How many ways can it choose the 20 volunteers to enroll in the study?

68. Suppose a pizza shop offers 4 choices of cheese and 9 toppings. If the order of the cheeses and toppings does not matter, how many different pizza selections are possible when choosing two cheeses and 2 toppings?

69. In the game of bingo, each card has 5 columns. Column 1 has spaces for 5 numbers, chosen from 1 to 15. Column 2 similarly has 5 numbers, chosen from 16 to 30. Column 3 has a free space in the middle, plus 4 numbers chosen from 31 to 45. The 5 numbers in columns 4 and 5 are chosen from 46 to 60 and from 61 to 75, respectively. The numbers in each card can be in any order. How many different bingo cards are there?

70. A television commercial for Little Caesars® pizza announced that, with the purchase of two pizzas, one could receive free any combination of up to five toppings on each pizza. The commercial shows a young child waiting in line at one of the company's stores who calculates that there are 1,048,576 possibilities for the toppings on the two pizzas. Verify the child's calculation. Use the fact that Little Caesars has 11 toppings to choose from. Assume

---

*Copyright © Marsha J. Falco.

that the order of the two pizzas matters; that is, if the first pizza has combination 1 and the second pizza has combination 2, that arrangement is different from combination 2 on the first pizza and combination 1 on the second.*

If the n objects in a permutations problem are not all distinguishable—that is, if there are n_1 of type 1, n_2 of type 2, and so on, for r different types—then the number of distinguishable permutations is

$$\frac{n!}{n_1!\, n_2! \cdots n_r!}.$$

Example *In how many ways can you arrange the letters in the word Mississippi?*

This word contains 1 m, 4 i's, 4 s's, and 2 p's. To use the formula, let $n = 11$, $n_1 = 1$, $n_2 = 4$, $n_3 = 4$, *and* $n_4 = 2$ *to get*

$$\frac{11!}{1!\, 4!\, 4!\, 2!} = 34{,}650$$

arrangements. The letters in a word with 11 different letters can be arranged in $11! = 39{,}916{,}800$ *ways.*

71. Find the number of distinguishable permutations of the letters in each of the given words.
 (a) martini **(b)** nunnery **(c)** grinding

72. A printer has 5 W's, 4 X's, 3 Y's, and 2 Z's. How many different "words" are possible that use all these letters? (A "word" does not have to have any meaning here.)

---

*Joseph F. Heiser, "Pascal and Gauss meet Little Caesars," *Mathematics Teacher*, 87 (September 1994): 389. In a letter to *Mathematics Teacher*, Heiser argued that the two combinations should be counted as the same, so the child has actually overcounted. In that case, there would be 524,800 possibilities.

73. Shirley is a shelf stocker at the local grocery store. She has 4 varieties of Stouffer's® frozen dinners, 3 varieties of Lean Cuisine® frozen dinners, and 5 varieties of Weight Watchers® frozen dinners. In how many distinguishable ways can she stock the shelves if
 (a) the dinners can be arranged in any order?
 (b) dinners from the same company are considered alike and have to be shelved together?
 (c) dinners from the same company are considered alike, but do not have to be shelved together?

74. A child has a set of different-shaped plastic objects. There are 2 pyramids, 5 cubes, and 6 spheres. In how many ways can she arrange them in a row
 (a) if they are all different colors?
 (b) if the same shapes must be grouped?
 (c) In how many distinguishable ways can they be arranged in a row if objects of the same shape are also the same color, but need not be grouped?

✓ Checkpoint Answers

1. **(a)** 720 **(b)** 24
2. **(a)** 24 **(b)** 720 **(c)** 1 **(d)** 30
3. 30 **4.** $8 \cdot 7 \cdot 6 \cdot 5 = 1680$
5. **(a)** 20 **(b)** 504 **(c)** 3 **(d)** 210 **(e)** 132
6. **(a)** 120 **(b)** 12 **(c)** 6
7. **(a)** 15 **(b)** 70 **(c)** 1
8. **(a)** 15 **(b)** 70 **(c)** 1
9. **(a)** 15,504 **(b)** 816 **(c)** 21,699
10. **(a)** 5040 **(b)** 455 **(c)** 28 **(d)** 360
11. **(a)** 5040 **(b)** 840
12. 120,526,770 **13.** 1260

9.3 ▶ Applications of Counting

Many of the probability problems involving *dependent* events that were solved with probability trees in Chapter 8 can also be solved by using counting principles—that is, permutations and combinations. Permutations and combinations are especially helpful when the number of choices is large. The use of counting rules to solve probability problems depends on the basic probability principle introduced in Section 8.3 and repeated here.

If event E is a subset of sample space S, then the probability that event E occurs, written $P(E)$, is

$$P(E) = \frac{n(E)}{n(S)}.$$

It is also helpful to keep in mind that, in probability statements,

"and" corresponds to multiplication

and

"or" corresponds to addition.

Example 1 From a potential jury pool with 1 Hispanic, 3 Caucasian, and 2 African-American members, 2 jurors are selected one at a time without replacement. Find the probability that 1 Caucasian and 1 African-American are selected.

Solution In Example 6 of Section 8.5, it was necessary to consider the order in which the jurors were selected. With combinations, it is not necessary: Simply count the number of ways in which 1 Caucasian and 1 African-American juror can be selected. The Caucasian can be selected in $_3C_1$ ways, and the African-American juror can be selected in $_2C_1$ ways. By the multiplication principle, both results can occur in

$$_3C_1 \cdot {}_2C_1 = 3 \cdot 2 = 6 \text{ ways,}$$

giving the numerator of the probability fraction. For the denominator, 2 jurors are selected from a total of 6 candidates. This can occur in $_6C_2 = 15$ ways. The required probability is

$$P(1 \text{ Caucasian and 1 African American}) = \frac{{}_3C_1 \cdot {}_2C_1}{{}_6C_2} = \frac{3 \cdot 2}{15} = \frac{6}{15} = \frac{2}{5} = .40.$$

This result agrees with the answer found earlier.

Example 2 From a baseball team of 15 players, 4 are to be selected to present a list of grievances to the coach.

(a) In how many ways can this be done?

Solution Four players from a group of 15 can be selected in $_{15}C_4$ ways. (Use combinations, since the order in which the group of 4 is selected is unimportant.) So,

$$_{15}C_4 = \frac{15!}{4! \, 11!} = \frac{15(14)(13)(12)}{4(3)(2)(1)} = 1365.$$

There are 1365 ways to choose 4 players from 15.

(b) One of the players is Michael Branson. Find the probability that Branson will be among the 4 selected.

Solution The probability that Branson will be selected is the number of ways the chosen group includes him, divided by the total number of ways the group of 4 can be chosen. If Branson must be one of the 4 selected, the problem reduces to finding the number of ways the additional 3 players can be chosen. There are 3 chosen from 14 players; this can be done in

$$_{14}C_3 = \frac{14!}{3! \, 11!} = 364$$

ways. The number of ways 4 players can be selected from 15 is

$$n = {}_{15}C_4 = 1365.$$

The probability that Branson will be one of the 4 chosen is

$$P(\text{Branson is chosen}) = \frac{364}{1365} \approx .267.$$

(c) Find the probability that Branson will not be selected.

Solution The probability that he will not be chosen is $1 - .267 = .733.$ ✓

✓ Checkpoint 1

The ski club has 8 women and 7 men. What is the probability that if the club elects 3 officers, all 3 of them will be women?

Answer: See page 567.

Example 3   **Business** A manufacturing company performs a quality-control analysis on the ceramic tile it produces. It produces the tile in batches of 24 pieces. In the quality-control analysis, the company tests 3 pieces of tile per batch. Suppose a batch of 24 tiles has 4 defective tiles.

(a) What is the probability that exactly 1 of the 3 tested tiles is defective?

Solution Let $P(1 \text{ defective})$ represent the probability of there being exactly 1 defective tile among the 3 tested tiles. To find this probability, we need to know how many ways we can select 3 tiles for testing. Since order does not matter, there are ${}_{24}C_3$ ways to choose 3 tiles:

$$ {}_{24}C_3 = \frac{24!}{21!\, 3!} = \frac{24 \cdot 23 \cdot 22}{3 \cdot 2 \cdot 1} = 2024. $$

There are ${}_4C_1$ ways of choosing 1 defective tile from the 4 in the batch. If we choose 1 defective tile, we must then choose 2 good tiles among the 20 good tiles in the batch. We can do this in ${}_{20}C_2$ ways. By the multiplication principle, there are

$$ {}_4C_1 \cdot {}_{20}C_2 = \frac{4!}{3!\, 1!} \cdot \frac{20!}{18!\, 2!} = 4 \cdot 190 = 760 $$

ways to choose exactly 1 defective tile.
Thus,

$$ P(1 \text{ defective}) = \frac{760}{2024} \approx .3755. $$

(b) If at least one of the tiles in a batch is defective, the company will not ship the batch. What is the probability that the batch is not shipped?

Solution The batch will not be shipped if 1, 2, or 3 of the tiles sampled are defective. We already found the probability of there being exactly 1 defective tile in part (a). We now need to find $P(2 \text{ defective})$ and $P(3 \text{ defective})$. To find $P(2 \text{ defective})$, we need to count the number of ways to choose 2 from the 4 defective tiles in the batch and choose 1 from the 20 good tiles in the batch:

$$ {}_4C_2 \cdot {}_{20}C_1 = \frac{4!}{2!\, 2!} \cdot \frac{20!}{19!\, 1!} = 6 \cdot 20 = 120. $$

To find $P(3 \text{ defective})$, we need to count the number of ways to choose 3 from the 4 defective tiles in the batch and choose 0 from the 20 good tiles in the batch:

$$ {}_4C_3 \cdot {}_{20}C_0 = \frac{4!}{1!\, 3!} \cdot \frac{20!}{20!\, 0!} = 4 \cdot 1 = 4. $$

We now have

$$ P(2 \text{ defective}) = \frac{120}{2024} \approx .0593 \text{ and } P(3 \text{ defective}) = \frac{4}{2024} \approx .0020. $$

Thus, the probability of rejecting the batch because 1, 2, or 3 tiles are defective is

$$ P(1 \text{ defective}) + P(2 \text{ defective}) + P(3 \text{ defective}) \approx .3755 + .0593 + .0020 $$
$$ = .4368. $$

(c) Use the complement rule to find the probability the batch will be rejected.

Solution We reject the batch if at least 1 of the sampled tiles is defective. The opposite of at least 1 tile being defective is that none are defective. We can find the probability that none of the 3 sampled tiles is defective by choosing 0 from the 4 defective tiles and choosing 3 from the 20 good tiles:

$$_4C_0 \cdot {_{20}C_3} = 1 \cdot 1140 = 1140.$$

Therefore, the probability that none of the sampled tiles is defective is

$$P(0 \text{ defective}) = \frac{1140}{2024} \approx .5632.$$

Using the complement rule, we have

$$P(\text{at least 1 defective}) \approx 1 - .5632 = .4368,$$

the same answer as in part (b). Using the complement rule can often save time when multiple probabilities need to be calculated for problems involving "at least 1." ☑ **2**

✓ **Checkpoint 2**

A batch of 15 granite slabs is mined, and 4 have defects. If the manager spot-checks 3 slabs at random, what is the probability that at least 1 slab is defective?

Answer: See page 567.

Example 4   In a common form of 5-card draw poker, a hand of 5 cards is dealt to each player from a deck of 52 cards. (For a review of a standard deck, see Figure 8.21 on page 490) There is a total of

$$_{52}C_5 = \frac{52!}{5! \ 47!} = 2{,}598{,}960$$

such hands possible. Find the probability of being dealt each of the given hands.

(a) Heart-flush hand (5 hearts)

Solution There are 13 hearts in a deck; there are

$$_{13}C_5 = \frac{13!}{5! \ 8!} = \frac{13(12)(11)(10)(9)}{5(4)(3)(2)(1)} = 1287$$

different hands containing only hearts. The probability of a heart flush is

$$P(\text{heart flush}) = \frac{1287}{2{,}598{,}960} \approx .000495.$$

(b) A flush of any suit (5 cards, all from 1 suit)

Solution There are 4 suits to a deck, so

$$P(\text{flush}) = 4 \cdot P(\text{heart flush}) = 4(.000495) \approx .00198.$$

(c) A full house of aces and eights (3 aces and 2 eights)

Solution There are $_4C_3$ ways to choose 3 aces from among the 4 in the deck and $_4C_2$ ways to choose 2 eights, so

$$P(3 \text{ aces, 2 eights}) = \frac{_4C_3 \cdot {_4C_2}}{_{52}C_5} \approx .00000923.$$

(d) Any full house (3 cards of one value, 2 of another)

Solution There are 13 values in a deck, so there are 13 choices for the first value mentioned, leaving 12 choices for the second value. (Order *is* important here, since a full house of aces and eights, for example, is not the same as a full house of eights and aces.)

$$P(\text{full house}) = \frac{13 \cdot {}_4C_3 \cdot 12 \cdot {}_4C_2}{{}_{52}C_5} \approx .00144.$$ ✓³

✓ **Checkpoint 3**

Find the probability of being dealt a poker hand (5 cards) with 4 kings.

Answer: See page 567.

Example 5 A cooler contains 8 different kinds of soda, among which 3 cans are Pepsi®, Classic Coke®, and Sprite®. What is the probability, when picking at random, of selecting the 3 cans in the particular order listed in the previous sentence?

Solution Use permutations to find the number of arrangements in the sample, because order matters:

$$n = {}_8P_3 = 8(7)(6) = 336.$$

Since each can is different, there is only 1 way to choose Pepsi, Classic Coke, and Sprite in that order, so the probability is

$$\frac{1}{336} = .0030.$$ ✓⁴

✓ **Checkpoint 4**

Martha, Leonard, Calvin, and Sheila will be handling the officer duties of president, vice president, treasurer, and secretary.

(a) If the offices are assigned randomly, what is the probability that Calvin is the president?

(b) If the offices are assigned randomly, what is the probability that Sheila is president, Martha is vice president, Calvin is treasurer, and Leonard is secretary?

Answers: See page 567.

Example 6 Suppose a group of 5 people is in a room. Find the probability that at least 2 of the people have the same birthday.

Solution "Same birthday" refers to the month and the day, not necessarily the same year. Also, ignore leap years, and assume that each day in the year is equally likely as a birthday. First find the probability that *no 2 people* among 5 people have the same birthday. There are 365 different birthdays possible for the first of the 5 people, 364 for the second (so that the people have different birthdays), 363 for the third, and so on. The number of ways the 5 people can have different birthdays is thus the number of permutations of 365 things (days) taken 5 at a time, or

$$_{365}P_5 = 365 \cdot 364 \cdot 363 \cdot 362 \cdot 361.$$

The number of ways that the 5 people can have the same or different birthdays is

$$365 \cdot 365 \cdot 365 \cdot 365 \cdot 365 = (365)^5.$$

Finally, the *probability* that none of the 5 people have the same birthday is

$$\frac{_{365}P_5}{(365)^5} = \frac{365 \cdot 364 \cdot 363 \cdot 362 \cdot 361}{365 \cdot 365 \cdot 365 \cdot 365 \cdot 365} \approx .973.$$

The probability that at least 2 of the 5 people *do* have the same birthday is $1 - .973 = .027$.

Example 6 can be extended for more than 5 people. In general, the probability that no 2 people among n people have the same birthday is

$$\frac{_{365}P_n}{(365)^n}.$$

The probability that at least 2 of the n people *do* have the same birthday is

$$1 - \frac{_{365}P_n}{(365)^n}. \quad \boxed{5}\checkmark$$

✓ Checkpoint 5

Evaluate $1 - \dfrac{_{365}P_n}{(365)^n}$ for

(a) $n = 3$;

(b) $n = 6$.

_____

Answers: See page 567.

The following table shows this probability for various values of n:

Number of People, n	Probability That At Least 2 Have the Same Birthday
5	.027
10	.117
15	.253
20	.411
22	.476
23	**.507**
25	.569
30	.706
35	.814
40	.891
50	.970
365	1

✓ Checkpoint 6

Set up (but do not calculate) the probability that at least 2 of the 9 members of the Supreme Court have the same birthday.

_____

Answer: See page 567.

The probability that 2 people among 23 have the same birthday is .507, a little more than half. Many people are surprised at this result; somehow it seems that a larger number of people should be required. $\boxed{6}\checkmark$

Using a graphing calculator, we can graph the probability formula in the previous example as a function of n, but the graphing calculator must be set to evaluate the function at integer points. Figure 9.11 was produced on a TI-84+ by letting $Y_1 = 1 - (365 \text{ nPr } X)/365^X$ on the interval $0 \le x \le 47$. (This domain ensures integer values for x.) Notice that the graph does not extend past $x = 39$. This is because $P(365, n)$ and 365^n are too large for the calculator when $n \ge 40$.

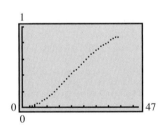

FIGURE 9.11

9.3 ▶ Exercises

Business   *Suppose in Example 3 that the number of defective tiles in a batch of 24 is 5 rather than 4. If 3 tiles are sampled at random, the management would like to know the probability that*

1.   exactly 1 of the sampled tiles is defective;

2.   the batch is rejected (that is, at least 1 sampled tile is defective).

Business   *A shipment of 8 computers contains 3 with defects. Find the probability that with a sample of the given size, drawn from the 8, will not contain a defective computer. (See Example 3.)*

3. 1   **4.** 2

5. 3   **6.** 5

A radio station runs a promotion at an auto show with a money box with 10 $100 tickets, 12 $50 tickets, and 20 $25 tickets. The box contains an additional 200 "dummy" tickets with no value. Three tickets are randomly drawn. Find the given probabilities. (See Examples 1 and 2).

7. All $100 tickets

8. All $50 tickets

9. Exactly two $25 tickets and no other money winners

10. One ticket of each money amount

11. No tickets with money

12. At least one money ticket

Two cards are drawn at random from an ordinary deck of 52 cards. (See Example 4.)

13. How many 2-card hands are possible?

Find the probability that the 2-card hand in Exercise 13 contains the given cards.

14. 2 kings

15. No deuces (2's)

16. 2 face cards

17. Different suits

18. At least 1 black card

19. No more than 1 diamond

20. Discuss the relative merits of using probability trees versus combinations to solve probability problems. When would each approach be most appropriate?

21. Several examples in this section used the rule $P(E') = 1 - P(E)$. Explain the advantage (especially in Example 6) of using this rule.

Natural Science *A shipment contains 8 igneous, 7 sedimentary, and 7 metamorphic rocks. If we select 5 rocks at random, find the probability that*

22. all 5 are igneous;

23. 3 are sedimentary;

24. only 1 is metamorphic.

25. In Exercise 59 in Section 9.2, we found the number of ways to pick 6 different numbers from 1 to 99 in a state lottery.
   (a) Assuming that order is unimportant, what is the probability of picking all 6 numbers correctly to win the big prize?
   (b) What is the probability if order matters?

26. In Exercise 25 (a), what is the probability of picking exactly 5 of the 6 numbers correctly?

27. Example 16 in Section 9.2 shows that the probability of winning the Powerball lottery is 1/195,249,054. If Juanita and Michelle each play Powerball on one particular evening, what is the probability that both will select the winning numbers if they make their selections independently of each other?

28. **Business** A cellular phone manufacturer randomly selects 5 phones from every batch of 50 produced. If at least one of the phones is found to be defective, then each phone in the batch is tested individually. Find the probability that the entire batch will need testing if the batch contains
   (a) 8 defective phones;
   (b) 2 defective phones.

29. **Social Science** Of the 15 members of President Barak Obama's first Cabinet, 4 were women. Suppose the president randomly selected 4 advisors from the cabinet for a meeting. Find the probability that the group of 4 would be composed as follows:
   (a) 3 woman and 1 man;
   (b) All men;
   (c) At least one woman.

30. **Business** A car dealership has 8 red, 9 silver, and 5 black cars on the lot. Ten cars are randomly chosen to be displayed in front of the dealership. Find the probability that
   (a) 4 are red and the rest are silver;
   (b) 5 are red and 5 are black;
   (c) 8 are red.

31. **Health** Twenty subjects volunteer for a study of a new cold medicine. Ten of the volunteers are ages 20–39, 8 are ages 40–59, and 2 are age 60 or older. If we select 7 volunteers at random, find the probability that
   (a) all the volunteers selected are ages 20–39;
   (b) 5 of the volunteers are ages 20–39 and 2 are age 60 or older;
   (c) 3 of the volunteers are ages 40–59.

For Exercises 32–34, refer to Example 6 in this section.

32. Set up the probability that at least 2 of the 43 men who have served as president of the United States have had the same birthday.*

33. Set up the probability that at least 2 of the 100 U.S. senators have the same birthday.

34. Set up the probability that at least 2 of the 50 U.S. governors have the same birthday.

---

*In fact, James Polk and Warren Harding were both born on November 2. Although Barack Obama is the 44th president, the 22nd and 24th presidents were the same man: Grover Cleveland.

One version of the New York State lottery game Quick Draw has players selecting 4 numbers at random from the numbers 1–80. The state picks 20 winning numbers. If the player's 4 numbers are selected by the state, the player wins $55.*

35. What is the probability of winning?

36. If the state picks 3 of the player's numbers, the player wins $5. What is the probability of winning $5?

37. What is the probability of having none of your 4 numbers selected by the state?

38. During the 1988 college football season, the Big Eight Conference ended the season in a "perfect progression," as shown in the following table:†

Won	Lost	Team
7	0	Nebraska (NU)
6	1	Oklahoma (OU)
5	2	Oklahoma State (OSU)
4	3	Colorado (CU)
3	4	Iowa State (ISU)
2	5	Missouri (MU)
1	6	Kansas (KU)
0	7	Kansas State (KSU)

Someone wondered what the probability of such an outcome might be.

(a) Assuming no ties and assuming that each team had an equally likely probability of winning each game,

find the probability of the perfect progression shown in the table.

(b) Under the same assumptions, find a general expression for the probability of a perfect progression in an *n*-team league.

 39. Use a computer or a graphing calculator and the Monte Carlo method with $n = 50$ to estimate the probabilities of the given hands at poker. (See the directions for Exercises 40–43 on page 504.) Assume that aces are either high or low. Since each hand has 5 cards, you will need $50 \cdot 5 = 250$ random numbers to "look at" 50 hands. Compare these experimental results with the theoretical results.

(a) A pair of aces
(b) Any two cards of the same value
(c) Three of a kind

 40. Use a computer or a graphing calculator and the Monte Carlo method with $n = 20$ to estimate the probabilities of the given 13-card bridge hands. Since each hand has 13 cards, you will need $20 \cdot 13 = 260$ random numbers to "look at" 20 hands.

(a) No aces
(b) 2 kings and 2 aces
(c) No cards of any suit—that is, only 3 suits represented

✓ Checkpoint Answers

1.	.123	2.	About .637	3.	.00001847
4.	(a) 1/4		(b) 1/24		
5.	(a) .008		(b) .040		
6.	$1 - {}_{365}P_9/365^9$				

*www.nylottery.org/index.php.

†From Richard Madsen, "On the Probability of a Perfect Progression." *American Statistics* 45, no. 3 (August 1991): 214.

9.4 ▶ Binomial Probability

In Section 9.1, we learned about probability distributions where we listed each outcome and its associated probability. After learning in Sections 9.2 and 9.3 how to count the number of possible outcomes, we are now ready to understand a special probability distribution known as the *binomial distribution*. This distribution occurs when the same experiment is repeated many times and each repetition is independent of previous ones. One outcome is designated a success and any other outcome is considered a failure. For example, you might want to find the probability of rolling 8 twos in 12 rolls of a die (rolling two is a success; rolling anything else is a failure). The individual trials (rolling the die once) are called **Bernoulli trials**, or **Bernoulli processes**, after the Swiss mathematician Jakob Bernoulli (1654–1705).

If the probability of a success in a single trial is p, then the probability of failure is $1 - p$ (by the complement rule). When Bernoulli trials are repeated a fixed number of times, the resulting distribution of outcomes is called a **binomial distribution**, or a **binomial experiment**. A binomial experiment must satisfy the following conditions.

Binomial Experiment

1. The same experiment is repeated a fixed number of times.
2. There are only two possible outcomes: success and failure.
3. The probability of success for each trial is constant.
4. The repeated trials are independent.

The basic characteristics of binomial experiments are illustrated by a recent poll of small businesses (250 employees or fewer) conducted by the National Federation of Independent Businesses. The poll found that 36% of small businesses pay for the health insurance of all or almost all full-time employees.* We use Y to denote the event that a small business does this, and N to denote the event that it does not. If we sample 5 small businesses at random and use .36 as the probability for Y, we will generate a binomial experiment, since all of the requirements are satisfied:

The sampling is repeated a fixed number of times (5);

there are only two outcomes of interest (Y or N);

the probability of success is constant ($p = .36$);

"at random" guarantees that the trials are independent.

To calculate the probability that all 5 randomly chosen businesses pay for health insurance, we use the product rule for independent events (Section 8.5) and $P(Y) = .36$ to obtain

$$P(YYYYY) = P(Y) \cdot P(Y) \cdot P(Y) \cdot P(Y) \cdot P(Y) = (.36)^5 \approx .006.$$

Determining the probability that 4 out of 5 businesses chose to pay for health insurance is slightly more complicated. The business that does not pay could be the first, second, third, fourth, or fifth business surveyed. So we have the following possible outcomes:

$$N\,Y\,Y\,Y\,Y$$
$$Y\,N\,Y\,Y\,Y$$
$$Y\,Y\,N\,Y\,Y$$
$$Y\,Y\,Y\,N\,Y$$
$$Y\,Y\,Y\,Y\,N$$

So the total number of ways in which 4 successes (and 1 failure) can occur is 5, which is the number $_5C_4$. The probability of each of these 5 outcomes is

$$P(Y) \cdot P(Y) \cdot P(Y) \cdot P(Y) \cdot P(N) = (.36)^4(1 - .36)^1 = (.36)^4(.64).$$

Since the 5 outcomes where there are 4 Ys and one N represent disjoint events, we multiply by $_5C_4 = 5$:

$$P(4 \ Ys \ \text{out of 5 trials}) = {}_5C_4(.36)^4(.64)^{5-4} = 5(.36)^4(.64)^1 \approx .054.$$

*www.nfib.com/.

The probability of obtaining exactly 3 *Y*s and 2 *N*s can be computed in a similar way. The probability of any one way of achieving 3 *Y*s and 2 *N*s will be

$$(.36)^3(.64)^2.$$

Again, the desired outcome can occur in more than one way. Using combinations, we find that the number of ways in which 3 *Y*s and 2 *N*s can occur is $_5C_3 = 10$. So, we have

$$P(3 \ Ys \ out \ of \ 5 \ trials) = {_5}C_3(.36)^3(.64)^{5-3} = 10(.36)^3(.64)^2 \approx .191. \checkmark$$

With the probabilities just generated and the answers to Checkpoint 1, we can write the probability distribution for the number of small businesses that pay for health insurance for all or almost all their full-time employees when 5 businesses are selected at random:

✓Checkpoint 1

Find the probability of obtaining

(a) exactly 2 businesses that pay for health insurance;

(b) exactly 1 business that pays for health insurance;

(c) exactly no business that pays for health insurance.

Answers: See page 574.

x	0	1	2	3	4	5
$P(x)$	.107	.302	.340	.191	.054	.006

When the outcomes and their associated probabilities are written in this form, it is very easy to calculate answers to questions such as, What is the probability that 3 or more businesses pay for the health insurance of their full-time employees? We see from the table that

$$P(3 \ or \ more \ Ys) = .191 + .054 + .006 = .251.$$

Similarly, the probability of one or fewer businesses paying for health insurance is

$$P(1 \ or \ fewer \ Ys) = .302 + .107 = .409.$$

The example illustrates the following fact.

⊞ TECHNOLOGY TIP
On the TI-84+ calculator, use "binompdf(*n,p,x*)" in the DISTR menu to compute the probability of exactly *x* successes in *n* trials (where *p* is the probability of success in a single trial). Use "binomcdf(*n,p,x*)" to compute the probability of at most *x* successes in *n* trials. Figure 9.12 shows the probability of exactly 3 successes in 5 trials and the probability of at most 3 successes in 5 trials, with the probability of success set at .36 for each case.

> **Binomial Probability**
>
> If p is the probability of success in a single trial of a binomial experiment, the probability of x successes and $n - x$ failures in n independent repeated trials of the experiment is
>
> $$_nC_x p^x (1 - p)^{n-x}.$$

```
binompdf(5,.36,3
)
          .191102976
binomcdf(5,.36,3
)
          .9402056704
■
```

FIGURE 9.12

Example 1   **Business** On March 26, 2009, a report from a study conducted by the Families and Work Institute found that 67% of workers age 29 or younger desire to have a job with more responsibility.* Suppose a random sample of 6 workers age 29 or younger is chosen. Find the probability of the given scenarios.

*www.familiesandwork.org.

(a) Exactly 4 of the 6 workers desire a job with more responsibility.

Solution We can think of the 6 workers sampled as independent trials, and a success occurs if a worker desires a job with more responsibility. This is a binomial experiment with $p = .67$, $n = 6$, and $x = 4$. By the binomial probability rule,

$$P(\text{exactly } 4) = {}_6C_4(.67)^4(.33)^{6-4}$$
$$= 15(.67)^4(.33)^2$$
$$\approx .329.$$

(b) None of the 6 workers desires a job with more responsibility.

Solution Let $x = 0$. Then we have

$$P(\text{exactly } 0) = {}_6C_0(.67)^0(.33)^{6-0}$$
$$= 1(.67)^0(.33)^6$$
$$\approx .001. \quad ✔^2$$

✔**Checkpoint 2**

According to the study in Example 1, 35% of workers age 29 or younger agreed with the statement, "It is better for all involved if the man earns the money and the woman takes care of the home and children." If 4 workers are selected at random, find the probability that

(a) 1 of 4 agreed with the statement;

(b) 3 out of 4 agreed with the statement.

Answers: See page 574.

Example 2 Suppose a family has 3 children.

(a) Find the probability distribution for the number of girls.

Solution Let $x =$ the number of girls in three births. According to the binomial probability rule, the probability of exactly one girl being born is

$$P(x = 1) = {}_3C_1\left(\frac{1}{2}\right)^1\left(\frac{1}{2}\right)^2 = 3\left(\frac{1}{2}\right)^3 = \frac{3}{8}.$$

The other probabilities in this distribution are found similarly, as shown in the following table:

x	0	1	2	3
$P(x)$	${}_3C_0\left(\frac{1}{2}\right)^0\left(\frac{1}{2}\right)^3 = \frac{1}{8}$	${}_3C_1\left(\frac{1}{2}\right)^1\left(\frac{1}{2}\right)^2 = \frac{3}{8}$	${}_3C_2\left(\frac{1}{2}\right)^2\left(\frac{1}{2}\right)^1 = \frac{3}{8}$	${}_3C_3\left(\frac{1}{2}\right)^3\left(\frac{1}{2}\right)^0 = \frac{1}{8}$

(b) Find the expected number of girls in a 3-child family.

Solution For a binomial distribution, we can use the following method (which is presented here with a "plausibility argument," but not a full proof): Because 50% of births are girls, it is reasonable to expect that 50% of a sample of children will be girls. Since 50% of 3 is $3(.50) = 1.5$, we conclude that the expected number of girls is 1.5. ✔^{3}

✔**Checkpoint 3**

Find the probability of getting 2 fours in 8 tosses of a die.

Answer: See page 574.

The expected value in Example 2(b) was the product of the number of births and the probability of a single birth being a girl—that is, the product of the number of trials and the probability of success in a single trial. The same conclusion holds in the general case.

Expected Value for a Binomial Distribution

When an experiment meets the four conditions of a binomial experiment with n fixed trials and constant probability of success p, the expected value is

$$E(x) = np.$$

Example 3 **Health** Data from the 2005–2006 National Health and Nutrition Examination Survey indicate that 35% of adults age 18–85 answered "Yes" to the question, "Over the past 30 days, did you do any vigorous activities for at least 10 minutes that caused heavy sweating, or large increases in breathing or heart rate?"* If we select 15 adults at random, find the following probabilities,

(a) The probability that exactly 5 engaged in vigorous activity in the last 30 days

Solution The experiment is repeated 15 times, with having engaged in vigorous activity being considered a success. The probability of success is .35. Since the selection is done at random, the trials are considered independent. Thus, we have a binomial experiment, and

$$P(x = 5) = {}_{15}C_5(.35)^5(.65)^{10} \approx .212.$$

(b) The probability that at most 3 engaged in vigorous activity in the last 30 days

Solution "At most 3" means 0, 1, 2, or 3 successes. We must find the probability for each case and then use the addition rule for disjoint events:

$$P(x = 0) = {}_{15}C_0(.35)^0(.65)^{15} \approx .002;$$
$$P(x = 1) = {}_{15}C_1(.35)^1(.65)^{14} \approx .013;$$
$$P(x = 2) = {}_{15}C_2(.35)^2(.65)^{13} \approx .048;$$
$$P(x = 3) = {}_{15}C_3(.35)^3(.65)^{12} \approx .111.$$

Thus,

$$P(\text{at most } 3) = .002 + .013 + .048 + .111 = .174.$$

(c) The expected number of adults who have engaged in vigorous activity in the last 30 days.

Solution Because this is a binomial experiment, we can use the formula $E(x) = np = 15(.35) = 5.25$. In repeated samples of 15 adults, the average number who engaged in vigorous activity is 5.25. ✓ 4

✓ **Checkpoint 4**

Suppose that in Example 3, 55% of adults said "Yes" to having engaged in moderate physical activity within the last 30 days. If 10 adults are selected at random, find the probability that

(a) exactly 2 said "Yes";

(b) at most 2 said "Yes."

(c) What is the expected number who say "Yes?"

Answers: See page 574.

Example 4 **Social Science** According to a study conducted by the American Veterinary Association in 2006, 37% of American households had a pet dog. If a sample of 10 random households is conducted, what is the probability that at least 1 household will have a dog?

---
*Based on data available at www.cdc.gov/nchs/nhanes.htm.

Solution We can treat this problem as a binomial experiment, with $n = 10$, $p = .37$, and x representing the number of households in the sample that have a dog. "At least 1 of 10" means 1 or 2 or 3, etc., up to 10. It will be simpler here to find the probability that none of the 10 selected households has a dog—that is, $P(x = 0)$—and then find the probability that at least 1 of the households has a dog, which is the value $1 - P(x = 0)$:

$$P(x = 0) = {}_{10}C_0(.37)^0(.63)^{10} \approx .0098$$
$$P(x \geq 1) = 1 - P(x = 0) \approx 1 - .0098 = .9902. \quad 5 \checkmark$$

✓**Checkpoint 5**

In Example 4, find the probability that

(a) at least 3 households have a dog;

(b) at most 5 of the households have a dog.

(c) What is the expected value?

―――――――――――

Answers: See page 574.

Example 5 If each member of a 9-person jury acts independently of the other members and makes the correct determination of guilt or innocence with probability .65, find the probability that the majority of the jurors will reach a correct verdict.*

Solution Since the jurors in this particular situation act independently, we can treat the problem as a binomial experiment. Thus, the probability that the majority of the jurors will reach the correct verdict is given by

$$P(\text{at least } 5) = {}_9C_5(.65)^5(.35)^4 + {}_9C_6(.65)^6(.35)^3 + {}_9C_7(.65)^7(.35)^2$$
$$+ {}_9C_8(.65)^8(.35)^1 + {}_9C_9(.65)^9$$
$$\approx .2194 + .2716 + .2162 + .1004 + .0207$$
$$= .8283.$$

🖱 **TECHNOLOGY TIP** Some spreadsheets provide binomial probabilities. In Microsoft Excel, for example, the command "=BINOMDIST (5, 9, .65, 0)" gives .21939, which is the probability for $x = 5$ in Example 5. Alternatively, the command "= BINOMDIST (4, 9, .65, 1)" gives .17172 as the probability that 4 or fewer jurors will make the correct decision. Subtract .17172 from 1 to get .82828 as the probability that the majority of the jurors will make the correct decision. This value agrees with the value found in Example 5.

―――――――――――

*Bernard Grofman, "A Preliminary Model of Jury Decision Making as a Function of Jury Size, Effective Jury Decision Rule, and Mean Juror Judgmental Competence," Frontiers in Economics (1979), pp. 98–110.

9.4 ▶ Exercises

In Exercises 1–39, see Examples 1–5.

Social Science *In 2008, the percentage of children under 18 years of age who lived with both parents was approximately 70%.* Find the probabilities that the given number of persons selected at random from 10 children under 18 years of age in 2008 lived with both parents.*

1. Exactly 6
2. Exactly 5
3. None
4. All
5. At least 1
6. At most 4

―――――――――――

*U.S Census Bureau, America's Families and Living Arrangments: 2008.

Social Science *The study in Exercise 1 also found that approximately 19% of children under 18 years of age lived with their mother only. Find the probabilities that the given number of persons selected at random from 10 children under 18 years of age in 2008 lived with their mother only.*

7. Exactly 2
8. Exactly 1
9. None
10. All
11. At least 1
12. At most 2

A coin is tossed 5 times. Find the probability of getting

13. all heads;
14. exactly 3 heads;
15. no more than 3 heads;
16. at least 3 heads.

17. How do you identify a probability problem that involves a binomial experiment?

18. Why do combinations occur in the binomial probability formula?

Business   *Researchers at the University of Virginia estimated that 34% of the mortgage foreclosures that occurred in the United States in 2008 were in the state of California.* If 15 foreclosed mortgages were selected at random, find the probability that*

19. exactly 3 were from California;

20. none was from California;

21. at most 2 were from California;

22. exactly 10 were not from California.

23. If 200 foreclosed mortgages were selected randomly, what would the expected number of California mortgages be?

Business   *The study from the National Federation of Independent Businesses (page 568) also found that approximately 56% of small businesses choose the cost of health care as the number-one challenge facing their business. If we select 8 small businesses at random, find the probability that the given number of businesses chose the cost of health care as the number-one challenge.*

24. all 8 businesses   **25.** all but 1 business

26. at most 2 businesses   **27.** at most 7 businesses

28. What is the expected number of businesses that chose the cost of health care as the number-one challenge?

Natural Science   *The probability that a birth will result in twins is .027.† Assuming independence (perhaps not a valid assumption), what are the probabilities that, out of 100 births in a hospital, there will be the given numbers of sets of twins?*

29. Exactly 2 sets of twins   **30.** At most 2 sets of twins

Social Science   *According to the Web site Answers.com, 10–13% of Americans are left handed. Assume that the percentage is 11%. If we select 9 people at random, find the probability that the number who are left handed is*

31. exactly 2;   **32.** at least 2;

33. none;   **34.** at most 3.

35. In a class of 35 students, how many left-handed students should the instructor expect?

Social Science   *Respondents to the 2006 General Social Survey (GSS) indicated that approximately 7.3% of Americans attend church services more than once a week.‡ If 16 Americans are chosen at random, find the given probabilities.*

36. Exactly 2 attend church services more than once a week

37. At most 3 attend church services more than once a week

Health   *Data from the 2005–2006 National Health and Nutrition Examination Survey (NHANES) estimates that 15.8% of American males are six feet tall or taller.*

38. If we select 9 males at random, what is the probability that at least 2 are six feet tall or taller?

39. If we select 5 males at random, will the probability that at least 2 are six feet tall or taller be higher or lower than the probability found for Exercise 38?

40. If we select 500 males at random, what is the expected number who will be six feet tall or taller?

41. **Social Science**   In the "Numbers" section of *Time* magazine, it was reported that 15.2% of low-birth-weight babies graduate from high school by age 19. It was also reported that 57.5% of their normal-birth-weight siblings graduated from high school by 19.†
   (a) If 40 low-birth-weight babies are tracked through high school, what is the probability that fewer than 15 will graduate from high school by age 19?
   (b) What are some of the factors that may contribute to the wide difference in high school success between these siblings? Do you believe that low birth weight is the primary cause of the difference? What other information do you need to better answer these questions?

42. **Natural Science**   In a placebo-controlled trial of Adderall XR®, a medication for attention deficit and hyperactivity disorder (ADHD), 22% of users of the drug reported loss of appetite. Only 2% of the patients taking the placebo reported loss of appetite.‡
   (a) If 100 patients who are taking Adderall XR are selected at random, what is the probability that 15 or more will experience loss of appetite?
   (b) If 100 patients who are taking the placebo are selected at random, what is the probability that 15 or more will experience loss of appetite?
   (c) Do you believe Adderall XR causes a loss of appetite? Why or why not?

43. **Natural Science**   DNA evidence has become an integral part of many court cases. When DNA is extracted from cells and body fluids, genetic information is represented by bands of information, which look similar to a bar code at a grocery store. It is generally accepted that, in unrelated people, the probability of a particular band matching is 1 in 4.§
   (a) If 5 bands are compared in unrelated people, what is the probability that all 5 of the bands match? (Express your answer in terms of "1 chance in ?".)

---

*www.virginia.edu/uvatoday/newsRelease.php?id=7838.

†*The World Almanac and Book of Facts*, 2001, p. 873.

‡Data available at www.norc.org/GSS+Website

*Based on data available at www.cdc.gov/nchs/nhanes.htm.

†"Numbers," *Time*, July 17, 2000, p. 21.

‡Advertisement in *Newsweek*, June 13, 2005, for Adderall XR®, marketed by Shire US, Inc.

§"Genetic Fingerprinting Worksheet." Centre for Innovation in Mathematics Teaching, http://www.cimt.plymouth.ac.uk

(b) If 20 bands are compared in unrelated people, what is the probability that all 20 of the bands match? (Express your answer in terms of "1 chance in ?".)

(c) If 20 bands are compared in unrelated people, what is the probability that 16 or more bands match? (Express your answer in terms of "1 chance in ?".)

(d) If you were deciding on a child's paternity and there were 16 matches out of 20 bands compared, would you believe that the person being tested was the father? Explain.

44. **Social Science** In England, a woman was found guilty of smothering her two infant children. Much of the Crown's case against her was based on the testimony from a pediatrician who indicated that the chances of 2 crib deaths occurring in both siblings was only about 1 in 73 million. This number was calculated by assuming that the probability

of a single crib death is 1 in 8500 and the probability of 2 crib deaths is 1 in 8500^2 (i.e., binomial).* Why is the use of binomial probability not correct in this situation?

✓ Checkpoint Answers

1. **(a)** About .340   **(b)** About .302   **(c)** About .107
2. **(a)** About .384   **(b)** About .111
3. About .2605
4. **(a)** About .0229   **(b)** About .0274   **(c)** 5.5
5. **(a)** About .7794   **(b)** About .8795   **(c)** 3.7

*Stephen J. Watkins, "Conviction by Mathematical Error?" *British Medical Journal* 320, no. 7226 (January 1, 2000):2–3.

9.5 ▶ Markov Chains

In Section 8.5, we touched on **stochastic processes**—mathematical models that evolve over time in a probabilistic manner. In the current section, we study a special kind of stochastic process called a **Markov chain**, in which the outcome of an experiment depends only on the outcome of the previous experiment. In other words, the next state of the system depends only on the present state, not on preceding states. Such experiments are common enough in applications to make their study worthwhile. Markov chains are named after the Russian mathematician A. A. Markov (1856–1922), who started the theory of stochastic processes. To see how Markov chains work, we look at an example.

Example 1 **Business** A small town has only two dry cleaners: Johnson and NorthClean. Johnson's manager hopes to increase the firm's market share by an extensive advertising campaign. After the campaign, a market research firm finds that there is a probability of .8 that a Johnson customer will bring his next batch of dirty items to Johnson and a .35 chance that a NorthClean customer will switch to Johnson for his next batch. Assume that the probability that a customer comes to a given cleaner depends only on where the last load of clothes was taken. If there is a .8 chance that a Johnson customer will return to Johnson, then there must be a $1 - .8 = .2$ chance that the customer will switch to NorthClean. In the same way, there is a $1 - .35 = .65$ chance that a NorthClean customer will return to NorthClean. If an individual bringing a load to Johnson is said to be in state 1 and an individual bringing a load to NorthClean is said to be in state 2, then these probabilities of change from one cleaner to the other are as shown in the following table:

		Second Load	
	State	1	2
First Load	1	.8	.2
	2	.35	.65

The information from the table can be written in other forms. Figure 9.13 is a **transition diagram** that shows the two states and the probabilities of going from one to another.

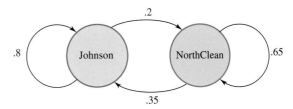

FIGURE 9.13

In a **transition matrix**, the states are indicated at the side and top, as follows:

$$
\begin{array}{c}
& \text{Second Load} \\
& \begin{array}{cc} \text{Johnson} & \text{NorthClean} \end{array} \\
\textit{First Load} \begin{array}{c} \text{Johnson} \\ \text{NorthClean} \end{array}
& \begin{bmatrix} .8 & .2 \\ .35 & .65 \end{bmatrix}.
\end{array}
$$

✓**Checkpoint 1**

You are given the transition matrix

$$
\begin{array}{c}
& \textit{State} \\
& \begin{array}{cc} 1 & 2 \end{array} \\
\textit{State} \begin{array}{c} 1 \\ 2 \end{array}
& \begin{bmatrix} .3 & .7 \\ .1 & .9 \end{bmatrix}.
\end{array}
$$

(a) What is the probability of changing from state 1 to state 2?

(b) What does the number .1 represent?

(c) Draw a transition diagram for this information.

Answers: See page 586.

> A **transition matrix** has the following features:
>
> 1. It is square, since all possible states must be used both as rows and as columns.
> 2. All entries are between 0 and 1, inclusive, because all entries represent probabilities.
> 3. The sum of the entries in any row must be 1, because the numbers in the row give the probability of changing from the state at the left to one of the states indicated across the top.

Example 2 **Business** Suppose that when the new promotional campaign began, Johnson had 40% of the market and NorthClean had 60%. Use the probability tree in Figure 9.14 to find how these proportions would change after another week of advertising.

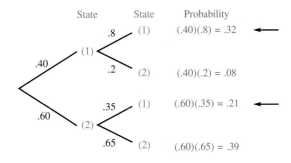

State 1: taking cleaning to Johnson
State 2: taking cleaning to NorthClean

FIGURE 9.14

Solution Add the numbers indicated with arrows to find the proportion of people taking their cleaning to Johnson after one week:

$$.32 + .21 = .53$$

Similarly, the proportion taking their cleaning to NorthClean is

$$.08 + .39 = .47.$$

The initial distribution of 40% and 60% becomes 53% and 47%, respectively, after 1 week.

These distributions can be written as the *probability vectors*

$$[.40 \quad .60] \quad \text{and} \quad [.53 \quad .47].$$

A **probability vector** is a one-row matrix, with nonnegative entries, in which the sum of the entries is equal to 1.

The results from the probability tree of Figure 9.14 are exactly the same as the result of multiplying the initial probability vector by the transition matrix (multiplication of matrices was discussed in Section 6.4):

$$[.4 \quad .6]\begin{bmatrix} .8 & .2 \\ .35 & .65 \end{bmatrix} = [.53 \quad .47].$$

If v denotes the original probability vector $[.4 \quad .6]$ and P denotes the transition matrix, then the market share vector after one week is $vP = [.53 \quad .47]$. To find the market share vector after two weeks, multiply the vector $vP = [.53 \quad .47]$ by P; this amounts to finding vP^2. ✓2

Checkpoint 2 shows that after 2 weeks, the market share vector is $vP^2 = [.59 \quad .41]$. To get the market share vector after three weeks, multiply this vector by P; that is, find vP^3. Do not use the rounded answer from Checkpoint 2. ✓3

Continuing this process gives each cleaner's share of the market after additional weeks:

✓**Checkpoint 2**

Find the product

$$[.53 \ .47]\begin{bmatrix} .8 & .2 \\ .35 & .65 \end{bmatrix}.$$

Answer: See page 586.

✓**Checkpoint 3**

Find each cleaner's market share after three weeks.

Answer: See page 586.

Weeks after Start	Johnson	NorthClean	
0	.4	.6	v
1	.53	.47	vP^1
2	.59	.41	vP^2
3	.61	.39	vP^3
4	.63	.37	vP^4
12	.64	.36	vP^{12}
13	.64	.36	vP^{13}

The results seem to approach the probability vector $[.64 \quad .36]$.

What happens if the initial probability vector is different from $[.4 \quad .6]$? Suppose $[.75 \quad .25]$ is used; then the same powers of the transition matrix as before give the following results:

Week after Start	Johnson	NorthClean	
0	.75	.25	v
1	.69	.31	vP^1
2	.66	.34	vP^2
3	.65	.35	vP^3
4	.64	.36	vP^4
5	.64	.36	vP^5
6	.64	.36	vP^6

The results again seem to be approaching the numbers in the probability vector [.64 .36], the same numbers approached with the initial probability vector [.4 .6]. In either case, the long-range trend is for a market share of about 64% for Johnson and 36% for NorthClean. The example suggests that this long-range trend does not depend on the initial distribution of market shares. This means that if the initial market share for Johnson was less than 64%, the advertising campaign has paid off in terms of a greater long-range market share. If the initial share was more than 64%, the campaign did not pay off.

REGULAR TRANSITION MATRICES

One of the many applications of Markov chains is in finding long-range predictions. It is not possible to make long-range predictions with all transition matrices, but for a large set of transition matrices, long-range predictions *are* possible. Such predictions are always possible with **regular transition matrices**. A transition matrix is **regular** if some power of the matrix contains all positive entries. A Markov chain is a **regular Markov chain** if its transition matrix is regular.

Example 3 Decide whether the given transition matrices are regular.

(a) $A = \begin{bmatrix} .3 & .1 & .6 \\ .0 & .2 & .8 \\ .3 & .7 & 0 \end{bmatrix}$.

Solution Square A:

$$A^2 = \begin{bmatrix} .27 & .47 & .26 \\ .24 & .60 & .16 \\ .09 & .17 & .74 \end{bmatrix}.$$

Since all entries in A^2 are positive, matrix A is regular.

(b) $B = \begin{bmatrix} .3 & 0 & .7 \\ 0 & 1 & 0 \\ 0 & 0 & 1 \end{bmatrix}$.

Solution Find various powers of B:

$$B^2 = \begin{bmatrix} .09 & 0 & .91 \\ 0 & 1 & 0 \\ 0 & 0 & 1 \end{bmatrix}; \quad B^3 = \begin{bmatrix} .027 & 0 & .973 \\ 0 & 1 & 0 \\ 0 & 0 & 1 \end{bmatrix}; \quad B^4 = \begin{bmatrix} .0081 & 0 & .9919 \\ 0 & 1 & 0 \\ 0 & 0 & 1 \end{bmatrix}.$$

✓ **Checkpoint 4**

Decide whether the given transition matrices are regular.

(a) $\begin{bmatrix} 0 & 1 \\ 1 & 0 \end{bmatrix}$

(b) $\begin{bmatrix} .45 & .55 \\ 1 & 0 \end{bmatrix}$

Answers: See page 586.

Notice that all of the powers of B shown here have zeros in the same locations. Thus, further powers of B will still give the same zero entries, so that no power of matrix B contains all positive entries. For this reason, B is not regular. ✓

NOTE If a transition matrix P has some zero entries, and P^2 does as well, you may wonder how far you must compute P^n to be certain that the matrix is not regular. The answer is that if zeros occur in identical places in both P^n and P^{n+1} for any n, then they will appear in those places for all higher powers of P, so P is not regular.

Suppose that v is any probability vector. It can be shown that, for a regular Markov chain with a transition matrix P, there exists a single vector V that does not depend on v, such that $v \cdot P^n$ gets closer and closer to V as n gets larger and larger.

> **Equilibrium Vector of a Markov Chain**
>
> If a Markov chain with transition matrix P is regular, then there is a unique vector v such that, for any probability vector v and for large values of n,
>
> $$v \cdot P^n \approx V.$$
>
> Vector V is called the equilibrium vector, or the fixed vector, of the Markov chain.

In the example with Johnson Cleaners, the equilibrium vector V is approximately [.64 .36]. Vector V can be determined by finding P^n for larger and larger values of n and then looking for a vector that the product $v \cdot P^n$ approaches. Such a strategy can be very tedious, however, and is prone to error. To find a better way, start with the fact that, for a large value of n,

$$v \cdot P^n \approx V,$$

as mentioned in the preceding box. We can multiply both sides of this result by P, $v \cdot P^n \cdot P \approx V \cdot P$, so that

$$v \cdot P^n \cdot P = v \cdot P^{n+1} \approx VP.$$

Since $v \cdot P^n \approx V$ for large values of n, it is also true that $v \cdot P^{n+1} \approx V$ for large values of n. (The product $v \cdot P^n$ approaches V, so that $v \cdot P^{n+1}$ must also approach V.) Thus, $v \cdot P^{n+1} \approx V$ and $v \cdot P^{n+1} \approx VP$, which suggests that

$$VP = V.$$

> If a Markov chain with transition matrix P is regular, then the equilibrium vector V satisties
>
> $$VP = V.$$

The equilibrium vector V can be found by solving a system of linear equations, as shown in the remaining examples.

Example 4   Find the long-range trend for the Markov chain in Examples 1 and 2, with transition matrix

$$P = \begin{bmatrix} .8 & .2 \\ .35 & .65 \end{bmatrix}.$$

Solution This matrix is regular, since all entries are positive. Let P represent this transition matrix and let V be the probability vector $[v_1 \quad v_2]$. We want to find V such that

$$VP = V,$$

or

$$[v_1 \quad v_2]\begin{bmatrix} .8 & .2 \\ .35 & .65 \end{bmatrix} = [v_1 \quad v_2].$$

Multiply on the left to get

$$[.8v_1 + .35v_2 \quad .2v_1 + .65v_2] = [v_1 \quad v_2].$$

Set corresponding entries from the two matrices equal to obtain

$$.8v_1 + .35v_2 = v_1; \quad .2v_1 + .65v_2 = v_2.$$

Simplify each of these equations:

$$-.2v_1 + .35v_2 = 0; \quad .2v_1 - .35v_2 = 0$$

These last two equations are really the same. (The equations in the system obtained from $VP = V$ are always dependent.) To find the values of v_1 and v_2, recall that $V = [v_1 \quad v_2]$ is a probability vector, so that

$$v_1 + v_2 = 1.$$

Find v_1 and v_2 by solving the system

$$-.2v_1 + .35v_2 = 0$$
$$v_1 + \quad v_2 = 1.$$

We can rewrite the second equation as $v_1 = 1 - v_2$. Now substitute for v_1 in the first equation:

$$-.2(1 - v_2) + .35v_2 = 0.$$

Solving for v_2 yields

$$-.2 + .2v_2 + .35v_2 = 0$$
$$-.2 + .55v_2 = 0$$
$$.55v_2 = .2$$
$$v_2 = .364.$$

Since $v_2 = .364$ and $v_1 = 1 - v_2$, it follows that $v_1 = 1 - .364 = .636$, and the equilibrium vector is $[.636 \quad .364] \approx [.64 \quad .36]$.

Example 5 **Business** The probability that a complex assembly line works correctly depends on whether the line worked correctly the last time it was used. The various probabilities are as given in the following transition matrix:

$$\begin{array}{c}\\ \text{Worked Properly Before} \\ \text{Did Not} \end{array} \begin{array}{cc} \text{Works} & \\ \text{Properly Now} & \text{Does Not} \\ \begin{bmatrix} .79 & .21 \\ .68 & .32 \end{bmatrix} \end{array}$$

Find the long-range probability that the assembly line will work properly.

Solution Begin by finding the equilibrium vector $[v_1 \quad v_2]$, where

$$[v_1 \quad v_2]\begin{bmatrix} .79 & .21 \\ .68 & .32 \end{bmatrix} = [v_1 \quad v_2].$$

Multiplying on the left and setting corresponding entries equal gives the equations

$$.79v_1 + .68v_2 = v_1 \quad \text{and} \quad .21v_1 + .32v_2 = v_2,$$

or

$$-.21v_1 + .68v_2 = 0 \quad \text{and} \quad .21v_1 - .68v_2 = 0.$$

Substitute $v_1 = 1 - v_2$ in the first of these equations to get

$$-.21(1 - v_2) + .68v_2 = 0$$
$$-.21 + .21v_2 + .68v_2 = 0$$
$$-.21 + .89v_2 = 0$$
$$.89v_2 = .21$$
$$v_2 = \frac{.21}{.89} = \frac{21}{89},$$

and $v_1 = 1 - \dfrac{21}{89} = \dfrac{68}{89}$. The equilibrium vector is $[68/89 \quad 21/89]$. In the long run,

the company can expect the assembly line to run properly $\dfrac{68}{89} \approx 76\%$ of the time. **5** ✓

✓**Checkpoint 5**

In Example 5, suppose the company modifies the line so that the transition matrix becomes

$$\begin{bmatrix} .85 & .15 \\ .75 & .25 \end{bmatrix}$$

Find the long-range probability that the assembly line will work properly.

Answer: See page 586.

Example 6 Find the equilibrium vector for the transition matrix

$$K = \begin{bmatrix} .2 & .6 & .2 \\ .1 & .1 & .8 \\ .3 & .3 & .4 \end{bmatrix}.$$

Solution Matrix K has all positive entries and thus is regular. For this reason, an equilibrium vector V must exist such that $VK = V$. Let $V = [v_1 \quad v_2 \quad v_3]$. Then

$$[v_1 \quad v_2 \quad v_3]\begin{bmatrix} .2 & .6 & .2 \\ .1 & .1 & .8 \\ .3 & .3 & .4 \end{bmatrix} = [v_1 \quad v_2 \quad v_3].$$

Use matrix multiplication on the left:

$$[.2v_1 + .1v_2 + .3v_3 \quad .6v_1 + .1v_2 + .3v_3 \quad .2v_1 + .8v_2 + .4v_3] = [v_1 \quad v_2 \quad v_3].$$

Set corresponding entries equal:

$$.2v_1 + .1v_2 + .3v_3 = v_1$$
$$.6v_1 + .1v_2 + .3v_3 = v_2$$
$$.2v_1 + .8v_2 + .4v_3 = v_3.$$

Simplify these equations:

$$-.8v_1 + .1v_2 + .3v_3 = 0$$
$$6v_1 - .9v_2 + .3v_3 = 0$$
$$.2v_1 + .8v_2 - .6v_3 = 0.$$

Since V is a probability vector,

$$v_1 + v_2 + v_3 = 1.$$

This gives a system of four equations in three unknowns:

$$v_1 + v_2 + v_3 = 1.$$
$$-.8v_1 + .1v_2 + .3v_3 = 0$$
$$.6v_1 - .9v_2 + .3v_3 = 0$$
$$.2v_1 + .8v_2 - .6v_3 = 0.$$

The system can be solved with the Gauss–Jordan method set forth in Section 6.2. Start with the augmented matrix

$$\begin{bmatrix} 1 & 1 & 1 & 1 \\ -.8 & .1 & .3 & 0 \\ .6 & -.9 & .3 & 0 \\ .2 & .8 & -.6 & 0 \end{bmatrix}.$$

The solution of this system is $v_1 = 5/23$, $v_2 = 7/23$, $v_3 = 11/23$, and so

$$V = \begin{bmatrix} \dfrac{5}{23} & \dfrac{7}{23} & \dfrac{11}{23} \end{bmatrix} \approx [.22 \quad .30 \quad .48]. \quad \checkmark$$

✓ Checkpoint 6

Find the equilibrium vector for the transition matrix

$$P = \begin{bmatrix} .3 & .7 \\ .5 & .5 \end{bmatrix}.$$

Answer: See page 586.

In Example 4, we found that [.64 .36] was the equilibrium vector for the regular transition matrix

$$P = \begin{bmatrix} .8 & .2 \\ .35 & .65 \end{bmatrix}.$$

Observe what happens when you take powers of the matrix P (the displayed entries have been rounded for easy reading, but the full decimals were used in the calculations):

$$P^2 = \begin{bmatrix} .71 & .29 \\ .51 & .49 \end{bmatrix}; \quad P^3 = \begin{bmatrix} .67 & .33 \\ .58 & .42 \end{bmatrix}; \quad P^4 = \begin{bmatrix} .65 & .35 \\ .61 & .39 \end{bmatrix};$$

$$P^5 = \begin{bmatrix} .64 & .36 \\ .62 & .38 \end{bmatrix}; \quad P^6 = \begin{bmatrix} .64 & .36 \\ .63 & .37 \end{bmatrix}; \quad P^{10} = \begin{bmatrix} .64 & .36 \\ .64 & .36 \end{bmatrix}.$$

As these results suggest, higher and higher powers of the transition matrix P approach a matrix having all identical rows—rows that have as entries the entries of the equilibrium vector V.

If you have the technology to compute matrix powers easily (such as a graphing calculator), you can approximate the equilibrium vector by taking higher and higher powers of the transition matrix until all its rows are identical. Figure 9.15 shows part of this process for the transition matrix

$$B = \begin{bmatrix} .79 & .21 \\ .68 & .32 \end{bmatrix}$$

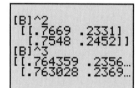
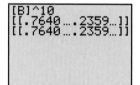

FIGURE 9.15

Figure 9.15 indicates that the equilibrium vector is [.764   .236], which is what was found algebraically in Example 5.

The results of this section can be summarized as follows.

Properties of Regular Markov Chains

Suppose a regular Markov chain has a transition matrix P.

1. As n gets larger and larger, the product $v \cdot P^n$ approaches a unique vector V for any initial probability vector v. Vector V is called the *equilibrium vector*, or *fixed vector*.
2. Vector V has the property that $VP = V$.
3. To find V, solve a system of equations obtained from the matrix equation $VP = V$ and from the fact that the sum of the entries of V is 1.
4. The powers P^n come closer and closer to a matrix whose rows are made up of the entries of the equilibrium vector V.

9.5 ▶ Exercises

Decide which of the given vectors could be a probability vector.

1. $\begin{bmatrix} \frac{1}{4} & \frac{3}{4} \end{bmatrix}$

2. $\begin{bmatrix} \frac{11}{16} & \frac{5}{16} \end{bmatrix}$

3. $\begin{bmatrix} 0 & 1 \end{bmatrix}$

4. $[.3 \quad .3 \quad .3]$

5. $[.3 \quad -.1 \quad .6]$

6. $\begin{bmatrix} \frac{2}{5} & \frac{3}{10} & .3 \end{bmatrix}$

Decide which of the given matrices could be a transition matrix. Sketch a transition diagram for any transition matrices.

7. $\begin{bmatrix} .7 & .2 \\ .5 & .5 \end{bmatrix}$

8. $\begin{bmatrix} \frac{1}{4} & \frac{3}{4} \\ 0 & 1 \end{bmatrix}$

9. $\begin{bmatrix} \frac{4}{9} & \frac{1}{3} \\ \frac{1}{5} & \frac{7}{10} \end{bmatrix}$

10. $\begin{bmatrix} 0 & 1 & 0 \\ .3 & .3 & .3 \\ 1 & 0 & 0 \end{bmatrix}$

11. $\begin{bmatrix} \frac{1}{2} & \frac{1}{4} & 1 \\ \frac{2}{3} & 0 & \frac{1}{3} \\ \frac{1}{3} & 1 & 0 \end{bmatrix}$

12. $\begin{bmatrix} .2 & .3 & .5 \\ 0 & 0 & 1 \\ .1 & .9 & 0 \end{bmatrix}$

In Exercises 13–15, write any transition diagrams as transition matrices.

13.

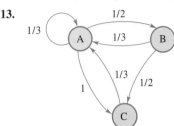

14.

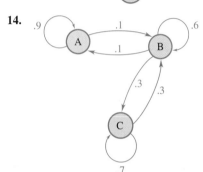

15.

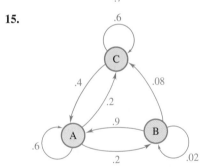

Decide whether the given transition matrices are regular. (See Example 3.)

16. $\begin{bmatrix} 1 & 0 \\ .25 & .75 \end{bmatrix}$

17. $\begin{bmatrix} .2 & .8 \\ .9 & .1 \end{bmatrix}$

18. $\begin{bmatrix} .3 & .5 & .2 \\ 1 & 0 & 0 \\ .5 & .1 & .4 \end{bmatrix}$

19. $\begin{bmatrix} 0 & 1 & 0 \\ .3 & .3 & .4 \\ 1 & 0 & 0 \end{bmatrix}$

20. $\begin{bmatrix} .25 & .40 & .30 & .05 \\ .18 & .23 & .59 & 0 \\ 0 & .15 & .36 & .49 \\ .28 & .32 & .24 & .16 \end{bmatrix}$

21. $\begin{bmatrix} .23 & .41 & 0 & .36 \\ 0 & .27 & .21 & .52 \\ 0 & 0 & 1 & 0 \\ .48 & 0 & .39 & .13 \end{bmatrix}$

Find the equilibrium vector for each of the given transition matrices. (See Examples 4 and 5.)

22. $\begin{bmatrix} .3 & .7 \\ .4 & .6 \end{bmatrix}$

23. $\begin{bmatrix} .55 & .45 \\ .19 & .81 \end{bmatrix}$

24. $\begin{bmatrix} \frac{5}{8} & \frac{3}{8} \\ \frac{7}{9} & \frac{2}{9} \end{bmatrix}$

25. $\begin{bmatrix} \frac{2}{3} & \frac{1}{3} \\ \frac{1}{8} & \frac{7}{8} \end{bmatrix}$

26. $\begin{bmatrix} .25 & .35 & .4 \\ .1 & .3 & .6 \\ .55 & .4 & .05 \end{bmatrix}$

27. $\begin{bmatrix} .16 & .28 & .56 \\ .43 & .12 & .45 \\ .86 & .05 & .09 \end{bmatrix}$

28. $\begin{bmatrix} .15 & .15 & .70 \\ .42 & .38 & .20 \\ .16 & .28 & .56 \end{bmatrix}$

29. $\begin{bmatrix} .44 & .31 & .25 \\ .80 & .11 & .09 \\ .26 & .31 & .43 \end{bmatrix}$

For each of the given transition matrices, use a graphing calculator or computer to find the first five powers of the matrix. Then find the probability that state 2 changes to state 4 after 5 repetitions of the experiment.

30. $\begin{bmatrix} .1 & .2 & .2 & .3 & .2 \\ .2 & .1 & .1 & .2 & .4 \\ .2 & .1 & .4 & .2 & .1 \\ .3 & .1 & .1 & .2 & .3 \\ .1 & .3 & .1 & .1 & .4 \end{bmatrix}$

31. $\begin{bmatrix} .3 & .2 & .3 & .1 & .1 \\ .4 & .2 & .1 & .2 & .1 \\ .1 & .3 & .2 & .2 & .2 \\ .2 & .1 & .3 & .2 & .2 \\ .1 & .1 & .4 & .2 & .2 \end{bmatrix}$

32. Health In a recent year, the percentage of patients at a doctor's office who received a flu shot was 26%. A campaign by the doctors and nurses was designed to increase the percentage of patients who obtain a flu shot. The doctors and nurses believed there was an 85% chance that someone who received a shot in year 1 would obtain a shot in year 2. They also believed that there was a 40% chance that a person who did not receive a shot in year 1 would receive a shot in year 2.

(a) Give the transition matrix for this situation.

(b) Find the percentages of patients in year 2 who received a flu shot.

(c) Find the long-range trend for the Markov chain representing receipt of flu shots at the doctor's office.

33. Social Science Six months prior to an election, a poll found that only 35% of state voters planned to vote for a casino gambling initiative. After a media blitz emphasizing the new jobs that are created as a result of casinos, a new poll found that among those who did not favor it previously, 30% now favored the initiative. Among those who favored the initiative initially, 90% still favored it.

(a) Give the transition matrix for this situation.

(b) Find the percentage who favored the gambling initiative after the media blitz.

(c) Find the long-term percentage who favor the initiative if the trends and media blitz continue.

34. **Business** The probability that a complex assembly line works correctly depends on whether the line worked correctly the last time it was used. There is a .91 chance that the line will work correctly if it worked correctly the time before and a .68 chance that it will work correctly if it did *not* work correctly the time before. Set up a transition matrix with this information, and find the long-run probability that the line will work correctly. (See Example 5.)

35. **Business** Suppose something unplanned occurred to the assembly line of Exercise 34, so that the transition matrix becomes

$$\begin{array}{c} \\ \text{Works} \\ \text{Doesn't Works} \end{array} \begin{array}{cc} \text{Works} & \text{Doesn't Work} \\ \left[\begin{array}{cc} .81 & .19 \\ .77 & .23 \end{array}\right]. \end{array}$$

Find the new long-run probability that the line will work properly.

36. **Natural Science** In Exercises 62 and 63 of Section 8.4 (p. 504), we discussed the effect on flower color of cross-pollinating pea plants. As shown there, since the gene for red is dominant and the gene for white is recessive, 75% of the pea plants have red flowers and 25% have white flowers, because plants with 1 red and 1 white gene appear red. If a red-flowered plant is crossed with a red-flowered plant known to have 1 red and 1 white gene, then 75% of the offspring will be red and 25% will be white. Crossing a red-flowered plant that has 1 red and 1 white gene with a white-flowered plant produces 50% red-flowered offspring and 50% white-flowered offspring.
    (a) Write a transition matrix using this information.
    (b) Write a probability vector for the initial distribution of colors.
    (c) Find the distribution of colors after 4 generations.
    (d) Find the long-range distribution of colors.

37. **Natural Science** Snapdragons with 1 red gene and 1 white gene produce pink-flowered offspring. If a red snapdragon is crossed with a pink snapdragon, the probabilities that the offspring will be red, pink, or white are 1/2, 1/2, and 0, respectively. If 2 pink snapdragons are crossed, the probabilities of red, pink, or white offspring are 1/4, 1/2, and 1/4, respectively. For a cross between a white and a pink snapdragon, the corresponding probabilities are 0, 1/2, and 1/2. Set up a transition matrix and find the long-range prediction for the fraction of red, pink, and white snapdragons.

38. **Natural Science** Markov chains can be utilized in research into earthquakes. Researchers in Italy give the following example of a transition matrix in which the rows are magnitudes of an earthquake and the columns are magnitudes of the next earthquake in the sequence.*

	2.5	2.6	2.7	2.8
2.5	3/7	1/7	2/7	1/7
2.6	1/2	0	1/4	1/4
2.7	1/3	1/3	0	1/3
2.8	1/4	1/2	0	1/4

Thus, the probability of a 2.5-magnitude earthquake being followed by a 2.8-magnitude earthquake is 1/7. If these trends were to persist, find the long-range trend for the probabilities of each magnitude for the subsequent earthquake.

39. **Social Science** An urban center finds that 60% of the population own a home (H), 39.5% are renters (R), and .5% are homeless (H). The study also finds the following transition probabilities per year.

$$\begin{array}{c} \\ O \\ R \\ H \end{array} \begin{array}{ccc} O & H & R \\ \left[\begin{array}{ccc} .90 & .10 & 0 \\ .09 & .909 & .001 \\ 0 & .34 & .66 \end{array}\right] \end{array}$$

    (a) Find the probability that residents own, rent, and are homeless after one year.
    (b) Find the long-range probabilities for the three categories.

40. **Business** An insurance company classifies its drivers into three groups: G_0 (no accidents), G_1 (one accident), and G_2 (more than one accident). The probability that a driver in G_0 will stay in G_0 after 1 year is .85, that he will become a G_1 is .10, and that he will become a G_2 is .05. A driver in G_1 cannot move to G_0. (This insurance company has a long memory!) There is a .80 probability that a G_1 driver will stay in G_1 and a .20 probability that he will become a G_2. A driver in G_2 must stay in G_2.
    (a) Write a transition matrix using this information.

    Suppose that the company accepts 50,000 new policyholders, all of whom are in group G_0. Find the number in each group
    (b) after 1 year;   (c) after 2 years;
    (d) after 3 years;   (e) after 4 years.
    (f) Find the equilibrium vector here. Interpret your result.

41. **Business** The difficulty with the mathematical model of Exercise 40 is that no "grace period" is provided; there should be a certain probability of moving from G_1 or G_2 back to G_0 (say, after 4 years with no accidents). A new

*Michele Lovallo, Vincenzo Lapenna, and Luciano Telesca, "Transition matrix analysis of earthquake magnitude sequences," *Chaos, Solitons, and Fractals* 24 (2005): 33–43.

system with this feature might produce the following transition matrix:

$$\begin{bmatrix} .85 & .10 & .05 \\ .15 & .75 & .10 \\ .10 & .30 & .60 \end{bmatrix}.$$

Suppose that when this new policy is adopted, the company has 50,000 policyholders in group G_0. Find the number in each group

(a) after 1 year;

(b) after 2 years;

(c) after 3 years.

(d) Find the equilibrium vector here. Interpret your result.

42. Suppose research on three major cell phone companies revealed the following transition matrix for the probability that a person with one cell phone carrier switches to another.

Will Switch to

	Company A	Company B	Company C
Company A	.91	.07	.02
Now has Company B	.03	.87	.10
Company C	.14	.04	.82

The current share of the market is [.26, .36, .38] for Companies A, B, and C, respectively. Find the share of the market held by each company after

(a) 1 year;   (b) 2 years;   (c) 3 years.

(d) What is the long-range prediction?

43. Business Data from *The Wall Street Journal* Web site indicated that the probability a new vehicle purchased in the United States in 2008 was from General Motors (GM) was .232, from Ford (F) was .150, from Toyota (T) was .159, and from other car manufacturers (O) was .459. Use the transition matrix below for market share changes from year to year to find

(a) the probability a vehicle was purchased from Ford in the next year;

(b) the long-term probability a vehicle is purchased from Toyota if the trends continue.

	GM	F	T	O
GM	.85	.04	.05	.06
F	.02	.91	.03	.04
T	.01	.01	.95	.03
O	.03	.02	.06	.89

44. Social Science At one liberal arts college, students are classified as humanities majors, science majors, or undecided. There is a 23% chance that a humanities major will change to a science major from one year to the next and a 40% chance that a humanities major will change to undecided. A science major will change to humanities with probability .12 and to undecided student with probability .38. An undecided student will switch to humanities or science with probabilities of .45 and .28, respectively. Find the long-range prediction for the fraction of students in each of these three majors.

45. Business In a queuing chain, we assume that people are queuing up to be served by, say, a bank teller. For simplicity, let us assume that once two people are in line, no one else can enter the line. Let us further assume that one person is served every minute, as long as someone is in line. Assume further that, in any minute, there is a probability of .4 that no one enters the line, a probability of .3 that exactly one person enters the line, and a probability of .3 that exactly two people enter the line, assuming that there is room. If there is not enough room for two people, then the probability that one person enters the line is .5. Let the state be given by the number of people in line.

(a) Give the transition matrix for the number of people in line:

$$\begin{array}{c} \\ 0 \\ 1 \\ 2 \end{array} \begin{array}{ccc} 0 & 1 & 2 \end{array} \\ \begin{bmatrix} ? & ? & ? \\ ? & ? & ? \\ ? & ? & ? \end{bmatrix}.$$

(b) Find the transition matrix for a 2-minute period.

(c) Use your result from part (b) to find the probability that a queue with no one in line has two people in line 2 minutes later.

Use a graphing calculator or computer for Exercises 46 and 47.

46. Business A company with a new training program classified each employee in one of four states: s_1, never in the program; s_2, currently in the program; s_3, discharged; s_4, completed the program. The transition matrix for this company is as follows.

	s_1	s_2	s_3	s_4
s_1	.4	.2	.05	.35
s_2	0	.45	.05	.5
s_3	0	0	1	0
s_4	0	0	0	1

(a) What percentage of employees who had never been in the program (state s_1) completed the program (state s_4) after the program had been offered five times?

(b) If the initial percentage of employees in each state was [.5 .5 0 0], find the corresponding percentages after the program had been offered four times.

47. Business Find the long-range prediction for the percentage of employees in each state for the company training program in Exercise 46.

✓**Checkpoint Answers**

1. **(a)** .7

   (b) The probability of changing from state 2 to state 1

   (c)

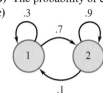

2. [.59 .41] (rounded)
3. [.61 .39] (rounded)
4. **(a)** No   **(b)** Yes
5. $5/6 \approx 83\%$
6. [5/12 7/12]

9.6 ▶ Decision Making

John F. Kennedy once remarked that he had assumed that, as president, it would be difficult to choose between distinct, opposite alternatives when a decision needed to be made. Actually, he found that such decisions were easy to make; the hard decisions came when he was faced with choices that were not as clear cut. Most decisions fall into this last category—decisions that must be made under conditions of uncertainty. In Section 9.1, we saw how to use expected values to help make a decision. Those ideas are extended in this section, where we consider decision making in the face of uncertainty. We begin with an example.

Example 1   **Business** Freezing temperatures are endangering the orange crop in central California. A farmer can protect his crop by burning smudge pots; the heat from the pots keeps the oranges from freezing. However, burning the pots is expensive, costing $20,000. The farmer knows that if he burns smudge pots, he will be able to sell his crop for a net profit (after the costs of the pots are deducted) of $50,000, provided that the freeze does develop and wipes out other orange crops in California. If he does nothing, he will either lose the $10,000 he has already invested in the crop if it does freeze or make a profit of $46,000 if it does not freeze. (If it does not freeze, there will be a large supply of oranges, and thus his profit will be lower than if there were a small supply.) What should the farmer do?

   Solution He should begin by carefully defining the problem. First, he must decide on the **states of nature**—the possible alternatives over which he has no control. Here, there are two: freezing temperatures and no freezing temperatures. Next, the farmer should list the things he can control—his actions or **strategies**. He has two possible strategies: to use smudge pots or not. The consequences of each action under each state of nature, called **payoffs**, are summarized in a **payoff matrix**, as follows, where the payoffs in this case are the profits for each possible combination of events:

		States of Nature	
		Freeze	No Freeze
Strategies of Farmer	Use Smudge Pots	$50,000	$26,000
	Do Not Use Pots	−$10,000	$46,000

✓ **Checkpoint 1**

Explain how each of the given payoffs in the matrix were obtained.

(a) −$10,000

(b) $50,000

Answers: See page 590.

To get the $26,000 entry in the payoff matrix, use the profit if there is no freeze, namely, $46,000, and subtract the $20,000 cost of using the pots.

Once the farmer makes the payoff matrix, what then? The farmer might be an optimist (some might call him a gambler); in this case, he might assume that the best will happen and go for the biggest number of the matrix ($50,000). For that profit, he must adopt the strategy "use smudge pots."

On the other hand, if the farmer is a pessimist, he would want to minimize the worst thing that could happen. If he uses smudge pots, the worst thing that could happen to him would be a profit of $26,000, which will result if there is no freeze. If he does not use smudge pots, he might face a loss of $10,000. To minimize the worst, he once again should adopt the strategy "use smudge pots."

Suppose the farmer decides that he is neither an optimist nor a pessimist, but would like further information before choosing a strategy. For example, he might call the weather forecaster and ask for the probability of a freeze. Suppose the forecaster says that this probability is only .2. What should the farmer do? He should recall the discussion of expected value and work out the expected profit for each of his two possible strategies. If the probability of a freeze is .2, then the probability that there is no freeze is .8. This information leads to the following expected values:

If smudge pots are used: $50,000(.2) + 26,000(.8) = 30,800$;

If no smudge pots are used: $-10,000(.2) + 46,000(.8) = 34,800$.

Here, the maximum expected profit, $34,800, is obtained if smudge pots are not used.

✓ **Checkpoint 2**

What should the farmer do if the probability of a freeze is .6? What is his expected profit?

Answer: See page 590.

As the example shows, the farmer's beliefs about the probabilities of a freeze affect his choice of strategies.

Example 2   **Business**   An owner of several greeting-card stores must decide in July about the type of displays to emphasize for Sweetest Day in October. He has three possible choices: emphasize chocolates, emphasize collectible gifts, or emphasize gifts that can be engraved. His success is dependent on the state of the economy in October. If the economy is strong, he will do well with the collectible gifts, while in a weak economy, the chocolates do very well. In a mixed economy, the gifts that can be engraved will do well. He first prepares a payoff matrix for all three possibilities, where the numbers in the matrix represent his profits in thousands of dollars:

	States of Nature		
	Weak Economy	Mixed	Strong Economy
Chocolates	85	30	75
Strategies Collectibles	45	45	110
Engraved	60	95	85

(a) What would an optimist do?

Solution If the owner is an optimist, he should aim for the biggest number on the matrix, 110 (representing $110,000 in profit). His strategy in this case would be to display collectibles.

(b) How would a pessimist react?

Solution A pessimist wants to find the best of the worst of all bad things that can happen. If he displays collectibles, the worst that can happen is a profit of $45,000. For displaying engravable items, the worst is a profit of $60,000, and for displaying chocolates, the worst is a profit of $30,000. His strategy here is to use the engravable items.

(c) Suppose the owner reads in a business magazine that leading experts believe that there is a 50% chance of a weak economy in October, a 20% chance of a mixed economy, and a 30% chance of a strong economy. How might he use this information?

Solution The owner can now find his expected profit for each possible strategy.

Chocolates $85(.5) + 30(.20) + 75(.30) = 71$;

Collectibles $45(.5) + 45(.20) + 110(.30) = 64.5$;

Engraved $60(.5) + 95(.20) + 85(.30) = 74.5$.

Here, the best strategy is to display gifts that can be engraved; the expected profit is 74.5, or $74,500. 3✓

✓**Checkpoint 3**

Suppose the owner reads another article, which gives the following predictions: a 35% chance of a weak economy, a 25% chance of an in-between economy, and a 40% chance of a strong economy. What is the best strategy now? What is the expected profit?

Answer: See page 590.

9.6 ▶ Exercises

1. **Business** A developer has $100,000 to invest in land. He has a choice of two parcels (at the same price): one on the highway and one on the coast. With both parcels, his ultimate profit depends on whether he faces light opposition from environmental groups or heavy opposition. He estimates that the payoff matrix is as follows (the numbers represent his profit):

Opposition

	Light	Heavy
Highway	$70,000	$30,000
Coast	$150,000	−$40,000

What should the developer do if he is
(a) an optimist?   **(b)** a pessimist?
(c) Suppose the probability of heavy opposition is .8. What is his best strategy? What is the expected profit?
(d) What is the best strategy if the probability of heavy opposition is only .4?

2. **Business** Mount Union College has sold out all tickets for a jazz concert to be held in the stadium. If it rains, the show will have to be moved to the gym, which has a much smaller seating capacity. The dean must decide in advance whether to set up the seats and the stage in the gym, in the stadium, or in both, just in case. The following payoff matrix shows the net profit in each case:

States of Nature

	Rain	No Rain
Set up in Stadium	−$1550	$1500
Set up in Gym	$1000	$1000
Set up in Both	$750	$1400

Strategies (Set up in Stadium, Set up in Gym, Set up in Both)

What strategy should the dean choose if she is
(a) an optimist?
(b) a pessimist?
(c) If the weather forecaster predicts rain with a probability of .6, what strategy should she choose to maximize the expected profit? What is the maximum expected profit?

3. **Business** An analyst must decide what fraction of the automobile tires produced at a particular manufacturing plant are defective. She has already decided that there are three possibilities for the fraction of defective items: .02, .09, and .16. She may recommend two courses of action: upgrade the equipment at the plant or make no upgrades. The following payoff matrix represents the *costs* to the company in each case, in hundreds of dollars:

Defectives

		.02	.09	.16
Strategies	Upgrade	130	130	130
	No Upgrade	28	180	450

What strategy should the analyst recommend if she is

(a) an optimist?

(b) a pessimist?

(c) Suppose the analyst is able to estimate probabilities for the three states of nature as follows:

Fraction of Defectives	Probability
.02	.70
.09	.20
.16	.10

Which strategy should she recommend? Find the expected cost to the company if that strategy is chosen.

4. **Business**   The research department of the Allied Manufacturing Company has developed a new process that it believes will result in an improved product. Management must decide whether to go ahead and market the new product or not. The new product may be better than the old one, or it may not be better. If the new product is better and the company decides to market it, sales should increase by $50,000. If it is not better and the old product is replaced with the new product on the market, the company will lose $25,000 to competitors. If management decides not to market the new product, the company will lose $40,000 if it is better and will lose research costs of $10,000 if it is not.

(a) Prepare a payoff matrix.

(b) If management believes that the probability that the new product is better is .4, find the expected profits under each strategy and determine the best action.

5. **Business**   A businessman is planning to ship a used machine to his plant in Nigeria. He would like to use it there for the next 4 years. He must decide whether to overhaul the machine before sending it. The cost of overhaul is $2600. If the machine fails when it is in operation in Nigeria, it will cost him $6000 in lost production and repairs. He estimates that the probability that it will fail is .3 if he does not overhaul it and .1 if he does overhaul it. Neglect the possibility that the machine might fail more than once in the 4 years.

(a) Prepare a payoff matrix.

(b) What should the businessman do to minimize his expected costs?

6. **Business**   A contractor prepares to bid on a job. If all goes well, his bid should be $25,000, which will cover his costs plus his usual profit margin of $4000. However, if a threatened labor strike actually occurs, his bid should be $35,000 to give him the same profit. If there is a strike and he bids $25,000, he will lose $5500. If his bid is too high, he may lose the job entirely, while if it is too low, he may lose money.

(a) Prepare a payoff matrix.

(b) If the contractor believes that the probability of a strike is .6, how much should he bid?

7. **Business**   An artist travels to craft fairs all summer long. She must book her booth at a June craft show six months in advance and decide if she wishes to rent a tent for an extra $500 in case it rains on the day of the show. If it does not rain, she believes she will earn $3000 at the show. If it rains, she believes she will earn only $2000, provided she has a tent. If she does not have a tent and it does rain, she will have to pack up and go home and will thus earn $0. Weather records over the last 10 years indicate that there is a .4 probability of rain in June.

(a) Prepare a profit matrix.

(b) What should the artist do to maximize her expected revenue?

8. **Business**   An investor has $50,000 to invest in stocks. She has two possible strategies: buy conservative blue-chip stocks or buy highly speculative stocks. There are two states of nature: the market goes up and the market goes down. The following payoff matrix shows the net amounts she will have under the various circumstances.

	Market Up	Market Down
Buy Blue Chip	$60,000	$46,000
Buy Speculative	$80,000	$32,000

What should the investor do if she is

(a) an optimist?

(b) a pessimist?

(c) Suppose there is a .6 probability of the market going up. What is the best strategy? What is the expected profit?

(d) What is the best strategy if the probability of a market rise is .2?

Sometimes the numbers (or payoffs) in a payoff matrix do not represent money (profits or costs, for example). Instead, they may represent utility. A utility is a number that measures the satisfaction (or lack of it) that results from a certain action. Utility numbers must be assigned by each individual, depending on how he or she feels about a situation. For example, one person might assign a utility of +20 for a week's vacation in San Francisco, with −6 being assigned if the vacation were moved to Sacramento. Work the problems that follow in the same way as the preceding ones.

9. **Social Science**   A politician must plan her reelection strategy. She can emphasize jobs or she can emphasize the environment. The voters can be concerned about jobs

or about the environment. Following is a payoff matrix showing the utility of each possible outcome.

$$\begin{array}{c} & & \textit{Voters} \\ & & \text{Jobs} \quad \text{Environment} \\ \textit{Candidate} \begin{array}{c} \text{Jobs} \\ \text{Environment} \end{array} & \begin{bmatrix} +40 & -10 \\ -12 & +30 \end{bmatrix} \end{array}$$

The political analysts feel that there is a .35 chance that the voters will emphasize jobs. What strategy should the candidate adopt? What is its expected utility?

10. In an accounting class, the instructor permits the students to bring a calculator or a reference book (but not both) to an examination. The examination itself can emphasize either numbers or definitions. In trying to decide which aid to take to an examination, a student first decides on the utilities shown in the following payoff matrix:

$$\begin{array}{c} & & \textit{Exam Emphasizes} \\ & & \text{Numbers} \quad \text{Definition} \\ \textit{Student Chooses} \begin{array}{c} \text{Calculator} \\ \text{Book} \end{array} & \begin{bmatrix} +50 & 0 \\ +15 & +35 \end{bmatrix} \end{array}$$

(a) What strategy should the student choose if the probability that the examination will emphasize numbers is .6? What is the expected utility in this case?

(b) Suppose the probability that the examination emphasizes numbers is .4. What strategy should the student choose?

✓ Checkpoint Answers

1. (a) If the crop freezes and smudge pots are not used, the farmer's profit is −$10,000 for labor costs.
   (b) If the crop freezes and smudge pots are used, the farmer makes a profit of $50,000.
2. Use smudge pots; $40,400
3. Engravable; $78,750

CHAPTER 9 ▶ Summary

KEY TERMS AND SYMBOLS

9.1 ▶ random variable
probability distribution
histogram
expected value
fair game

9.2 ▶ **n!** (n factorial)
multiplication principle
permutations
combinations

9.4 ▶ Bernoulli trials (processes)
binomial experiment
binomial probability

9.5 ▶ stochastic processes
Markov chain
state
transition diagram
transition matrix
probability vector

regular transition matrix
regular Markov chain
equilibrium vector (fixed vector)

9.6 ▶ states of nature
strategies
payoffs
payoff matrix

CHAPTER 9 KEY CONCEPTS

Expected Value of a Probability Distribution   For a random variable x with values $x_1, x_2, \ldots, x_n$ and probabilities $p_1, p_2, \ldots, p_n$, the expected value is

$$E(x) = x_1 p_1 + x_2 p_2 + \cdots + x_n p_n.$$

Multiplication Principle   If there are m_1 ways to make a first choice, m_2 ways to make a second choice, and so on, then there are $m_1 m_2 \cdots m_n$ different ways to make the entire sequence of choices.

The number of **permutations** of n elements taken r at a time is $_nP_r = \dfrac{n!}{(n-r)!}$.

The number of **combinations** of n elements taken r at a time is

$$_nC_r = \frac{n!}{(n-r)!\, r!}.$$

Binomial Experiments have the following characteristics: (1) The same experiment is repeated several times; (2) there are only *two* outcomes, labeled success and failure; (3) the probability of success is the same for each trial; and (4) the trials are independent. If the probability of success in a single trial is p, the probability of x successes in n trials is

$$_nC_xp^x(1-p)^{n-x}.$$

Markov Chains A **transition matrix** must be square, with all entries between 0 and 1 inclusive, and the sum of the entries in any row must be 1. A Markov chain is *regular* if some power of its transition matrix P contains all positive entries. The long-range probabilities for a regular Markov chain are given by the **equilibrium**, or **fixed**, **vector** V, where, for any initial probability vector v, the products vP^n approach V as n gets larger and $VP = V$. To find V, solve the system of equations formed by $VP = V$ and the fact that the sum of the entries of V is 1.

Decision Making A **payoff matrix**, which includes all available strategies and states of nature, is used in decision making to define the problem and the possible solutions. The expected value of each strategy can help to determine the best course of action.

CHAPTER 9 REVIEW EXERCISES

In Exercises 1–3, (a) sketch the histogram of the given probability distribution, and (b) find the expected value.

1.

x	0	1	2	3
$P(x)$	.22	.54	.16	.08

2.

x	−3	−2	−1	0	1	2	3
$P(x)$	.15	.20	.25	.18	.12	.06	.04

3.

x	−10	0	10
$P(x)$	$\dfrac{1}{3}$	$\dfrac{1}{3}$	$\dfrac{1}{3}$

4. Health The probability distribution for the previous number of children a pregnant mother has given birth to can be estimated using data from the North Carolina Birth Registry as follows.*

x = Number of children now living	0	1	2	3	4
$P(x)$	.40898	.32788	.16616	.06281	.02110

x = Number of children now living	5	6	7	8	9
$P(x)$	.00771	.00321	.00132	.00061	.00023

Find the expected value.

*Based on data available at www.odum.unc.edu. Data modified slightly for 9 previous children or less.

5. Social Science Data from The American Community Survey yields the following probability distribution for x, the number of bedrooms for the dwellings in which Americans live.*

x	0	1	2	3	4	5
$P(x)$	.0138	.1049	.2722	.3909	.1748	.0434

Find the expected number of bedrooms.

In Exercises 6 and 7, (a) give the probability distribution, and (b) find the expected value.

6. Business A grocery store has 10 bouquets of flowers for sale, 3 of which are red rose displays. Two bouquets are selected at random, and the number of rose bouquets is noted.

7. Social Science In a class of 10 students, 3 did not do their homework. The professor selects 3 members of the class to present solutions to homework problems on the board and records how many of those selected did not do their homework.

Solve the given problems.

8. Suppose someone offers to pay you $100 if you draw 3 cards from a standard deck of 52 cards and all the cards are hearts. What should you pay for the chance to win if it is a fair game?

9. You pay $2 to play a game of "Over/Under," in which you will roll two dice and note the sum of the results. You can bet that the sum will be less than 7 (under), exactly 7, or greater than 7 (over). If you bet "under" and you win, you get your $2 back, plus $2 more. If you bet 7 and you win, you get your $2 back, plus $4, and if you bet "over" and

*Based on data available at www.census.gov/acs.

win, you get your $2 back, plus $2 more. What are the expected winnings for each type of bet?

10. A lottery has a first prize of $10,000, two second prizes of $1000 each, and two $100 third prizes. Ten thousand tickets are sold, at $2 each. Find the expected winnings of a person buying 1 ticket.

11. **Social Science** It can be estimated that 25% of renters pay $1140 or more a month in rent.* If we randomly select 5 households that rent, the probability distribution for x, the number of the renters that pay $1140 or more in rent, is given as follows:

x	0	1	2	3	4	5
$P(x)$	.2373	.3955	.2637	.0879	.0146	.0010

Find the expected value for x.

12. **Business** In October 2008, David Pogue of The *New York Times* estimated Apple® Computer's total worldwide market share at approximately 7.5%. If we select 3 computers at random and define x to be the number of Apple computers, the probability distribution is as follows:

x	0	1	2	3
$P(x)$	.7915	.1925	.0156	.0004

Find $E(x)$.

13. In how many ways can 8 different taxis line up at the airport?

14. How many variations are possible for gold, silver, and bronze medalists in the 50-meter swimming race if there are 8 finalists?

15. In how many ways can a sample of 3 computer monitors be taken from a batch of 12 identical monitors?

16. If 4 of the 12 monitors in Exercise 15 are broken, in how many ways can the sample of 3 include the following?
   (a) 1 broken monitor;
   (b) no broken monitors;
   (c) at least 1 broken monitor.

17. In how many ways can 6 students from a class of 30 be arranged in the first row of seats? (There are 6 seats in the first row.)

18. In how many ways can the six students in Exercise 17 be arranged in a row if a certain student must be first?

19. In how many ways can the 6 students in Exercise 17 be arranged if half the students are science majors and the other half are business majors and if
   (a) like majors must be together?
   (b) science and business majors are alternated?

20. Explain under what circumstances a permutation should be used in a probability problem and under what circumstances a combination should be used.

21. Discuss under what circumstances the binomial probability formula should be used in a probability problem.

Suppose 2 cards are drawn without replacement from an ordinary deck of 52 cards. Find the probabilities of the given results.

22. Both cards are black.   23. Both cards are hearts.

24. Exactly 1 is a face card.   25. At most 1 is an ace.

An ice cream stand contains 4 custard flavors, 6 ice cream flavors, and 2 frozen yogurt selections. Three customers come to the window. If each customer's selection is random, find the probability that the selections include

26. all ice cream;   27. all custard;

28. at least one frozen yogurt;

29. one custard, one ice cream, and one frozen yogurt;

30. at most one ice cream.

31. In this exercise, we study the connection between sets (from Chapter 8) and combinations.
   (a) Given a set with n elements, what is the number of subsets of size 0? of size 1? of size 2? of size n?
   (b) Using your answer from part (a), give an expression for the total number of subsets of a set with n elements.
   (c) Using your answer from part (b) and a result from Chapter 8, explain why the following equation must be true:

$$_nC_0 + {_nC_1} + {_nC_2} + \cdots + {_nC_n} = 2^n.$$

   (d) Verify the equation in part (c) for $n = 4$ and $n = 5$.

Health *According to the U.S. National Center for Health Statistics, 36% of deaths are a result of major cardiovascular disease. If 7 deaths are selected at random, find the probability that*

32. exactly 2 of the deaths were from major cardiovascular disease;

33. at least 1 of the deaths was from major cardiovascular disease.

Natural Science *Researchers studied scarring patterns on the skin of humpback whales in Alaska and estimate that 78% of the whales have been previously entangled in fishing nets.* Suppose that 6 whales are selected at random, and let x be the number of whales with scars indicating previous entanglement.*

34. Give the probability distribution for x.

35. What is the expected number of whales indicating previous entanglement?

---

*Janet L. Neilson, Christine M. Gabriele, and Janice M. Straley, "Humpback Whale Entanglement in Fishing Gear in Northern Southeastern Alaska," *Proceedings of the Fourth Glacier Bay Science Symposium*, 2007, pp. 204–207.

---

*Based on data available at www.census.gov/acs.

36. Business As of February 2009, 22% of the Janus Health Global Life Sciences Fund (a high growth investment mutual fund) was invested in foreign stocks. If 4 stocks from the fund are picked at random, find the probability that the given numbers of stocks are foreign stocks.
  (a) All 4 stocks
  (b) At least 1 stock
  (c) At most 2 stocks

37. Business In 2008, 15% of the credit unions insured by the National Credit Union Association (NCUA) had $100 million or more in assets.* If we select 5 credit unions at random,
  (a) give the probability distribution for x, the number of credit unions with $100 million or more in assets;
  (b) give the expected value for the number of credit unions with $100 million or more in assets.

Decide whether each matrix is a regular transition matrix.

38. $\begin{bmatrix} 0 & 1 \\ .77 & .23 \end{bmatrix}$

39. $\begin{bmatrix} -.2 & .4 \\ .3 & .7 \end{bmatrix}$

40. $\begin{bmatrix} .21 & .15 & .64 \\ .50 & .12 & .38 \\ 1 & 0 & 0 \end{bmatrix}$

41. $\begin{bmatrix} .22 & 0 & .78 \\ .40 & .33 & .27 \\ 0 & .61 & .39 \end{bmatrix}$

42. Business Using e-mail for professional correspondence has become a major component of a worker's day. A study classified e-mail use into 3 categories for an office day: no use, light use (1–60 minutes), and heavy use (more than 60 minutes). Researchers observed a pool of 100 office workers over a month and developed the following transition matrix of probabilities from day to day:

	Current Day		
Previous Day	No Use	Light Use	Heavy Use
No use	.35	.15	.50
Light Use	.30	.35	.35
Heavy Use	.15	.30	.55

Suppose the initial distribution for the three states is [.2, .4, .4]. Find the distribution after
  (a) 1 day;
  (b) 2 days.
  (c) What is the long-range prediction for the distribution of e-mail use?

43. Business An analyst at a major brokerage firm that invests in Europe, North America, and Asia has examined the investment records for a particular international stock mutual fund over several years. The analyst constructed the following transition matrix for the probability of switching the location of an equity from year to year:

*Based on data available at www.ncua.org.

	Current Year		
	Europe	North America	Asia
Previous Year — Europe	.80	.14	.06
North America	.04	.85	.11
Asia	.03	.13	.84

If the initial investment vector is 15% in Europe, 60% in North America, and 25% in Asia,
  (a) find the percentages in Europe, North America, and Asia after 1 year;
  (b) find the percentages in Europe, North America, and Asia after 3 years;
  (c) find the long-range percentages in Europe, North America, and Asia.

44. Social Science A candidate for city council can come out in favor of a new factory, be opposed to it, or waffle on the issue. The change in votes for the candidate depends on what her opponent does, with payoffs as shown in the following matrix:

	Opponent		
Candidate	Favors	Waffles	Opposes
Favors	0	−1000	−4000
Waffles	1000	0	−500
Opposes	5000	2000	0

  (a) What should the candidate do if she is an optimist?
  (b) What should she do if she is a pessimist?
  (c) Suppose the candidate's campaign manager feels that there is a 40% chance that the opponent will favor the plant and a 35% chance that he will waffle. What strategy should the candidate adopt? What is the expected change in the number of votes?
  (d) The opponent conducts a new poll that shows strong opposition to the new factory. This changes the probability that he will favor the factory to 0 and the probability that he will waffle to .7. What strategy should our candidate adopt? What is the expected change in the number of votes now?

45. Social Science When teaching, an instructor can adopt a strategy using either active learning or lecturing to help students learn best. A class often reacts very differently to these two strategies. A class can prefer lecturing or active learning. A department chair constructs the following payoff matrix of the average point gain (out of 500 possible points) on the final exam after studying many classes that use active learning and many that use lecturing and polling students as to their preference:

	Students in class prefer	
Instructor uses	Lecture	Active Learning
Lecture	50	−80
Active Learning	−30	100

(a) If the department chair uses the preceding information to decide how to teach her own classes, what should she do if she is an optimist?

(b) What about if she is a pessimist?

(c) If the polling data shows that there is a 75% chance that a class will prefer the lecture format, what strategy should she adopt? What is the expected payoff?

(d) If the chair finds out that her next class has had more experience with active learning, so that there is now a 60% chance that the class will prefer active learning, what strategy should she adopt? What is the expected payoff?

Exercises 46 and 47 are taken from actuarial examinations given by the Society of Actuaries.*

46. Business A company is considering the introduction of a new product that is believed to have probability .5 of being successful and probability .5 of being unsuccessful. Successful products pass quality control 80% of the time. Unsuccessful products pass quality control 25% of the time. If the product is successful, the net profit to the company will be $40 million; if unsuccessful, the net loss will be $15 million. Determine the expected net profit if the product passes quality control.

(a) $23 million   **(b)** $24 million
(c) $25 million   **(d)** $26 million
(e) $27 million

47. Business A merchant buys boxes of fruit from a grower and sells them. Each box of fruit is either Good or Bad. A Good box contains 80% excellent fruit and will earn $200 profit on the retail market. A Bad box contains 30% excellent fruit and will produce a loss of $1000. The a priori probability of receiving a Good box of fruit is .9. Before the merchant decides to put the box on the market, he can sample one piece of fruit to test whether it is excellent. Based on that sample, he has the option of rejecting the box without paying for it. Determine the expected value of the right to sample. (*Hint:* If the merchant samples the fruit, what are the probabilities of accepting a Good box, accepting a Bad box, and not accepting the box? What are these probabilities if he does not sample the fruit?)

(a) 0   **(b)** $16   **(c)** $34
(d) $72   **(e)** $80

48. Business An issue of *Mathematics Teacher* included "Overbooking Airline Flights," an article by Joe Dan Austin. In this article, Austin developed a model for the expected income for an airline flight. With appropriate assumptions, the probability that exactly x of n people with reservations show up at the airport to buy a ticket is given by the binomial probability formula. Assume the following: Six reservations have been accepted for 3 seats, $p = .6$ is the probability that a person with a reservation will show up, a ticket costs $100, and the airline must pay $100 to anyone with a reservation who does not get a ticket. Complete the following table:

Number Who Show Up (x)	0	1	2	3	4	5	6
Airline's Income							
$P(x)$							

(a) Use the table to find $E(I)$, the expected income from the 3 seats.

(b) Find $E(I)$ for $n = 3$, $n = 4$, and $n = 5$. Compare these answers with $E(I)$ for $n = 6$. For these values of n, how many reservations should the airline book for the 3 seats in order to maximize the expected revenue?

---

*Problems from "Course 130 Examination, Operations Research," of the Education and Examination Committee of the Society of Actuaries. Reprinted by permission of the Society of Actuaries.

Quick Draw® from the New York State Lottery

At bars and restaurants in the state of New York, patrons can play an electronic lottery game called Quick Draw.* A similar game is available in many other states. There are 10 ways for a patron to play this game. Prior to the draw, a person may bet $1 on games called 10-spot, 9-spot, 8-spot, 7-spot, 6-spot, 5-spot, 4-spot, 3-spot, 2-spot, and 1-spot. Depending on the game, the player will choose numbers from 1 to 80. For the 10-spot game, the player chooses 10 numbers; for a 9-Spot game, the player chooses 9 numbers; etc. Every four minutes, the State of New York chooses 20 numbers at random from the numbers 1 to 80. For example, if a player chose the 6-Spot game, he or she will have picked 6 numbers. If 3, 4, 5, or 6 of the numbers the player picked are also numbers the state picked randomly, then the player will win money. Each game has different ways to win, with differing payoff amounts. Notice with the 10-Spot, 9-Spot, 8-Spot, and 7-Spot, a player can win by matching 0 numbers correctly. The accompanying tables show the payoffs for the different games. Notice that a player does not have to match all the numbers he or she picked in order to win.

10-Spot Game

Numbers Matched	Winnings per $1 Played
10	$100,000
9	$5,000
8	$300
7	$45
6	$10
5	$2
0	$5

9-Spot Game

Numbers Matched	Winnings per $1 Played
9	$30,000
8	$3,000
7	$125
6	$20
5	$5
0	$2

8-Spot Game

Numbers Matched	Winnings per $1 Played
8	$10,000
7	$550
6	$75
5	$6
0	$2

7-Spot Game

Numbers Matched	Winnings per $1 Played
7	$5,000
6	$100
5	$20
4	$2
0	$1

6-Spot Game

Numbers Matched	Winnings per $1 Played
6	$1,000
5	$55
4	$6
3	$1

5-Spot Game

Numbers Matched	Winnings per $1 Played
5	$300
4	$20
3	$2

*More information on Quick Draw can be found at www.nylottery.org; click on "Daily Games."

4-Spot Game

Numbers Matched	Winnings per $1 Played
4	$55
3	$5
2	$1

3-Spot Game

Numbers Matched	Winnings per $1 Played
3	$23
2	$2

2-Spot Game

Numbers Matched	Winnings per $1 Played
2	$10

1-Spot Game

Numbers Matched	Winnings per $1 Played
1	$2

With our knowledge of counting, it is possible for us to calculate the probability of winning for these different games.

Example 1 Find the probability distribution for the number of matches for the 6-spot game.

Solution Let us define x to be the number of matches when playing 6-spot. The outcomes of x are then $0, 1, 2, \ldots, 6$. To find the probabilities of these matches, we need to do a little thinking. First, we need to know how many ways a player can pick 6 numbers from the selection of 1 to 80. Since the order in which the player picks the numbers does not matter, the number of ways to pick 6 numbers is

$$_{80}C_6 = \frac{80!}{74! \, 6!} = 300,500,200.$$

To find the probability of the outcomes of 0 to 6, we can think of the 80 choices broken into groups: 20 winning numbers the state picked and 60 losing numbers the state did not pick. If x, the number of matches, is 0, then the player picked 0 numbers from the 20 winning numbers and 6 from the 60 losing numbers. Using the multiplication principle, we find that this quantity is

$$_{20}C_0 \cdot {}_{60}C_6 = \left(\frac{20!}{20! \, 0!}\right)\left(\frac{60!}{54! \, 6!}\right) = (1)(50,063,860) = 50,063,860.$$

Therefore,

$$P(x = 0) = \frac{_{20}C_0 \cdot {}_{60}C_6}{_{80}C_6} = \frac{50,063,860}{300,500,200} \approx .16660.$$

Similarly for $x = 1, 2, \ldots, 6$, and completing the probability distribution table, we have

x	$P(x)$
0	$\dfrac{_{20}C_0 \cdot {}_{60}C_6}{_{80}C_6} \approx .16660$
1	$\dfrac{_{20}C_1 \cdot {}_{60}C_5}{_{80}C_6} \approx .36349$
2	$\dfrac{_{20}C_2 \cdot {}_{60}C_4}{_{80}C_6} \approx .30832$
3	$\dfrac{_{20}C_3 \cdot {}_{60}C_3}{_{80}C_6} \approx .12982$
4	$\dfrac{_{20}C_4 \cdot {}_{60}C_2}{_{80}C_6} \approx .02854$
5	$\dfrac{_{20}C_5 \cdot {}_{60}C_1}{_{80}C_6} \approx .00310$
6	$\dfrac{_{20}C_6 \cdot {}_{60}C_0}{_{80}C_6} \approx .00013$

Example 2 Find the expected winnings for a $1 bet on the 6-spot game.

Solution To find the expected winnings, we take the winnings for each number of matches and subtract our $1 initial payment fee. Thus, we have the following:

x	Net Winnings	$P(x)$
0	−$1	0.16660
1	−$1	.36349
2	−$1	.30832
3	$0	.12982
4	$5	.02854
5	$54	.00310
6	$999	.00013

The expected winnings are

$$
\begin{aligned}
E(\text{winnings}) &= (-1)\cdot.16660 + (-1)\cdot.36349 \\
&\quad + (-1)\cdot.30832 + 0\cdot.12982 + 5(.02854) \\
&\quad + 54(.00310) + 999(.00013) \\
&= -.39844.
\end{aligned}
$$

Thus, for every $1 bet on the 6-Spot game, a player would lose about 40 cents. Put another way, the state gets about 40 cents, on average, from every $1 bet on 6-spot.

EXERCISES

1. If New York State initiates a promotion where players earn "double payoffs" for the 6-spot game, (that is, if a player matched 3 numbers, she would win $2; if she matched 4 numbers, she would win $12; etc.), find the expected winnings.

2. Would it be in the state's interest to offer such a promotion? Why or why not?

3. Find the probability distribution for the 4-spot game.

4. Find the expected winnings for the 4-spot game.

5. If the state offers double payoffs for the 4-spot game, what are the expected winnings?

Introduction to Statistics

Statistics has applications to almost every aspect of modern life. The digital age is creating a wealth of data that needs to be summarized, visualized, and analyzed, from the earnings of major-league baseball teams to movies' box-office receipts and the sales for the soft-drink industry. See Exercises 26 and 27 on pages 615 and 616, and Exercises 54–58 on page 640.

CASE 10: Statistics in the Law: The *Castañeda* Decision

Statistics is the science that deals with the collection and summarization of data. Methods of statistical analysis make it possible to draw conclusions about a population on the basis of data from a sample of the population. Statistical models have become increasingly useful in manufacturing, government, agriculture, medicine, and the social sciences and in all types of research. An Indianapolis race-car team, for example, is using statistics to improve its performance by gathering data on each run around the track. The team samples data 300 times a second and uses computers to process the data. In this chapter, we give a brief introduction to some of the key topics from statistical methodology.

10.1 ▶ Frequency Distributions

Researchers often wish to learn characteristics or traits of a specific **population** of individuals, objects, or units. The traits of interest are called **variables**, and it is these that we measure or label. Often, however, a population of interest is very large or constantly changing, so measuring each unit is impossible. Thus, researchers are forced to collect data on a subset of the population of interest, called a **sample**.

Sampling is a complex topic, but the universal aim of all sampling methods is to obtain a sample that "represents" the population of interest. One common way of obtaining a representative sample is to perform simple random sampling, in which every unit of the population has an equal chance to be selected to be in the sample. Suppose we wanted to study the height of students enrolled in a class. To obtain a random sample, we could place slips of paper containing the names of everyone in class in a hat, mix the papers, and draw 10 names blindly. We would then record the height (the variable of interest) for each student selected.

A simple random sample can be difficult to obtain in real life. For example, suppose you want to take a random sample of voters in your congressional district to see which candidate they prefer in the next election. If you do a telephone survey, you have a representative sample of people who are at home to answer the telephone, but those who work a lot of hours and are rarely home to answer the phone, those who have an unlisted number, those who cannot afford a telephone, and those who refuse to answer telephone surveys are underrepresented. Such people may have an opinion different from those of the people you interview.

A famous example of an inaccurate poll was made by the *Literary Digest* in 1936. Its survey indicated that Alfred Landon would win the presidential election; in fact, Franklin Roosevelt won with 62% of the popular vote. The *Digest*'s major error was mailing its surveys to a sample of those listed in telephone directories. During the Depression, many poor people did not have telephones, and the poor voted overwhelmingly for Roosevelt. Modern pollsters use sophisticated techniques to ensure that their sample is as representative as possible.

Once a sample has been collected and all data of interest is recorded, the data must be organized so that conclusions may be more easily drawn. With numeric responses, one method of organization is to group the data into intervals, usually of equal size.

Example 1　**Business**　The following list gives the 2008–2009 tuition (in thousands of dollars) for a random sample of 30 private colleges that offer four-year degrees or higher:*

23	22	38	25	11	16	15	26	23	24
37	18	21	36	36	28	18	9	39	17
27	24	10	32	24	27	22	24	28	39

Identify the population and the variable, group the data into intervals, and find the frequency of each interval.

Solution　The population is all private colleges that offer a four-year degree or higher. The variable of interest is the tuition (in thousands of dollars). The highest

---

*Data from http://chronicle.com/.

number in the list is 39, and the lowest number is 9; one convenient way to group the data is in intervals of size 5, starting with 5–9 and ending with 35–39. This grouping gives an interval for each number in the list and results in seven equal intervals of a convenient size. Too many intervals of smaller size would not simplify the data enough, while too few intervals of larger size would conceal information that the data might provide. A rule of thumb is to use from 6 to 15 intervals.

First tally the number of schools in each interval. Then total the tallies in each interval, as in the following table:

Tuition Amount	Tally	Frequency
5–9	|	1
10–14	||	2
15–19	⊬⊬	5
20–24	⊬⊬ ||||	9
25–29	⊬⊬ |	6
30–34	|	1
35–39	⊬⊬ |	6
	Total =	30

This table is an example of **grouped frequency distribution**.

The frequency distribution in Example 1 shows information about the data that might not have been noticed before. For example, the interval with the largest number of colleges is 20–24. However, some information has been lost; for example, we no longer know exactly how many colleges charged 39 (thousand dollars) in tuition.

PICTURING DATA

The information in a grouped frequency distribution can be displayed graphically with a **histogram**, which is similar to a bar graph. In a histogram, the number of observations in each interval determines the height of each bar, and the size of each interval determines the width of each bar. If equally sized intervals are used, all the bars have the same width.

A **frequency polygon** is another form of graph that illustrates a grouped frequency distribution. The polygon is formed by joining consecutive midpoints of the tops of the histogram bars with straight-line segments. Sometimes the midpoints of the first and last bars are joined to endpoints on the horizontal axis where the next midpoint would appear. (See Figure 10.1 on the next page.)

Example 2   A grouped frequency distribution of college tuition was found in Example 1. Draw a histogram and a frequency polygon for this distribution.

Solution First, draw a histogram, shown in blue in Figure 10.1. To get a frequency polygon, connect consecutive midpoints of the tops of the bars. The frequency polygon is shown in red.

✔**Checkpoint 1**

An accounting firm selected 24 complex tax returns prepared by a certain tax preparer. The number of errors per return were as follows:

8 12 0 6 10 8 0 14
8 12 14 16 4 14 7 11
9 12 7 15 11 21 22 19

Prepare a grouped frequency distribution for this data. Use intervals 0–4, 5–9, and so on.

Answer: See page 607.

✔**Checkpoint 2**

Make a histogram and a frequency polygon for the distribution found in Checkpoint 1.

Answer: See page 607.

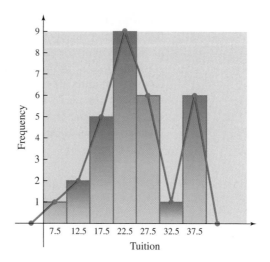

FIGURE 10.1

TECHNOLOGY TIP   As noted in Section 9.1, most graphing calculators can display histograms. Many will also display frequency polygons (which are usually labeled LINE or xyLINE in calculator menus). When dealing with grouped frequency distributions, however, certain adjustments must be made on a calculator:

1. *A calculator list of outcomes must consist of single numbers, not intervals.* The table in Example 1, for instance, cannot be entered as shown. To convert the first column of the table for calculator use, choose one number in each interval—say, 7 in the interval 5–9, 12 in the interval 10–14, 17 in the interval 15–19, etc. Then use 7, 12, 17, . . . as the list of outcomes to be entered into the calculator. The frequency list (the last column of the table) remains the same.

2. *The histogram's bar width affects the shape of the graph.* If you use a bar width of 4 in Example 1, the calculator may produce a histogram with gaps in it. To avoid this, use the interval $5 \leq x < 10$ in place of $5 \leq x \leq 9$, and similarly for the other intervals, and make 5 the bar width.

Following this procedure, we obtain the calculator-generated histogram and frequency polygon in Figure 10.2 for the data from Example 1. Note that the width of each histogram bar is 5. Some calculators cannot display both the histogram and the frequency polygon on the same screen, as is done here.

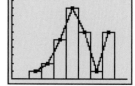

FIGURE 10.2

Stem-and-leaf plots allow us to organize the data into a distribution without the disadvantage of losing the original information. In a **stem-and-leaf plot**, we separate the digits in each data point into two parts consisting of the first one or two digits (the stem) and the remaining digit (the leaf). We also provide a key to show the reader the units of the data that was recorded.

Example 3 Construct a stem-and-leaf plot for the data in Example 1.

Solution Since the data is made up of two-digit numbers, we use the first digit for the stems: 0, 1, 2, and 3. The second digits provide the leaves. For example, if we look at the second row of the stem-and-leaf plot, we have a stem value of 1 and leaf values of 0 and 1. This corresponds to entries of 10 and 11, meaning one college had tuition of $10 (thousand) and another college had tuition of $11 (thousand). In this example, each row corresponds to an interval in the frequency table. The stems and leaves are separated by a vertical line.

Stem	Leaves
0	9
1	01
1	56788
2	122334444
2	567788
3	2
3	667899

Units: 3|9 = 39 thousand dollars

If we turn the page on its side, the distribution looks like a histogram, but still retains each of the original values. We used each stem digit twice, because, as with a histogram, using too few intervals conceals useful information about the shape of the distribution. ³✓

✓ **Checkpoint 3**

Make a stem-and-leaf plot for the data in Example 1, using one stem each for 0, 1, 2, and 3.

Answer: See page 607.

Example 4 List the original data for the following stem-and-leaf plot of resting pulses taken on the first day of class for 36 students:

Stem	Leaves
4	8
5	278
6	034455688888
7	02222478
8	2269
9	00002289

Units: 9|0 = 90 beats per minute

✓ **Checkpoint 4**

List the original data for the following heights (inches) of students:

Stem	Leaves
5	9
6	00012233334444
6	55567777799
7	0111134
7	558

Units: 7|5 = 75 inches

Answer: See page 607.

The first stem and its leaf correspond to the data point 48 beats per minute. Similarly, the rest of the data are 52, 57, 58, 60, 63, 64, 64, 65, 65, 66, 68, 68, 68, 68, 68, 70, 72, 72, 72, 72, 74, 77, 78, 82, 82, 86, 89, 90, 90, 90, 90, 92, 92, 98, and 99 beats per minute. ⁴✓

ASSESSING THE SHAPE OF A DISTRIBUTION

Histograms and stem-and-leaf plots are very useful in assessing what is called the **shape** of the distribution. One common shape of data is seen in Figure 10.3(a). When all the bars of a histogram are approximately the same height, we say the data has a **uniform** shape. In Figure 10.3(b), we see a histogram that is said to be bell shaped, or **normal**. We use the "normal" label when the frequency peaks in the middle and tapers off equally on each side. When the data does not taper off equally on each side, we say the data is **skewed**. If the data tapers off further to the left, we say the data is **left skewed** (Figure 10.3(c)). When the data tapers off further to the right, we say the data is **right skewed** (Figure 10.3(d)). (Notice that with skewed data, we say "left skewed" or "right skewed" to refer to the tail, and not the peak of the data.)

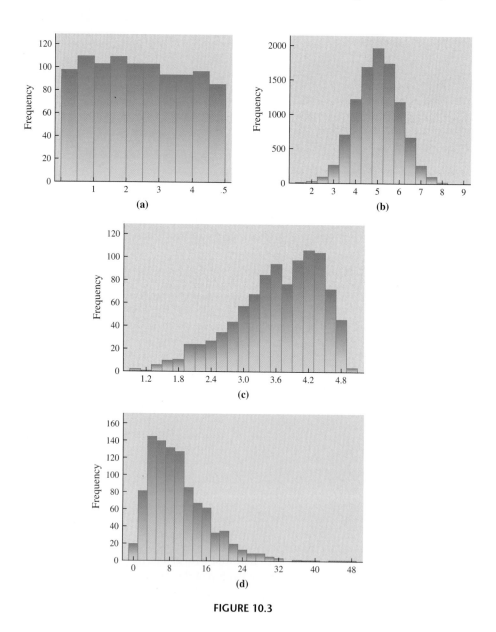

FIGURE 10.3

Example 5 **Health** Characterize the shapes of the given distributions for 1000 adult males.

(a) Height (inches); see Figure 10.4.

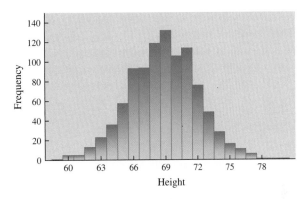

FIGURE 10.4

Solution The shape is **normal** because the shape peaks in the middle and tapers equally on each side.

(b) Body mass index (kg/m²); see Figure 10.5.

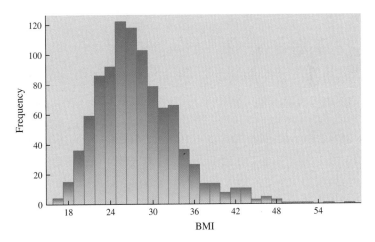

FIGURE 10.5

Solution The shape is **right skewed** because the tail is to the right. 5 ✓

It is important to note that most data is *not* normal, as we will see in the upcoming exercises and the next section. Using the label "normal" is a bit of a misnomer, because many important distributions, such as income, house prices, and infant birth weights, are skewed. It is also important to know that not all distributions have an easy-to-classify shape. This is especially true when samples are small.

✓**Checkpoint 5**

Characterize the shape of the distribution from the following stem-and-leaf plot of ages (years):

Stem	Leaves
1	88888
2	22334
2	5579
3	333344
3	59
4	3344
4	667779
5	34
5	5679
6	1
6	
7	13
7	678

(*Units*: 7|8 = 78 years

Answer: See page 607.

10.1 ▶ Exercises

The data for Exercises 1–4 consists of a random sample of 50 births taken from the 2007 North Carolina Birth Registry.* For each variable, (a) group the data as indicated; (b) prepare a frequency distribution with columns for intervals and frequencies; (c) construct a histogram; (d) construct a frequency polygon. (See Examples 1 and 2).

1. The variable is the age, in years, of the mother giving birth. Use 8 intervals, starting with 14–17 (inclusive).

15	26	27	32	24	24	35	29	44	20
25	20	18	31	22	30	25	38	37	22
28	20	21	23	34	30	27	24	33	29
26	20	18	15	24	28	24	31	20	20
21	24	25	33	28	36	26	27	35	19

2. The variable is weeks of gestation of the infant. Use 9 intervals, starting with 27–28 (inclusive).

42	40	42	40	39	39	38	36	38	40
41	34	36	34	41	38	40	38	37	40
37	39	39	37	40	39	39	39	27	40
41	34	39	43	36	41	38	31	40	30
40	41	44	39	32	37	41	38	39	39

3. The variable is weight (in pounds) gained by the mother during pregnancy. Use 10 intervals, starting with 0–4 (inclusive).

8	13	15	22	25	20	35	29	5	37
49	35	49	35	32	28	42	25	25	45
47	35	45	5	30	32	16	33	19	30
40	32	39	36	7	22	28	30	0	20
10	10	35	31	41	31	25	26	20	11

4. The variable is weight (in grams) of the infant at birth. Use 8 intervals, starting with 1000–1499 (inclusive).

2608 3374 3260 3459 3204 3090 2835 3175 2778 4536
3289 2693 2693 2211 3742 3374 3799 3657 3232 3374
3459 3062 3572 2835 3600 3629 3572 3572 1106 3856
3686 3119 3033 3289 2552 3033 3005 1531 3090 1616
2523 3430 3204 2778 1644 2098 3884 3827 3941 3175

Finance   *The data for Exercises 5–8 consists of random sample of 30 households from the 2007 American Community Survey.† Construct a frequency distribution and a histogram for each data set.*

5. Household income (in thousands of dollars):

159	83	15	17	80	159
127	53	102	46	79	46
149	100	99	179	27	171
14	52	33	230	49	22
39	27	9	13	86	38

6. Monthly mortgage payment (in dollars):

430	330	740	860	940	280
2400	1000	1800	300	2400	300
2000	350	3200	2100	710	1100
1300	1100	500	500	2000	800
1000	160	1400	900	700	740

7. Monthly electric bill (in dollars):

80	110	50	110	200	130
50	150	60	370	400	80
70	200	50	120	80	100
520	90	160	250	70	190
190	120	30	180	310	230

8. Annual property insurance costs (in dollars):

600	500	380	1900	370	1200
330	800	800	690	1100	100
970	600	400	600	540	3300
2400	460	2200	1300	600	1500
780	1000	1300	320	1000	4000

Construct a frequency distribution and a histogram for the data in Exercises 9 and 10.

9. **Business**   The ages (in years) of the 30 highest-earning chief executive officers in 2008, according to *Forbes:**

63	43	62	65	73	55
66	56	66	70	58	61
47	53	50	55	63	62
69	57	58	58	58	49
54	59	50	62	54	53

10. **Social Science**   The commuting time (in minutes) for 30 adults chosen at random:†

20	10	15	50	40	25
20	20	10	25	40	35
10	15	45	15	75	1
19	10	20	5	30	40
35	20	7	13	25	45

Construct a stem-and-leaf plot for the data in the indicated exercise. (See Example 3.)

11. Exercise 1 (use stems, 1, 1, 2, 2, 3, 3, 4)
12. Exercise 2   13. Exercise 3
14. Exercise 4 (round grams to the nearest hundred)
15. Exercise 5 (round incomes to the nearest ten thousand)
16. Exercise 6 (round dollars to the nearest hundred)

---

*http://arc.icss.unc.edu/dvn/dv/NCVITAL.

†Based on data from www.census.gov/acs.

*www.forbes.com.

†www.census.gov/acs.

17. Exercise 7

18. Exercise 8 (round dollars to the nearest hundred)

19. Social Science   The following data gives the percentage of residents with a high school diploma for the 50 states and the District of Columbia in 2007:*

80	85	80	90	85	90
91	83	89	84	88	86
84	89	87	91	87	89
81	88	88	87	83	81
80	86	87	82	82	89
89	86	91	84	88	91
88	90	79	83	81	
87	89	86	89	79	
86	80	90	87	90	

Create a stem-and-leaf plot for this data.

20. Social Science   The following data gives the percentage of residents with a bachelor's degree for the 50 states and the District of Columbia:*

21	26	20	28	23	34
26	27	27	22	28	34
25	29	35	33	26	30
19	25	38	34	30	17
30	30	25	25	24	25
35	22	31	32	25	23
35	24	19	26	22	
26	29	25	26	25	
48	20	27	24	29	

Create a stem-and-leaf plot for this data.

Describe the shape of each of the given histograms. (See Example 5.)

21.

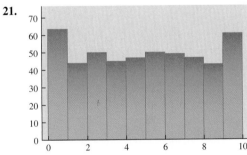

22.

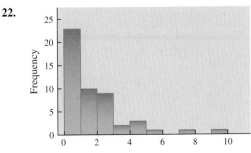

The Statistical Abstract of the United States: 2009.

23.

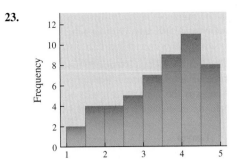

24.

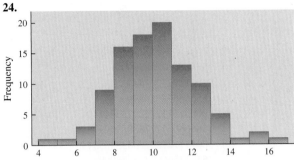

25.

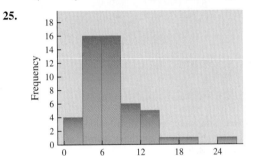

26. The grade distribution for scores on a final exam is shown in the following stem-and-leaf plot:

Stem	Leaves
2	7
3	
3	
4	01
4	899
5	4
5	5
6	122
6	58
7	00124
7	9
8	0044
8	5679
9	00223334
9	5788

Units: $9|8 = 98\%$

(a) What is the shape of the grade distribution?
(b) How many students earned 90% or better?
(c) How many students earned less than 60%?

27. **Finance** The loan-to-asset ratio for credit unions is the percentage of the value of the assets that are encumbered in loans. Following is the stem-and-leaf plot of loan-to-asset ratio values for the credit unions in Massachusetts for 2008:*

Stem	Leaves
1	4
1	
2	0133
2	889
3	0334
3	556666677888899
4	00011123344444
4	55556677888899
5	0000111122222223344444
5	56666667777788889999
6	00111122222233333334444444444
6	55555566677788889999
7	00011111111112222333333344444444
7	55556666666677777777778888999
8	00000011223444
8	666778
9	023

Units: $9|3 = 93\%$

(a) What is the shape of the distribution?
(b) How many credit unions have loan-to-asset ratios of exactly 70%?
(c) Do more credit unions have ratios in the 30s or in the 40s?

28. **Health** The percentage of adults who smoke regularly is summarized for the 50 U.S. states and the District of Columbia in the following stem-and-leaf plot:†

Stem	Leaves
1	0
1	
1	4
1	67777777
1	8888888889999
2	000000011111
2	2222223333
2	44555
2	
2	8

Units: $2|8 = 28\%$

*www.ncua.org.

†www.cdc.gov/mmwr.

Notice that this plot has the leaves divided into five categories instead of two.
(a) Describe the shape of the distribution.
(b) How many states have a smoking percentage of 20% or higher?
(c) What is the lowest percentage? Can you guess which state that is?

29. **Business** The following stem-and-leaf plot gives the average insurance expenditure per insured vehicle (in tens of dollars) for the 50 states and the District of Columbia:*

Stem	Leaves
5	55689
6	012345567788999
7	0234455899
8	2444445
9	234689
10	2567
11	1288

Units: $11|8 = \$1180$

(a) Describe the shape of the distribution.
(b) How many states have an average expenditure of over $1000?
(c) How many states have an average expenditure of $840?

30. **Business** For the 22 states that produce large numbers of broiler chickens, the following stem-and-leaf plot gives the production in millions of live pounds:†

Stem	Leaves
0	0012234
0	8
1	02333
1	66
2	2
3	2
3	4
4	78
5	
5	
6	4
6	7

Units: $6|7 = 67$ million pounds

(a) Describe the shape of the distribution.
(b) How many states produce fewer than 10 million pounds?

*www.naic.org.

†U.S. Department of Agriculture.

✓ Checkpoint Answers

1.

Interval	Frequency
0–4	3
5–9	7
10–14	9
15–19	3
20–24	2
	Total: 24

2.

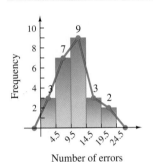

Number of errors

3.

Stem	Leaves
0	9
1	0156788
2	122334444567788
3	2667899

Units: $3|9 = 39$ thousand dollars

4. 59, 60, 60, 60, 61, 62, 62, 63, 63, 63, 63, 64, 64, 64, 64, 65, 65, 65, 66, 67, 67, 67, 67, 67, 69, 69, 70, 71, 71, 71, 71, 73, 74, 75, 75, 78

5. Right skewed

10.2 ▶ Measures of Central Tendency

Often, we want to summarize data numerically with a measure that represents a "typical" outcome. There are several ways to do this, and we generally call such a summary a "measure of center." In this section, we learn about the three most common measures of center: the mean, median, and mode.

MEAN

The three most important measures of central tendency are the mean, the median, and the mode. The most used of these is the mean, which is similar to the expected value of a probability distribution. The **arithmetic mean** (or just the "mean") of a set of numbers is the sum of the numbers, divided by the total number of numbers. We write the sum of n numbers $x_1, x_2, x_3, \ldots, x_n$ in a compact way with **summation notation**, also called **sigma notation**. With the Greek letter Σ (sigma), the sum

$$x_1 + x_2 + x_3 + \cdots + x_n$$

is written

$$x_1 + x_2 + x_3 + \cdots + x_n = \sum_{i=1}^{n} x_i.$$

In statistics, $\sum_{i=1}^{n} x_i$ is often abbreviated as just Σx. The symbol $\bar{x}$ (read "x-bar") is used to represent the mean of a sample.

Mean

The mean of the n numbers $x_1, x_2, x_3, \ldots, x_n$ is

$$\bar{x} = \frac{x_1 + x_2 + \cdots + x_n}{n} = \frac{\Sigma x}{n}.$$

TECHNOLOGY TIP Computing the mean is greatly simplified by the statistical capabilities of most scientific and graphing calculators. Calculators vary considerably in how data is entered, so read your instruction manual to learn how to enter lists of data and the corresponding frequencies. On scientific calculators with statistical capabilities, there are keys for finding most of the measures of central tendency discussed in this section. On graphing calculators, most or all of these measures can be obtained with a single keystroke. (Look for a *one-variable statistics* option, which is often labeled 1-VAR, in the STAT menu or its CALC submenu.)

Example 1 **Business** The number of businesses filing for bankruptcy for the years 2004–2008 are given in the following table:*

Year	Petitions Filed
2004	34,817
2005	39,201
2006	19,695
2007	28,322
2008	43,546

Find the mean number of business bankruptcies filed annually during this period.

Solution Let $x_1 = 34{,}817$, $x_2 = 39{,}201$, and so on. Here, $n = 5$, since there are 5 numbers in the list, so

$$\bar{x} = \frac{34{,}817 + 39{,}201 + 19{,}695 + 28{,}322 + 43{,}546}{5} \approx 33{,}116.$$

The mean number of business bankruptcy petitions filed during the given years is 33,116. ✓

The mean of data that has been arranged into a frequency distribution is found in a similar way. For example, suppose the following quiz score data is collected:

✔ **Checkpoint 1**

Find the mean dollar amount of the following purchases of eight students selected at random at the campus bookstore during the first week of classes:

$250.56	$567.32
$45.29	$321.56
$120.22	$561.04
$321.07	$226.90

Answer: See page 617.

*www.uscourts.gov/.

Value	Frequency
84	2
87	4
88	7
93	4
99	3
Total:	20

TECHNOLOGY TIP
  The mean of the five numbers in Example 1 is easily found by using the $\bar{x}$ key on a scientific calculator or the one-variable statistics key on a graphing calculator. A graphing calculator will also display additional information, which will be discussed in the next section.

The value 84 appears twice, 87 four times, and so on. To find the mean, first add 84 two times, 87 four times, and so on; or get the same result faster by multiplying 84 by 2, 87 by 4, and so on, and then adding the results. Dividing the sum by 20, the total of the frequencies, gives the mean:

$$\bar{x} = \frac{(84 \cdot 2) + (87 \cdot 4) + (88 \cdot 7) + (93 \cdot 4) + (99 \cdot 3)}{20}$$

$$= \frac{168 + 348 + 616 + 372 + 297}{20}$$

$$= \frac{1801}{20}$$

$$\bar{x} = 90.05.$$

Verify that your calculator gives the same result.

Example 2   **Social Science** An instructor of a finite-mathematics class at a small liberal-arts college collects data on the age of her students. The data is recorded in the following frequency distribution:

Age	Frequency	Age × Frequency
18	12	$18 \cdot 12 = 216$
19	9	$19 \cdot 9 = 171$
20	5	$20 \cdot 5 = 100$
21	2	$21 \cdot 2 = 42$
22	2	$22 \cdot 2 = 44$
Total: 30		Total: 573

✓**Checkpoint 2**

Find $\bar{x}$ for the following frequency distribution for the variable of years of schooling for a sample of construction workers.

Years	Frequency
7	2
9	3
11	6
13	4
15	4
16	1

Answer: See page 617.

Find the mean age.

  Solution The age 18 appears 12 times, 19 nine times, and so on. To find the mean, first multiply 18 by 12, 19 by 9, and so on, to get the column "Age × Frequency," which has been added to the frequency distribution. Adding the products from this column gives a total of 573. The total from the frequency column is 30. The mean age is

$$\bar{x} = \frac{573}{30} = 19.1. \quad \text{2}✓$$

The mean of grouped data is found in a similar way. For grouped data, intervals are used, rather than single values. To calculate the mean, it is assumed that all of the values in a given interval are located at the midpoint of the interval. The letter x is used to represent the midpoints, and f represents the frequencies, as shown in the next example.

Example 3 **Social Science** The grouped frequency distribution for annual tuition (in thousands of dollars) for the 30 private colleges described in Example 1 of Section 10.1 is as follows:

Tuition Amount	Midpoint, x	Frequency, f	Product, xf
5–9	7	1	7
10–14	12	2	24
15–19	17	5	85
20–24	22	9	198
25–29	27	6	162
30–34	32	1	32
35–39	37	6	222
		Total: 30	Total: 730

Find the mean from the grouped frequency distribution.

Solution A column for the midpoint of each interval has been added. The numbers in this column are found by adding the endpoints of each interval and dividing by 2. For the interval 5–9, the midpoint is $(5 + 9)/2 = 7$. The numbers in the product column on the right are found by multiplying each frequency by its corresponding midpoint. Finally, we divide the total of the product column by the total of the frequency column to get

$$\bar{x} = \frac{730}{30} \approx 24.3.$$

Note that information is always lost when the data is grouped. It is more accurate to use the original data, rather than the grouped frequency, when calculating the mean, but the original data might not be available. Furthermore, the mean based upon the grouped data is typically not too different from the mean based upon the original data, and there may be situations in which the extra accuracy is not worth the extra effort. ✓³

NOTE 1. The midpoint of an interval in a grouped frequency distribution may be a value that none of the data assumes. For example, if we grouped the tuition data for the 30 private colleges into the intervals 6–11, 12–17, 18–23, 24–29, 30–35, 36–41, the midpoints would be 8.5, 14.5, 20.5, 26.5, 32.5, and 38.5, respectively, even though all the data as reported were whole numbers.

2. If we had used different intervals in Example 3, the mean would have come out to be a slightly different number. This is demonstrated in Checkpoint 4. ✓⁴

✓ **Checkpoint 3**

Find the mean of the following grouped frequency distribution for the number of classes completed thus far in the college careers of a random sample of 52 students:

Classes	Frequency
0–5	6
6–10	10
11–20	12
21–30	15
31–40	9

Answer: See page 617.

✓ **Checkpoint 4**

Find the mean for the college tuition data using the following intervals for the grouped frequency distribution:

Tuition Amount	Frequency
6–11	3
12–17	3
18–23	7
24–29	10
30–35	1
36–41	6

Answer: See page 617.

The formula for the mean of a grouped frequency distribution is as follows.

> ### Mean of a Grouped Distribution
>
> The mean of a distribution in which x represents the midpoints, f denotes the frequencies, and $n = \Sigma f$ is
>
> $$\bar{x} = \frac{\Sigma(xf)}{n}.$$

The mean of a random sample is a random variable, and for this reason it is sometimes called the **sample mean**. The sample mean is a random variable because it assigns a number to the experiment of taking a random sample. If a different random sample were taken, the mean would probably have a different value, with some values being more probable than others. For example, if another set of 30 private colleges were selected in Example 3, the mean tuition amount might have been 31.4.

We saw in Section 9.1 how to calculate the expected value of a random variable when we know its probability distribution. The expected value is sometimes called the **population mean**, denoted by the Greek letter μ. In other words,

$$E(x) = \mu.$$

Furthermore, it can be shown that the expected value of $\bar{x}$ is also equal to μ; that is,

$$E(\bar{x}) = \mu.$$

For instance, consider again the 30 private colleges in Example 3. We found that $\bar{x} = 24.3$, but the value of μ, the average for all tuition amounts, is unknown. If a good estimate of μ were needed, the best guess (based on this data) is 24.3.

MEDIAN

Asked by a reporter to give the average height of the players on his team, a Little League coach lined up his 15 players by increasing height. He picked out the player in the middle and pronounced this player to be of average height. This kind of average, called the **median**, is defined as the middle entry in a set of data arranged in either increasing or decreasing order. If the number of entries is even, the median is defined to be the mean of the two middle entries. The following table shows how to find the median for the two sets of data {8, 7, 4, 3, 1} and {2, 3, 4, 7, 9, 12} after each set has been arranged in increasing order.

Odd Number of Entries	Even Number of Entries
1	2
3	3
Median = 4	4 ⎫
7	7 ⎭ *Median* = $\frac{4+7}{2}$ = 5.5
8	9
	12

📄 **NOTE** As shown in the table, when the number of entries is even, the median is not always equal to one of the data entries.

Example 4 Find the median number of hours worked per week

(a) for a sample of 7 male students whose work hours were

$$0, 7, 10, 20, 22, 25, 30.$$

Solution The median is the middle number, in this case 20 hours per week. (Note that the numbers are already arranged in numerical order.) In this list, three numbers are smaller than 20 and three are larger.

(b) for a sample of 11 female students whose work hours were

$$20, 0, 20, 30, 35, 30, 20, 23, 16, 38, 25.$$

Solution First, arrange the numbers in numerical order, from smallest to largest, or vice versa:

$$0, 16, 20, 20, 20, 23, 25, 30, 30, 35, 38.$$

The middle number can now be determined; the median is 23 hours per week.

(c) for a sample of 10 students of either gender whose work hours were

$$25, 18, 25, 20, 16, 12, 10, 0, 35, 32.$$

Solution Write the numbers in numerical order:

$$0, 10, 12, 16, 18, 20, 25, 25, 32, 35.$$

There are 10 numbers here; the median is the mean of the two middle numbers, or

$$\text{median} = \frac{18 + 20}{2} = 19.$$

The median is 19 hours per week.

⚠ **CAUTION** Remember, the data must be arranged in numerical order before you locate the median. 5✓

Both the mean and the median of a sample are examples of a **statistic**, which is simply a number that gives summary information about a sample. In some situations, the median gives a truer representative or typical element of the data than the mean does. For example, suppose that in an office there are 10 salespersons, 4 secretaries, the sales manager, and Ms. Daly, who owns the business. Their annual salaries are as follows: support staff, $30,000 each; salespersons, $50,000 each; manager, $70,000; and owner, $400,000. The mean salary is

$$\bar{x} = \frac{(30,000)4 + (50,000)10 + 70,000 + 400,000}{16} = \$68,125.$$

However, since 14 people earn less than $68,125 and only 2 earn more, the mean does not seem very representative. The median salary is found by ranking the salaries by size: $30,000, $30,000, $30,000, $30,000, $50,000, $50,000, . . . ,

---

✓**Checkpoint 5**

Find the median for the given heights in inches.

(a) 60, 72, 64, 75, 72, 65, 68, 70

(b) 73, 58, 77, 66, 69, 69, 66, 68, 67

Answers: See page 617.

🖱 **TECHNOLOGY TIP**
Many graphing calculators (including most TI- and Casio models) display the median when doing one-variable statistics. You may have to scroll down to a second screen to find it.

$400,000. There are 16 salaries (an even number) in the list, so the mean of the 8th and 9th entries will give the value of the median. The 8th and 9th entries are both $50,000, so the median is $50,000. In this example, the median is more representative of the distribution than the mean is.

When the data includes extreme values (such as $400,000 in the preceding example), the mean may not provide an accurate picture of a typical value. So the median is often a better measure of center than the mean for data with extreme values, such as income levels and house prices. In general, the median is a better measure of center whenever we see right-skewed or left-skewed distributions.

MODE

Sue's scores on 10 class quizzes include one 7, two 8's, six 9's, and one 10. She claims that her average grade on quizzes is 9, because most of her scores are 9's. This kind of "average," found by selecting the most frequent entry, is called the **mode**.

Example 5 Find the mode for the given data sets.

(a) Ages of retirement: 55, 60, 63, 63, 70, 55, 60, 65, 68, 65, 65, 71, 65, 65

Solution The number 65 occurs more often than any other, so it is the mode. It is sometimes convenient, but not necessary, to place the numbers in numerical order when looking for the mode.

(b) Total cholesterol score: 180, 200, 220, 260, 220, 205, 255, 240, 190, 300, 240

Solution Both 220 and 240 occur twice. This list has *two* modes, so it is bimodal.

(c) Prices of new cars: $25,789, $43,231, $33,456, $19,432, $22,971, $29,876

Solution No number occurs more than once. This list has no mode. ✓

The mode has the advantages of being easily found and not being influenced by data that are extreme values. It is often used in samples where the data to be "averaged" are not numerical. A major disadvantage of the mode is that there may be more than one, in case of ties, or there may be no mode at all when all entries occur with the same frequency.

The mean is the most commonly used measure of central tendency. Its advantages are that it is easy to compute, it takes all the data into consideration, and it is reliable—that is, repeated samples are likely to give similar means. A disadvantage of the mean is that it is influenced by extreme values, as illustrated in the salary example.

The median can be easy to compute and is influenced very little by extremes. A disadvantage of the median is the need to rank the data in order; this can be tedious when the number of items is large.

Example 6 **Business** A sample of 10 working adults was asked "How many hours did you work last week?" Their responses were as follows:

$$40, 35, 43, 40, 30, 40, 45, 40, 55, 20.^*$$

Find the mean, median, and mode of the data.

*www.norc.org/GSS+Website.

✔**Checkpoint 6**

Find the mode for each of the given data sets.

(a) Highway miles per gallon of an automobile: 25, 28, 32, 19, 15, 25, 30, 25

(b) Price paid for last haircut or styling: $11, $35, $35, $10, $0, $12, $0, $35, $38, $42, $0, $25

(c) Class enrollment in six sections of calculus: 30, 35, 26, 28, 29, 19

Answers: See page 617.

✔**Checkpoint 7**

Following is a list of the number of movies seen at a theater in the last three months by nine students selected at random:

1, 0, 2, 5, 2, 0, 0, 1, 4

(a) Find the mean.
(b) Find the median.
(c) Find the mode.

Answers: See page 617.

Solution The mean number of hours worked is

$$\bar{x} = \frac{40 + 35 + 43 + 40 + 30 + 40 + 45 + 40 + 55 + 20}{10} = 38.8 \text{ hours.}$$

After the numbers are arranged in order from smallest to largest, the middle number, or median, is 40 hours.

The number 40 occurs more often than any other, so it is the mode.

10.2 ▶ Exercises

Find the mean for each data set. Round to the nearest tenth. (See Example 1.)

1. Secretarial salaries (U.S. dollars):

$21,900, $22,850, $24,930, $29,710, $28,340, $40,000.

2. Starting teaching salaries (U.S. dollars):

$38,400, $39,720, $28,458, $29,679, $33,679.

3. Earthquakes on the Richter scale:

3.5, 4.2, 5.8, 6.3, 7.1, 2.8, 3.7, 4.2, 4.2, 5.7.

4. Body temperatures of self-classified "healthy" students (degrees Fahrenheit):

96.8, 94.1, 99.2, 97.4, 98.4, 99.9, 98.7, 98.6.

5. Lengths of foot (inches) for adult men:

9.2, 10.4, 13.5, 8.7, 9.7.

Find the mean for each distribution. Round to the nearest tenth. (See Examples 2 and 3.)

6. Scores on a quiz, on a scale from 0 to 10:

Value	Frequency
7	4
8	6
9	7
10	11

7. Age (years) of students in an introductory accounting class:

Value	Frequency
19	3
20	5
21	25
22	8
23	2
24	1
28	1

8. Commuting distance (miles) for students at a university:

Value	Frequency
0	15
1	12
2	8
5	6
10	5
17	2
20	1
25	1

9. Estimated miles per gallon of automobiles:

Value	Frequency
9	5
11	10
15	12
17	9
20	6
28	1

10–14. *Find the median of the data in Exercises 1–5. (See Example 4.)*

Find the mode or modes for each of the given lists of numbers. (See Example 5.)

15. Ages (years) of children in a day-care facility:

1, 2, 2, 1, 2, 2, 1, 1, 2, 2, 3, 4, 2, 3, 4, 2, 3, 2, 3.

16. Ages (years) in the intensive care unit at a local hospital:

68, 64, 23, 68, 70, 72, 72, 68.

17. Heights (inches) of students in a statistics class:

62, 65, 71, 74, 71, 76, 71, 63, 59, 65, 65, 64, 72, 71, 77, 63, 65.

18. Minutes of pain relief from acetaminophen after childbirth:

60, 240, 270, 180, 240, 210, 240, 300, 330, 360, 240, 120.

19. Grade point averages for 5 students:

$$3.2, 2.7, 1.9, 3.7, 3.9.$$

20. When is the median the most appropriate measure of central tendency?

21. Under what circumstances would the mode be an appropriate measure of central tendency?

For grouped data, the modal class is the interval containing the most data values. Give the mean and modal class for each of the given collections of grouped data. (See Example 3.)

22. **Health** Weight gain (in pounds) for 50 mothers giving birth:*

Interval	Frequency
0–4	1
5–9	4
10–14	4
15–19	3
20–24	5
25–29	8
30–34	9
35–39	8
40–44	3
45–49	5

23. Weight of 50 newly born infants (in grams):

Interval	Frequency
1000–1499	1
1500–1999	3
2000–2499	2
2500–2999	9
3000–3499	21
3500–3999	13
4000–4499	0
4500–4999	1

24. To predict the outcome of the next congressional election, you take a survey of your friends. Is this a random sample of the voters in your congressional district? Explain why or why not.

Work each problem. (See Example 6.)

25. **Social Science** The following table shows the number of nations participating in the winter Olympic games from 1972 to 2006:*

Year	Nations Participating
1972	35
1976	37
1980	37
1984	49
1988	57
1992	64
1994	67
1998	72
2002	77
2006	80

Find the following statistics for the data:
(a) mean;
(b) median;
(c) mode.

26. **Business** The following table gives the value (in millions of dollars) of the 10 most valued baseball teams as estimated by *Forbes* in 2007:†

Rank	Team	Value
1	New York Yankees	1306
2	New York Mets	824
3	Boston Red Sox	816
4	Los Angels Dodgers	694
5	Chicago Cubs	642
6	Los Angeles Angels of Anaheim	500
7	Atlanta Braves	497
8	San Francisco Giants	494
9	St. Louis Cardinals	484
10	Philadelphia Phillies	481

(a) Find the mean value of these teams.
(b) Find the median value of these teams.
(c) What might account for the difference between these values?

---

*http://arc.irss.unc.edu/dvn/dv/NCVITAL.

*The New York Times Almanac: 2008.

†www.forbes.com.

27. Business The 12 movies that have earned the most revenue (in millions of dollars) from U.S. domestic box-office receipts are given in the table:*

Rank	Title	U.S. Box-Office Receipts
1	*Titanic*	601
2	*The Dark Knight*	533
3	*Star Wars*	461
4	*Shrek 2*	436
5	*E. T.: The Extra-Terrestrial*	435
6	*Star Wars: Episode I—The Phantom Menace*	431
7	*Pirates of the Caribbean: Dead Man's Chest*	423
8	*Spider-Man*	404
9	*Star Wars: Episode III—Revenge of the Sith*	380
10	*The Lord of the Rings: The Return of the King*	377
11	*Spider-Man 2*	373
12	*The Passion of the Christ*	370

(a) Find the mean value in dollars for this group of movies.

(b) Find the median value in dollars for this group of movies.

28. Natural Science The number of recognized blood types varies by species, as indicated in the following table.†

Animal	Number of Blood Types
Pig	16
Cow	12
Chicken	11
Horse	9
Human	8
Sheep	7
Dog	7
Rhesus Monkey	6
Mink	5
Rabbit	5
Mouse	4
Rat	4
Cat	2

Find the mean, median, and mode of this data.

29. Business The revenue (in millions of dollars) for the Starbucks Corporation for 1999–2008 is given in the table:*

Year	Revenue
1999	1680.2
2000	2169.2
2001	2649.0
2002	3288.9
2003	4075.5
2004	5294.3
2005	6369.3
2006	7786.9
2007	9411.5
2008	10,383.0

(a) Calculate the mean and median for this data.

(b) What year's revenue revenue is closest to the mean?

Natural Science *The table gives the average monthly high and low temperatures, in degrees Fahrenheit, for Raleigh, NC, over the course of a year:*†

Month	High	Low
January	49	30
February	53	32
March	61	40
April	71	48
May	78	57
June	84	65
July	88	69
August	86	68
September	80	62
October	70	49
November	61	42
December	52	33

Find the mean and median for each of the given subgroups.

30. The high temperatures   **31.** The low temperatures

Business *For each of Exercises 32 and 33, a frequency distribution and its histogram have been constructed from the 2009 Fan Cost index (FCI) report from Team Marketing Report®. The FCI is a measure of how much it costs a family of four to attend a major-league baseball game by taking into account ticket prices, parking, and the costs for food, drink, a program, and a cap.‡ Determine the*

---

*www.imdb.com as of April 18, 2009.

†*The Handy Science Answer Book*, Carnegie Library of Pittsburgh, Pennsylvania, p. 264.

*www.morningstar.com.

†www.weather.com.

‡http://www.teammarketing.com/fancost/.

shape of the distribution from the histogram, and then decide if the mean or median is a better measure of center. If the mean is the better measure, calculate the value. If the median is the better measure, give the midpoint of the interval that contains it.

32. The frequency distribution and histogram for the average ticket price:

Price (Dollars)	Frequency
10–19.99	10
20–29.99	13
30–39.99	4
40–49.99	1
50–59.99	1
60–69.99	0
70–79.99	1

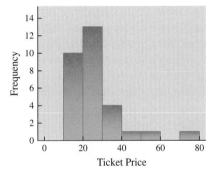

Ticket Price

33. **Business** The frequency distribution and the histogram for the Fan Cost Index (FCI) are given below.

FCI (Dollars)	Frequency
100–149.99	5
150–199.99	13
200–249.99	8
250–299.99	1
300–349.99	2
350–399.99	0
400–449.99	1

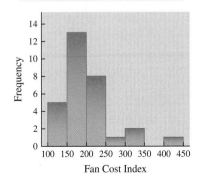

Fan Cost Index

34. **Health** The following stem-and-leaf plot gives the distribution for the percentage of children without health insurance in 2006 (rounded to the nearest percent) for the 50 U.S. states and the District of Columbia.*

Stem	Leaves
0	4445
0	666666777777
0	888888999999
1	000001
1	222333
1	44455
1	77
1	888
2	1

Units: $2|1 = 21\%$

(a) Describe the shape of the distribution.
(b) Find the median percentage.

35. **Health** The following stem-and-leaf plot gives the percentages of all residents (rounded to the nearest percent) without health insurance for the 50 U.S. states and the District of Columbia.

Stem	Leaves
0	888999
1	00000011111
1	222233333
1	44455555
1	6777777
1	8889
2	0011
2	2
2	4

Units: $2|4 = 24\%$

(a) Describe the shape of the distribution.
(b) Find the median percentage.

✓ Checkpoint Answers

1. $301.75

2. $\bar{x} = 11.75$

3. 18.90

4. 24.7

5. **(a)** 69 inches   **(b)** 68 inches

6. **(a)** 25 miles per gallon   **(b)** $0 and $35
    (c) No mode

7. **(a)** About 1.7   **(b)** 1   **(c)** 0

*www.census.gov.

10.3 ▶ Measures of Variation

The mean, median, and mode are measures of central tendency for a list of numbers, but tell nothing about the *spread* of the numbers in the list. For example, look at the following data sets of number of times per week three people ate meals at restaurants over the course of five weeks:

Jill:	3	5	6	3	3
Miguel:	4	4	4	4	4
Sharille:	10	1	0	0	9

Each of these three data sets has a mean of 4, but the amount of dispersion or variation within the lists is different. This difference may reflect different dining patterns over time. Thus, in addition to a measure of central tendency, another kind of measure is needed that describes how much the numbers vary.

The largest number of restaurant meals for Jill is 6, while the smallest is 3, a difference of 3. For Miguel, the difference is 0; for Sharille, it is 10. The difference between the largest and smallest number in a sample is called the **range**, one example of a measure of variation. The range is 3 for Jill, 0 for Miguel, and 10 for Sharille. The range has the advantage of being very easy to compute and gives a rough estimate of the variation among the data in the sample. However, it depends only on the two extremes and tells nothing about how the other data is distributed between the extremes.

TECHNOLOGY TIP
Many graphing calculators show the largest and smallest numbers in a list when displaying one-variable statistics, usually on the second screen of the display.

✓**Checkpoint 1**

Find the range for this sample of the number of miles from students' homes to college: 15, 378, 5, 210, 125.

Answer: See page 627.

Example 1 **Business** Find the range for each given data set for a small sample of people.

(a) Price paid for last haircut (with tip): 10, 0, 15, 30, 20, 18, 50, 120, 75, 95, 0, 5

Solution The highest number here is 120; the lowest is 0. The range is the difference of these numbers, or

$$120 - 0 = 120.$$

(b) Amount spent for last vehicle servicing: 30, 19, 125, 150, 430, 50, 225

Solution Range $= 430 - 19 = 411.$ ✓

To find another useful measure of variation, we begin by finding the **deviations from the mean**—the differences found by subtracting the mean from each number in a distribution.

Example 2 Find the deviations from the mean for the following sample of ages.

$$32, \quad 41, \quad 47, \quad 53, \quad 57.$$

Solution Adding these numbers and dividing by 5 gives a mean of 46 years. To find the deviations from the mean, subtract 46 from each number in the sample. For example, the first deviation from the mean is $32 - 46 = -14$; the last is $57 - 46 = 11$ years. All of the deviations are listed in the following table.

Age	Deviation from Mean
32	−14
41	−5
47	1
53	7
57	11

To check your work, find the sum of the deviations. It should always equal 0. (The answer is always 0 because the positive and negative deviations cancel each other out.) ✓

✓**Checkpoint 2**

Find the deviations from the mean for the following sample of number of miles traveled by various people to a vacation location:

135, 60, 50, 425, 380.

Answer: See page 627.

To find a measure of variation, we might be tempted to use the mean of the deviations. However, as just mentioned, this number is always 0, no matter how widely the data is dispersed. To avoid the problem of the positive and negative deviations averaging to 0, we could take absolute values and find $\Sigma|x - \bar{x}|$ and then divide it by n to get the *mean deviation*. However, statisticians generally prefer to square each deviation to get nonnegative numbers and then take the square root of the mean of the squared variations in order to preserve the units of the original data (such as inches, pounds). (Using squares instead of absolute values allows us to take advantage of some algebraic properties that make other important statistical methods much easier.) The squared deviations for the data in Example 2 are shown in the following table:

Number	Deviation from Mean	Square of Deviation
32	−14	196
41	−5	25
47	1	1
53	7	49
57	11	121

In this case, the mean of the squared deviations is

$$\frac{196 + 25 + 1 + 49 + 121}{5} = \frac{392}{5} = 78.4.$$

This number is called the **population variance**, because the sum was divided by $n = 5$, the number of items in the original list.

Since the deviations from the mean must add up to 0, if we know any 4 of the 5 deviations, the 5th can be determined. That is, only $n - 1$ of the deviations are free to vary, so we really have only $n - 1$ independent pieces of information, or *degrees of freedom*. Using $n - 1$ as the divisor in the formula for the mean gives

$$\frac{196 + 25 + 1 + 49 + 121}{5 - 1} = \frac{392}{4} = 98.$$

This number, 98, is called the **sample variance** of the distribution and is denoted s^2, because it is found by averaging a list of squares. In this case, the population and sample variances differ by quite a bit. But when n is relatively large, as is the case in real-life applications, the difference between them is rather small.

Sample Variance

The variance of a sample of n numbers $x_1, x_2, x_3, \ldots, x_n$, with mean $\bar{x}$, is

$$s^2 = \frac{\Sigma(x - \bar{x})^2}{n - 1}.$$

When computing the sample variance by hand, it is often convenient to use the following shortcut formula, which can be derived algebraically from the definition in the preceding box:

$$s^2 = \frac{\Sigma x^2 - n\bar{x}^2}{n - 1}.$$

To find the sample variance, we square the deviations from the mean, so the variance is in squared units. To return to the same units as the data, we use the *square root* of the variance, called the **sample standard deviation**, denoted s.

Sample Standard Deviation

The standard deviation of a sample of n numbers $x_1, x_2, x_3, \ldots, x_n$, with mean $\bar{x}$, is

$$s = \sqrt{\frac{\Sigma(x - \bar{x})^2}{n - 1}}.$$

 NOTE The **population standard deviation** is

$$\sigma = \sqrt{\frac{\Sigma(x - \bar{x})^2}{n}},$$

where n is the population size.

TECHNOLOGY TIP When a graphing calculator computes one-variable statistics for a list of data, it usually displays the following information (not necessarily in this order, and sometimes on two screens) and possibly other information as well:

Information	Notation
Number of data entries	n or $N\Sigma$
Mean	$\bar{x}$ or mean Σ
Sum of all data entries	Σx or TOT Σ
Sum of the squares of all data entries	Σx^2
Sample standard deviation	Sx or sx or $x\sigma_{n-1}$ or SSDEV
Population standard deviation	σx or $x\sigma_n$ or PSDEV
Largest/smallest data entries	maxX/minX or MAXΣ/MINΣ
Median	Med or MEDIAN

📄 **NOTE**   In the rest of this section, we shall deal exclusively with the sample variance and the sample standard deviation. So whenever standard deviation is mentioned, it means "sample standard deviation," not population standard deviation.

As its name indicates, the standard deviation is the most commonly used measure of variation. The standard deviation is a measure of the variation from the mean. The size of the standard deviation indicates how spread out the data is from the mean.

Example 3   Find the standard deviation for the following sample of the lengths (in minutes) of eight consecutive cell phone conversations by one person:

$$2, \quad 8, \quad 3, \quad 2, \quad 6, \quad 11, \quad 31, \quad 9.$$

Work by hand, using the shortcut variance formula on page 620.

Solution   Arrange the work in columns, as shown in the table in the margin. Now use the first column to find the mean:

$$\bar{x} = \frac{\sum x}{8} = \frac{72}{8} = 9 \text{ minutes.}$$

The total of the second column gives $\sum x^2 = 1280$. The variance is

$$s^2 = \frac{\sum x^2 - n\bar{x}^2}{n-1}$$

$$= \frac{1280 - 8(9)^2}{8-1}$$

$$= 90.3 \text{ (rounded),}$$

and the standard deviation is

$$s \approx \sqrt{90.3} \approx 9.5 \text{ minutes.} \quad \text{✓}^3$$

Time	Square of the Time
2	4
8	64
3	9
2	4
6	36
11	121
31	961
9	81
72	1280

 **Checkpoint 3**

Find the standard deviation for a sample of the number of miles traveled by various people to a vacation location:

135, 60, 50, 425, 380.

Answer: See page 627.

🖱 **TECHNOLOGY TIP**   The screens in Figure 10.6 show two ways to find variance and standard deviation on a TI-84+ calculator: with the LIST menu and with the STAT menu. The data points are first entered in a list—here, L_5. See your instruction book for details.

 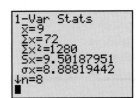

FIGURE 10.6

In a spreadsheet, enter the data in cells A1 through A8. Then, in cell A9, type "=VAR (A1..A8)" and press Enter. The standard deviation can be calculated either by taking the square root of cell A9 or by typing "=STDEV (A1..A8)" in cell A10 and pressing Enter.

⊘ **CAUTION** We must be careful to divide by $n - 1$, not n, when calculating the standard deviation of a sample. Many calculators are equipped with statistical keys that compute the variance and standard deviation. Some of these calculators use $n - 1$, and others use n for these computations; some may have keys for both. Check your calculator's instruction book before using a statistical calculator for the exercises.

One way to interpret the standard deviation uses the fact that, for many populations, most of the data is within three standard deviations of the mean. (See Section 10.4.) This implies that, in Example 3, most of the population data from which this sample is taken is between

$$\bar{x} - 3s = 9 - 3(9.5) = -19.5$$

and

$$\bar{x} + 3s = 9 + 3(9.5) = 37.5.$$

For Example 3, the preceding calculations imply that most phone conversations are less than 37.5 minutes long. This approach of determining whether sample observations are beyond 3 standard deviations of the mean is often employed in conducting quality control in many industries.

For data in a grouped frequency distribution, a slightly different formula for the standard deviation is used.

Standard Deviation for a Grouped Distribution

The standard deviation for a sample distribution with mean $\bar{x}$, where x is an interval midpoint with frequency f and $n = \Sigma f$, is

$$s = \sqrt{\frac{\Sigma f x^2 - n\bar{x}^2}{n - 1}}.$$

The formula indicates that the product fx^2 is to be found for each interval. Then all the products are summed, n times the square of the mean is subtracted, and the difference is divided by one less than the total frequency—that is, by $n - 1$. The square root of this result is s, the standard deviation. The standard deviation found by this formula may (and probably will) differ somewhat from the standard deviation found from the original data.

⊘ **CAUTION** In calculating the standard deviation for either a grouped or an ungrouped distribution, using a rounded value for the mean or variance may produce an inaccurate value.

Example 4 The following frequency distribution gives the 2008–2009 annual tuition (in hundreds of dollars) for a random sample of 30 community colleges:*

---

*Based on data from *The Chronicle of Higher Education*, at http://chronicle.com/.

Class	Frequency f
5–9.99	3
10–14.99	4
15–19.99	6
20–24.99	3
25–29.99	6
30–34.99	4
35–39.99	1
40–44.99	1
45–49.99	2

Find the sample standard deviation s for this data.

Solution We first need to find the mean $\bar{x}$ for this grouped data. We find the midpoint of each interval and label it x. We multiply the frequency by the midpoint x to obtain fx:

Class	Frequency f	Midpoint x	fx
5–9.99	3	7.5	22.5
10–14.99	4	12.5	50
15–19.99	6	17.5	105
20–24.99	3	22.5	67.5
25–29.99	6	27.5	165
30–34.99	4	32.5	130
35–39.99	1	37.5	37.5
40–44.99	1	42.5	42.5
45–49.99	2	47.5	95
	Total = 30		Total = 715

Therefore,

$$\bar{x} = \frac{715}{30} \approx 23.8.$$

Now that we have the mean value, we can modify our table to include columns for x^2 and fx^2. We obtain the following results:

Class	Frequency f	x^2	fx^2
5–9.99	3	56.25	168.75
10–14.99	4	156.25	625.00
15–19.99	6	306.25	1837.50
20–24.99	3	506.25	1518.75
25–29.99	6	756.25	4537.50
30–34.99	4	1056.25	4225.00
35–39.99	1	1406.25	1406.25
40–44.99	1	1806.25	1806.25
45–49.99	2	2256.25	4512.50
	Total = 30		20,637.50

✓ **Checkpoint 4**

Find the standard deviation for the following grouped frequency distribution of the number of classes completed thus far in the college careers of a random sample of 52 students:

Classes	Frequency
0–5	6
6–10	10
11–20	12
21–30	15
31–40	9

Answer: See page 627.

We now use the formula for the standard deviation with $n = 30$ to find s:

$$s = \sqrt{\frac{\Sigma f x^2 - n\bar{x}^2}{n - 1}}$$

$$= \sqrt{\frac{20{,}637.5 - 30(23.8)^2}{30 - 1}}$$

$$\approx 11.21. \quad \overset{4}{✓}$$

📄 **NOTE** A calculator is almost a necessity for finding a standard deviation. With a nongraphing calculator, a good procedure to follow is first to calculate $\bar{x}$. Then, for each x, square that number, and multiply the result by the appropriate frequency. If your calculator has a key that accumulates a sum, use it to accumulate the total in the last column of the table. With a graphing calculator, simply enter the midpoints and the frequencies, and then ask for the one-variable statistics.

10.3 ▶ Exercises

1. How are the variance and the standard deviation related?

2. Why can't we use the sum of the deviations from the mean as a measure of dispersion of a distribution?

Finance *In Exercises 3–10, expenditures (in millions of dollars) for various government services in 2005 are given for the five largest counties in the United States by population: Los Angeles, CA; Cook, IL; Harris, TX; Maricopa, AZ; and Orange, CA.* Find the range and the standard deviation for each given category.*

3. Housing: 5, 10, 3, 11, 15

4. Public Welfare: 4614, 11, 33, 695, 735

5. Health: 1770, 39, 200, 77, 322

6. Hospitals: 2916, 897, 880, 162, 0

7. Police Protection: 1118, 94, 363, 57, 270

8. Correction: 969, 389, 69, 324, 252

9. Highways: 251, 136, 372, 103, 36

10. Parks and Recreation: 227, 112, 26, 7, 1

Find the standard deviation for the grouped data in Exercises 11 and 12. (See Example 4.)

11. Number of credits for a sample of college students:

College Credits	Frequency
0–24	4
25–49	3
50–74	6
75–99	3
100–124	5
125–149	9

12. Scores on a calculus exam:

Scores	Frequency
30–39	1
40–49	6
50–59	13
60–69	22
70–79	17
80–89	13
90–99	8

13. Natural Science Twenty-five laboratory rats used in an experiment to test the food value of a new product made the following weight gains in grams:

---

*Statistical Abstract of the United States: 2009.

```
5.25   5.03   4.90   4.97   5.03
5.12   5.08   5.15   5.20   4.95
4.90   5.00   5.13   5.18   5.18
5.22   5.04   5.09   5.10   5.11
5.23   5.22   5.19   4.99   4.93
```

Find the mean gain and the standard deviation of the gains.

14. Business An assembly-line machine turns out washers with the following thicknesses (in millimeters):

```
1.20   1.01   1.25   2.20   2.58   2.19   1.29   1.15
2.05   1.46   1.90   2.03   2.13   1.86   1.65   2.27
1.64   2.19   2.25   2.08   1.96   1.83   1.17   2.24
```

Find the mean and standard deviation of these thicknesses.

An application of standard deviation is given by Chebyshev's theorem. (P. L. Chebyshev was a Russian mathematician who lived from 1821 to 1894.) This theorem, which applies to any distribution of numerical data, states,

For any distribution of numerical data, at least $1 - 1/k^2$ of the numbers lie within k standard deviations of the mean.

Example *For any distribution, at least*

$$1 - \frac{1}{3^2} = 1 - \frac{1}{9} = \frac{8}{9}$$

of the numbers lie within 3 standard deviations of the mean. Find the fraction of all the numbers of a data set lying within the given numbers of standard deviations from the mean.

15. 2   **16.** 4   **17.** 1.5

In a certain distribution of numbers, the mean is 50, with a standard deviation of 6. Use Chebyshev's theorem to tell what percent of the numbers are

18. between 32 and 68;

19. between 26 and 74;

20. less than 38 or more than 62;

21. less than 32 or more than 68;

22. less than 26 or more than 74.

Business *The following table gives the total amounts of sales (in millions of dollars) for aerobic, basketball, and cross-training shoes in the United States from 2001–2007:**

	Aerobic	Basketball	Cross-training
2001	281	761	1476
2002	239	789	1421
2003	222	890	1407
2004	237	877	1327
2005	261	878	1437
2006	262	964	1516
2007	268	987	1561

23. Find the mean and standard deviation for the aerobic shoe sales.

24. Find the mean and standard deviation for the basketball shoe sales.

25. Find the mean and standard deviation for the cross-training shoe sales.

26. Which type of shoe has the most variation in its sales? Explain.

27. Natural Science The number of recognized blood types of various animal species is given in the following table:*

Animal	Number of Blood Types
Pig	16
Cow	12
Chicken	11
Horse	9
Human	8
Sheep	7
Dog	7
Rhesus Monkey	6
Mink	5
Rabbit	5
Mouse	4
Rat	4
Cat	2

In Exercise 28 of the previous section, the mean was found to be 7.38.

(a) Find the variance and the standard deviation of this data.

(b) How many of these animals have blood types that are within 1 standard deviation of the mean?

28. Social Science The table shows the salaries (in thousands of dollars) of the nine highest-paid state governors as of September 2007:†

State	Salary
CA	212
NY	179
MI	177
NJ	175
VA	175
PA	164
WA	163
TN	160
IL	151

(a) Find the mean salary of these governors. Which state has the governor with the salary closest to the mean?

---

*www.nsga.org.

**The Handy Science Answer Book*, Carnegie Library of Pittsburgh, Pennsylvania, p. 264.

†*The World Almanac and Book of Facts*: 2008.

(b) Find the standard deviation for the data.

(c) What percentage of the governors had salaries within 1 standard deviation of the mean?

(d) What percentage of the governors had salaries within 3 standard deviations of the mean?

29. Health The amounts of time that it takes for various slow-growing tumors to double in size are listed in the following table:*

Type of Cancer	Doubling Time (days)
Breast cancer	84
Rectal cancer	91
Synovioma	128
Skin cancer	131
Lip cancer	143
Testicular cancer	153
Esophageal cancer	164

(a) Find the mean and standard deviation of this data.

(b) How many of these cancers have doubling times that are within 2 standard deviations of the mean?

(c) If a person had a nonspecified tumor that was doubling every 200 days, discuss whether this particular tumor was growing at a rate that would be expected.

30. Business The Quaker Oats Company conducted a survey to determine whether a proposed premium, to be included with purchases of the firm's cereal, was appealing enough to generate new sales.† Four cities were used as test markets, where the cereal was distributed with the premium, and four cities were used as control markets, where the cereal was distributed without the premium. The eight cities were chosen on the basis of their similarity in terms of population, per-capita income, and total cereal purchase volume. The results were as follows:

		Percent Change in Average Market Shares per Month
Test Cities	1	+18
	2	+15
	3	+7
	4	+10
Control Cities	1	+1
	2	−8
	3	−5
	4	0

(a) Find the mean of the change in market share for the four test cities.

(b) Find the mean of the change in market share for the four control cities.

(c) Find the standard deviation of the change in market share for the test cities.

(d) Find the standard deviation of the change in market share for the control cities.

(e) Find the difference between the mean of part (a) and the mean of part (b). This represents the estimate of the percent change in sales due to the premium.

(f) The two standard deviations from part (c) and part (d) were used to calculate an "error" of ± 7.95 for the estimate in part (e). With this amount of error, what is the smallest and largest estimate of the increase in sales? (*Hint*: Use the answer to part (e).)

On the basis of the results of this exercise, the company decided to mass-produce the premium and distribute it nationally.

31. Business The following table gives 10 samples of three measurements made during a production run:

SAMPLE NUMBER

1	2	3	4	5	6	7	8	9	10
2	3	−2	−3	−1	3	0	−1	2	0
−2	−1	0	1	2	2	1	2	3	0
1	4	1	2	4	2	2	3	2	2

(a) Find the mean $\bar{x}$ for each sample of three measurements.

(b) Find the standard deviation s for each sample of three measurements.

(c) Find the mean $\bar{\bar{x}}$ of the sample means.

(d) Find the mean $\bar{s}$ of the sample standard deviations.

(e) The upper and lower control limits of the sample means here are $\bar{\bar{x}} \pm 1.954\bar{s}$. Find these limits. If any of the measurements are outside these limits, the process is out of control. Decide whether this production process is out of control.

32. Discuss what the standard deviation tells us about a distribution.

Social Science *Shown in the following table are the reading scores of a second-grade class given individualized instruction and the reading scores of a second-grade class given traditional instruction in the same school:*

Scores	Individualized Instruction	Traditional Instruction
50–59	2	5
60–69	4	8
70–79	7	8
80–89	9	7
90–99	8	6

---

*Vincent Collins, R. Kenneth Lodffer, and Harold Tivey, "Observations on Growth Rates of Human Tumors," *American Journal of Roentgen*, 76, no. 5 (November 1956): 988–1000.

†This example was supplied by Jeffery S. Berman, senior analyst, Marketing Information, Quaker Oats Company.

33. Find the mean and standard deviation for the individualized-instruction scores.

34. Find the mean and standard deviation for the traditional-instruction scores.

 35. Discuss a possible interpretation of the differences in the means and the standard deviations in Exercises 33 and 34.

✓ **Checkpoint Answers**

1. 373

2. Mean is 210; deviations are −75, −150, −160, 215, and 170.

3. 179.5 miles   **4.** 10.92 classes

10.4 ▶ Normal Distributions and Boxplots

Suppose a bank is interested in improving its services to customers. The manager decides to begin by finding the amount of time tellers spend on each transaction, rounded to the nearest minute. The times for 75 different transactions are recorded, with the results shown in the following table, where the frequencies listed in the second column are divided by 75 to find the empirical probabilities:

Time	Frequency	Probability
1	3	$3/75 = .04$
2	5	$5/75 \approx .07$
3	9	$9/75 = .12$
4	12	$12/75 = .16$
5	15	$15/75 = .20$
6	11	$11/75 \approx .15$
7	10	$10/75 \approx .13$
8	6	$6/75 = .08$
9	3	$3/75 = .04$
10	1	$1/75 \approx .01$

Figure 10.7(a) shows a histogram and frequency polygon for the data. The heights of the bars are the empirical probabilities, rather than the frequencies. The transaction times are given to the nearest minute. Theoretically, at least, they could have been timed to the nearest tenth of a minute, or hundredth of a minute, or even more precisely. In each case, a histogram and frequency polygon could be drawn. If the times are measured with smaller and smaller units, there are more bars in the histogram and the frequency polygon begins to look more and more like the curve in Figure 10.7(b) instead of a polygon. Actually, it is possible for the transaction times to take on any real-number value greater than 0. A distribution in which the outcomes can take on any real-number value within some interval is a **continuous distribution**. The graph of a continuous distribution is a curve.

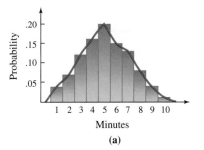

(a)

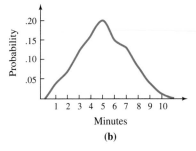

(b)

FIGURE 10.7

The distribution of heights (in inches) of college women is another example of a continuous distribution, since these heights include infinitely many possible measurements, such as 53, 58.5, 66.3, 72.666, and so on. Figure 10.8 shows the continuous distribution of heights of college women. Here, the most frequent heights occur near the center of the interval displayed.

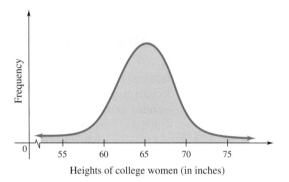

Heights of college women (in inches)

FIGURE 10.8

NORMAL DISTRIBUTIONS

As discussed on page 602, we say that data is normal (or normally distributed) when its graph is well approximated by a bell-shaped curve. (See Figure 10.9.) We call the graphs of such distributions **normal curves**. Examples of distributions that are approximately normal are the heights of college women and cholesterol levels in adults. We use the Greek letters μ (mu) to denote the mean and σ (sigma) to denote the standard deviation of a normal distribution.

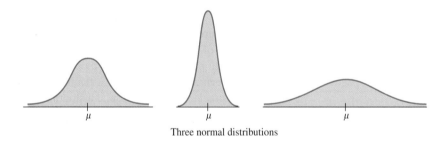

Three normal distributions

FIGURE 10.9

There are many normal distributions, depending on μ and σ. Some of the corresponding normal curves are tall and thin, and others short and wide, as shown in Figure 10.9. But every normal curve has the following properties:

1. Its peak occurs directly above the mean μ.
2. The curve is symmetric about the vertical line through the mean. (That is, if you fold the graph along this line, the left half of the graph will fit exactly on the right half).
3. The curve never touches the x-axis—it extends indefinitely in both directions.
4. The area under the curve (and above the horizontal axis) is 1. (As can be shown with calculus, this is a consequence of the fact that the sum of the probabilities in any distribution is 1.)

A normal distribution is completely determined by its mean μ and standard deviation σ.* A small standard deviation leads to a tall, narrow curve like the one in the center of Figure 10.9, because most of the data is close to the mean. A large standard deviation means the data is very spread out, producing a flat, wide curve like the one on the right in Figure 10.9.

Since the area under a normal curve is 1, parts of this area can be used to determine certain probabilities. For instance, Figure 10.10(a) is the probability distribution of the annual rainfall in a certain region. The probability that the annual rainfall will be between 25 and 35 inches is the area under the curve from 25 to 35. The general case, shown in Figure 10.10(b), can be stated as follows.

> The area of the shaded region under the normal curve from a to b is the probability that an observed data value will be between a and b.

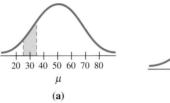

(a)   **(b)**

FIGURE 10.10

To use normal curves effectively, we must be able to calculate areas under portions of them. These calculations have already been done for the normal curve with mean $\mu = 0$ and standard deviation $\sigma = 1$ (which is called the **standard normal curve**) and are available in Table 2 at the back of the book. Examples 1 and 2 demonstrate how to use Table 2 to find such areas. Later, we shall see how the standard normal curve may be used to find areas under any normal curve.

The horizontal axis of the standard normal curve is usually labeled z. Since the standard deviation of the standard normal curve is 1, the numbers along the horizontal axis (the z-values) measure the number of standard deviations above or below the mean $z = 0$.

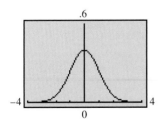

FIGURE 10.11

🖱 **TECHNOLOGY TIP** Some graphing calculators (such as the TI-84+ and most Casios) have the ability to graph a normal distribution, given its mean and standard deviation, and to find areas under the curve between two x-values. For an area under the curve, some calculators will give the corresponding z-value. For details, see your instruction book. (Look for "distribution" or "probability distribution.") A calculator-generated graph of the standard normal curve is shown in Figure 10.11.

---

*As shown in more advanced courses, its graph is the graph of the function

$$f(x) = \frac{1}{\sigma\sqrt{2\pi}}\, e^{-(x-\mu)^2/(2\sigma^2)},$$

where $e \approx 2.71828$ is the real number introduced in Section 4.1.

Example 1 Find the given areas under the standard normal curve.

(a) The area between $z = 0$ and $z = 1$, the shaded region in Figure 10.12

Solution Find the entry 1 in the z-column of Table 2. The entry next to it in the A-column is .3413, which means that the area between $z = 0$ and $z = 1$ is .3413. Since the total area under the curve is 1, the shaded area in Figure 10.12 is 34.13% of the total area under the normal curve.

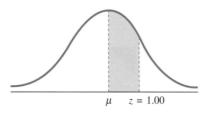

μ $z = 1.00$

FIGURE 10.12

(b) The area between $z = -2.43$ and $z = 0$

Solution Table 2 lists only positive values of z. But the normal curve is symmetric around the mean $z = 0$, so the area between $z = 0$ and $z = -2.43$ is the same as the area between $z = 0$ and $z = 2.43$. Find 2.43 in the z-column of Table 2. The entry next to it in the A-column shows that the area is .4925. Hence, the shaded area in Figure 10.13 is 49.25% of the total area under the curve. ✓ ✓

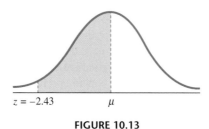

$z = -2.43$ μ

FIGURE 10.13

✓ **Checkpoint 1**

Find the percent of the area between the mean and

(a) $z = 1.51$;

(b) $z = -2.04$.

(c) Find the percent of the area in the shaded region.

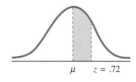

μ $z = .72$

Answers: See page 640.

✓ **Checkpoint 2**

If your calculator can graph probability distributions and find areas, use it to find the areas requested in Example 1.

Answers: See page 640.

 TECHNOLOGY TIP Because of their convenience and accuracy, graphing calculators and computers have made normal-curve tables less important. Figure 10.14 shows how part (b) of Example 1 can be done on a TI-84+ calculator using a command from the DISTR menu. The second result in the calculator screen gives the area between $-\infty$ and $z = -2.43$; the entry $-1\text{E}99$ represents $-1 \cdot 10^{99}$, which is used to approximate $-\infty$.

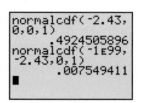

FIGURE 10.14

Many statistical software packages are widely used today. All of these packages are set up in a way that is similar to a spreadsheet, and they all can be used to generate normal curve values. In addition, most spreadsheets can perform a wide range of statistical calculations.

Example 2 Use technology or Table 2 to find the percent of the total area for the given areas under the standard normal curve.

(a) The area between .88 standard deviations *below* the mean and 2.35 standard deviations *above* the mean (that is, between $z = -.88$ and $z = 2.35$)

Solution First, draw a sketch showing the desired area, as in Figure 10.15. From Table 2, the area between the mean and .88 standard deviations below the mean is .3106. Also, the area from the mean to 2.35 standard deviations above the mean is .4906. As the figure shows, the total desired area can be found by *adding* these numbers:

$$\begin{array}{r} .3106 \\ +.4906 \\ \hline .8012 \end{array}$$

The shaded area in Figure 10.15 represents 80.12% of the total area under the normal curve.

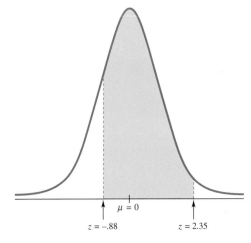

$z = -.88$ $\mu = 0$ $z = 2.35$

FIGURE 10.15

(b) The area between .58 standard deviations above the mean and 1.94 standard deviations above the mean

Solution Figure 10.16 on the next page shows the desired area. The area between the mean and .58 standard deviations above the mean is .2190. The area between the mean and 1.94 standard deviations above the mean is .4738. As the figure shows, the desired area is found by *subtracting* one area from the other:

$$\begin{array}{r} .4738 \\ -.2190 \\ \hline .2548 \end{array}$$

The shaded area of Figure 10.16 represents 25.48% of the total area under the normal curve.

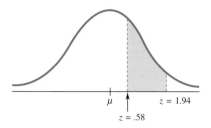

FIGURE 10.16

Find the given standard normal-curve areas as percentages of the total area.

(a) Between .31 standard deviations below the mean and 1.01 standard deviations above the mean

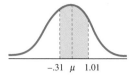

(b) Between .38 standard deviations and 1.98 standard deviations below the mean

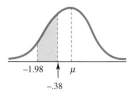

(c) To the right of 1.49 standard deviations above the mean

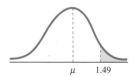

(d) What percent of the area is within 1 standard deviation of the mean? within 2 standard deviations of the mean? within 3 standard deviations of the mean? What can you conclude from the last answer?

Answers: See page 640.

(c) The area to the right of 2.09 standard deviations above the mean

Solution The total area under a normal curve is 1. Thus, the total area to the right of the mean is $1/2$, or .5000. From Table 2, the area from the mean to 2.09 standard deviations above the mean is .4817. The area to the right of 2.09 standard deviations is found by subtracting .4817 from .5000:

$$\begin{array}{r} .5000 \\ -.4817 \\ \hline .0183 \end{array}$$

A total of 1.83% of the total area is to the right of 2.09 standard deviations above the mean. Figure 10.17 (which is not to scale) shows the desired area. ✔³

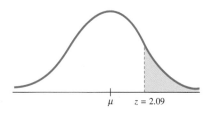

FIGURE 10.17

The key to finding areas under *any* normal curve is to express each number *x* on the horizontal axis in terms of standard deviations above or below the mean. The **z-score** for *x* is the number of standard deviations that *x* lies from the mean (positive if *x* is above the mean, negative if *x* is below the mean).

Example 3   If a normal distribution has mean 60 and standard deviation 5, find the given *z*-scores.

(a) The *z*-score for $x = 65$

Solution Since 65 is 5 units above 60 and the standard deviation is 5, 65 is 1 standard deviation above the mean. So its *z*-score is 1.

(b) The z-score for $x = 52.5$

> **Solution** The z-score is -1.5, because 52.5 is 7.5 units below the mean (since $52.5 - 60 = -7.5$) and 7.5 is 1.5 standard deviations (since $7.5/5 = 1.5$). ✓

✓ **Checkpoint 4**

Find each z-score, using the information in Example 3.

(a) $x = 36$

(b) $x = 55$

Answers: See page 640.

In Example 3(b) we found the z-score by taking the difference between 52.5 and the mean and dividing this difference by the standard deviation. The same procedure works in the general case.

> If a normal distribution has mean μ and standard deviation σ, then the z-score for the number x is
>
> $$z = \frac{x - \mu}{\sigma}.$$

The importance of z-scores is the following fact, whose proof is omitted.

> **Area under a Normal Curve**
>
> The area under a normal curve between $x = a$ and $x = b$ is the same as the area under the standard normal curve between the z-score for a and the z-score for b.

Therefore, by converting to z-scores and using a graphing calculator or Table 2 for the standard normal curve, we can find areas under any normal curve. Since these areas are probabilities (as explained earlier), we can now handle a variety of applications.

Graphing calculators, computer programs, and CAS programs (such as DERIVE) can be used to find areas under the normal curve and, hence, probabilities. The equation of the standard normal curve, with $\mu = 0$ and $\sigma = 1$, is

$$f(x) = (1/\sqrt{2\pi})e^{-x^2/2}.$$

A good approximation of the area under this curve (and above $y = 0$) can be found by using the x-interval $[-4, 4]$. However, calculus is needed to find such areas.

Example 4 **Business** Dixie Office Supplies finds that its sales force drives an average of 1200 miles per month per person, with a standard deviation of 150 miles. Assume that the number of miles driven by a salesperson is closely approximated by a normal distribution.

(a) Find the probability that a salesperson drives between 1200 and 1600 miles per month.

Solution Here, $\mu = 1200$ and $\sigma = 150$, and we must find the area under the normal distribution curve between $x = 1200$ and $x = 1600$. We begin by finding the z-score for $x = 1200$:

$$z = \frac{x - \mu}{\sigma} = \frac{1200 - 1200}{150} = \frac{0}{150} = 0.$$

The z-score for $x = 1600$ is

$$z = \frac{x - \mu}{\sigma} = \frac{1600 - 1200}{150} = \frac{400}{150} = 2.67.*$$

So the area under the curve from $x = 1200$ to $x = 1600$ is the same as the area under the standard normal curve from $z = 0$ to $z = 2.67$, as indicated in Figure 10.18. A graphing calculator or Table 2 shows that this area is .4962. Therefore, the probability that a salesperson drives between 1200 and 1600 miles per month is .4962.

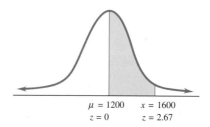

$$\mu = 1200 \qquad x = 1600$$
$$z = 0 \qquad z = 2.67$$

FIGURE 10.18

(b) Find the probability that a salesperson drives between 1000 and 1500 miles per month.

Solution As shown in Figure 10.19, z-scores for both $x = 1000$ and $x = 1500$ are needed.

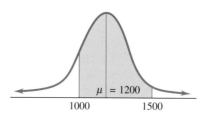

$$\mu = 1200$$
$$1000 \qquad 1500$$

FIGURE 10.19

For $x = 1000$,
$$z = \frac{1000 - 1200}{150}$$
$$= \frac{-200}{150}$$
$$= -1.33.$$

For $x = 1500$,
$$z = \frac{1500 - 1200}{150}$$
$$= \frac{300}{150}$$
$$= 2.00.$$

*All z-scores here are rounded to two decimal places.

From Table 2, $z = 1.33$ leads to an area of .4082, while $z = 2.00$ corresponds to .4773. A total of $.4082 + .4773 = .8855$, or 88.55%, of all drivers travel between 1000 and 1500 miles per month. From this calculation, the probability that a driver travels between 1000 and 1500 miles per month is .8855. ⁵✓

✓**Checkpoint 5**

With the data from Example 4, find the probability that a salesperson drives between 1000 and 1450 miles per month.

Answer: See page 640.

Example 5 **Health** With data from the 2005–2006 National Health and Nutritional Examination Survey (NHANES), we can use 196 (mg/dL) as an estimate of the mean total cholesterol level for all Americans and 44 (mg/dL) as an estimate of the standard deviation.* Assuming total cholesterol levels to be normally distributed, what is the probability that an American chosen at random has a cholesterol level higher than 250? If 200 Americans are chosen at random, how many can we expect to have total cholesterol higher than 250?

Solution Here, $\mu = 196$ and $\sigma = 44$. The probability that a randomly chosen American has cholesterol higher than 250 is the area under the normal curve to the right of $x = 250$. The z-score for $x = 250$ is

$$z = \frac{x - \mu}{\sigma} = \frac{250 - 196}{44} = \frac{54}{44} = 1.23.$$

From Table 2, we see that the area to the right of 1.23 is $.5 - .3907 = .1093$, which is 10.93% of the total area under the curve. Therefore, the probability of a randomly chosen American having cholesterol higher than 250 is .1093.

With 10.93% of Americans having total cholesterol higher than 250, selecting 200 Americans at random yields

$$10.93\% \text{ of } 200 = .1093 \cdot 200 = 21.86.$$

Approximately 22 of these Americans can be expected to have a total cholesterol level higher than 250. ⁶✓

✓**Checkpoint 6**

Using the mean and standard deviation from Example 5, find the probability an adult selected at random has a cholesterol level below 150.

Answer: See page 640.

📄 **NOTE** Notice in Example 5 that $P(z \geq 1.23) = P(z > 1.23.)$. The area under the curve is the same whether we include the endpoint or not. Notice also that $P(z = 1.23) = 0$, because no area is included.

🛑 **CAUTION** When calculating the normal probability, it is wise to draw a normal curve with the mean and the z-scores every time. This practice will avoid confusion as to whether you should add or subtract probabilities.

As mentioned earlier, z-scores are standard deviations, so $z = 1$ corresponds to 1 standard deviation above the mean, and so on. As found in Checkpoint 3(d) of this section, 68.26% of the area under a normal curve lies within 1 standard deviation of the mean. Also, 95.46% lies within 2 standard deviations of the mean, and 99.74% lies within 3 standard deviations of the mean. These results, summarized in Figure 10.20, can be used to get quick estimates when you work with normal curves.

---

*Based on data available at www.cdc.gov/nchs/nhanes.htm.

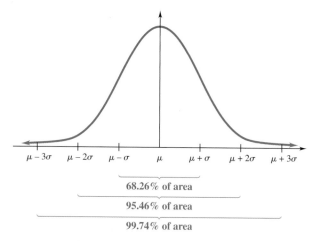

68.26% of area

95.46% of area

99.74% of area

FIGURE 10.20

BOXPLOTS

The normal curve is useful because you can easily read various characteristics of the data from the picture. Boxplots are another graphical means of presenting key characteristics of a data set. The idea is to arrange the data in increasing order and choose three numbers Q_1, Q_2, and Q_3 that divide it into four equal parts, as indicated schematically in the following diagram:

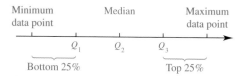

The number Q_1 is called the **first quartile**, the median Q_2 is called the **second quartile**, and Q_3 is called the **third quartile**. The minimum, Q_1, Q_2, Q_3, and the maximum are often called the five-number summary, and they are used to construct a boxplot, as illustrated in Examples 6 and 7.

Example 6　**Business**　The following table gives the revenues (in billions of U.S. dollars) for Apple and Microsoft Corporations for the given years:* Construct a boxplot for the Apple revenue data.

Year	1999	2000	2001	2002	2003	2004	2005	2006	2007	2008
Apple	6.1	8.0	5.4	5.7	6.2	8.3	13.9	19.3	24.0	32.5
Microsoft	19.7	23.0	25.3	28.4	32.2	36.8	39.8	44.3	51.1	60.4

Solution　We first have to order the revenues from low to high:

5.4, 5.7, 6.1, 6.2, **8.0**, **8.3**, 13.9, 19.3, 24.0, 32.5

---

*www.morningstar.com.

The minimum revenue is 5.4, and the maximum revenue is 32.5. Since there is an even number of revenues, the median revenue Q_2 is 8.15 (halfway between the two center entries). To find Q_1, which separates the lower 25% of the data from the rest, we first calculate

$$25\% \text{ of } n \text{ (rounded up to the nearest integer),}$$

where n is the number of data points. Here, $n = 10$, and so $.25(10) = 2.5$, which rounds up to 3. Now count to the *third* revenue (in order) to get $Q_1 = 6.1$.

Similarly, since Q_3 separates the lower 75% of the data from the rest, we calculate

$$75\% \text{ of } n \text{ (rounded up to the nearest integer).}$$

When $n = 10$, we have $.75(10) = 7.5$, which rounds to 8. Count to the *eighth* revenue, getting $Q_3 = 19.3$.

The five key numbers for constructing the boxplot are

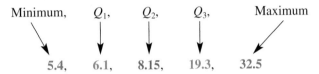

Minimum, Q_1, Q_2, Q_3,   Maximum

5.4,   6.1,   8.15,   19.3,   32.5

Draw a horizontal line parallel to the number axis, from the minimum to the maximum score. Around this line, construct a box whose ends are at Q_1 and Q_3, and mark the location of Q_2 by a vertical line in the box, as shown in Figure 10.21.

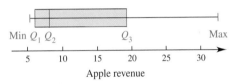

Min Q_1 Q_2 Q_3 Max

5   10   15   20   25   30

Apple revenue

FIGURE 10.21

Boxplots are useful in showing the location of the middle 50% of the data. This is the region of the box between Q_1 and Q_3. Boxplots are also quite useful in comparing two distributions that are measured on the same scale, as we will see in Example 7.

Example 7   **Business** Construct a boxplot for the Microsoft revenue data in Example 6 with the Apple revenue boxplot on the same graph.

Solution Microsoft had increasing revenue each year, so the data is already ranked low to high:

19.7, 23.0, 25.3, 28.4, **32.2**, **36.8**, 39.8, 44.3, 51.1, 60.4.

The minimum is 19.7, the maximum is 60.4, and the median $Q_2 = 34.5$. Again, $n = 10$, and so

$$25\% \text{ of } n = .25(10) = 2.5, \text{ which rounds up to 3,}$$

so that $Q_1 = 25.3$ (the *third* revenue). Similarly,

$$75\% \text{ of } n = .75(10) = 7.5, \text{ which rounds up to 8,}$$

so that $Q_3 = 44.3$ (the *eighth* revenue).

We can now use the minimum, Q_1, Q_2, Q_3, and the maximum to place the boxplot of the Microsoft revenue above the Apple boxplot, as in Figure 10.22.

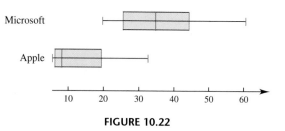

FIGURE 10.22

When we compare the revenue distributions in this way, we see how much more revenue Microsoft generated in the studied years than Apple. Because the box for Microsoft is wider, and the distance from the minimum to the maximum is also wider for Microsoft than Apple, we can also say there is a greater degree of variability for Microsoft. ✓

✓ **Checkpoint 7**

Create a boxplot for the weights (in kilograms) for eight first-year students:

88, 79, 67, 69, 58, 53, 89, 57.

Answer: See page 640.

🖱 **TECHNOLOGY TIP** Many graphing calculators can graph boxpots for single-variable data. The procedure is similar to plotting data with the STAT PLOT menu.

10.4 ▶ Exercises

1. The peak in a normal curve occurs directly above _____.

2. The total area under a normal curve (above the horizontal axis) is _____.

3. How are z-scores found for normal distributions with $\mu \neq 0$ or $\sigma \neq 1$?

4. How is the standard normal curve used to find probabilities for normal distributions?

Find the percentage of the area under a normal curve between the mean and the given number of standard deviations from the mean. (See Example 2.)

5. 1.75

6. .26

7. −.43

8. −2.4

Find the percentage of the total area under the standard normal curve between the given z-scores. (See Examples 1 and 2.)

9. $z = 1.41$ and $z = 2.83$

10. $z = .64$ and $z = 2.11$

11. $z = -2.48$ and $z = -.05$

12. $z = -1.63$ and $z = -1.08$

13. $z = -3.05$ and $z = 1.36$

14. $z = -2.91$ and $z = -.51$

Find a z-score satisfying each of the given conditions. (Hint: Use Table 2 backward or a graphing calculator.)

15. 5% of the total area is to the right of z.

16. 1% of the total area is to the left of z.

17. 15% of the total area is to the left of z.

18. 25% of the total area is to the right of z.

19. For any normal distribution, what is the value of $P(x \leq \mu)$? of $P(x \geq \mu)$?

20. Using Chebyshev's theorem and the normal distribution, compare the probability that a number will lie within 2 standard deviations of the mean of a probability distribution. (See Exercises 15–22 of Section 10.3.) Explain what you observe.

21. Repeat Exercise 20, using 3 standard deviations.

Assume the distributions in Exercises 22–30 are all normal. (See Example 4.)

22. **Business**   According to the label, a regular can of Campbell's™ soup holds an average of 305 grams, with a standard deviation of 4.2 grams. What is the probability that a can will be sold that holds more than 306 grams?

23. **Business**   A jar of Adams Old Fashioned Peanut Butter contains 453 grams, with a standard deviation of 10.1 grams.

Find the probability that one of these jars contains less than 450 grams.

24. **Business** A General Electric soft-white three-way light-bulb has an average life of 1200 hours, with a standard deviation of 50 hours. Find the probability that the life of one of these bulbs will be between 1150 and 1300 hours.

25. **Business** A 100-watt lightbulb has an average brightness of 1640 lumens, with a standard deviation of 62 lumens. What is the probability that a 100-watt bulb will have a brightness between 1600 and 1700 lumens?

26. **Social Science** The scores on a standardized test in a suburban high school have a mean of 80, with a standard deviation of 12. What is the probability that a student will have a score less than 60?

27. **Health** Using the data from the same study as in Example 5, we find that the average HDL cholesterol level is 51.6 mg/dL, with a standard deviation of 14.3 mg/dL. Find the probability that an individual will have an HDL cholesterol level greater than 60 mg/dL.

28. **Business** The production of cars per day at an assembly plant has mean 120.5 and standard deviation 6.2. Find the probability that fewer than 100 cars are produced on a random day.

29. **Business** Starting salaries for accounting majors have mean $45,000, with standard deviation $3,200. What is the probability an individual will start at a salary above $53,000?

30. **Social Science** The driving distance to work for residents of a certain community has mean 21 miles and standard deviation 3.6 miles. What is the probability that an individual drives between 10 and 20 miles to work?

Business *Scores on the Graduate Management Association Test (GMAT) are approximately normally distributed. The mean score for 2007–2008 was 540, with a standard deviation of 100.* For the following exercises, find the probability that a GMAT test taker selected at random earns a score in the given range, using the normal distribution as a model.*

31. Between 540 and 700

32. Between 300 and 540

33. Between 300 and 700

34. Less than 400

35. Greater than 750

36. Between 600 and 700

37. Between 300 and 400

Social Science *New studies by Federal Highway Administration traffic engineers suggest that speed limits on many thoroughfares are set arbitrarily and often are artificially low. According to traffic engineers, the ideal limit should be the "85th-percentile speed," the speed at or below which 85% of the traffic moves. Assuming that speeds are normally distributed, find the 85th-percentile speed for roads with the given conditions.*

---
*www.gmac.com.

38. The mean speed is 55 mph, with a standard deviation of 10 mph.

39. The mean speed is 40 mph, with a standard deviation of 5 mph.

Social Science *One professor uses the following system for assigning letter grades in a course:*

Grade	Total Points
A	Greater than $\mu + \frac{3}{2}\sigma$
B	$\mu + \frac{1}{2}\sigma$ to $\mu + \frac{3}{2}\sigma$
C	$\mu - \frac{1}{2}\sigma$ to $\mu + \frac{1}{2}\sigma$
D	$\mu - \frac{3}{2}\sigma$ to $\mu - \frac{1}{2}\sigma$
F	Below $\mu - \frac{3}{2}\sigma$

What percentage of the students receive the given grades?

40. A

41. B

42. C

43. Do you think the system in Exercises 40–42 would be more likely to be fair in a large freshman class in psychology or in a graduate seminar of five students? Why?

Health *In nutrition, the recommended daily allowance of vitamins is a number set by the government as a guide to an individual's daily vitamin intake. Actually, vitamin needs vary drastically from person to person, but the needs are very closely approximated by a normal curve. To calculate the recommended daily allowance, the government first finds the average need for vitamins among people in the population and then the standard deviation. The recommended daily allowance is defined as the mean plus 2.5 times the standard deviation.*

44. What percentage of the population will receive adequate amounts of vitamins under this plan?

Find the recommended daily allowance for the following vitamins.

45. Mean = 550 units, standard deviation = 46 units

46. Mean = 1700 units, standard deviation = 120 units

47. Mean = 155 units, standard deviation = 14 units

48. Mean = 1080 units, standard deviation = 86 units

Social Science   *The mean performance score of a large group of fifth-grade students on a math achievement test is 88. The scores are known to be normally distributed. What percentage of the students had scores as follows?*

49. More than 1 standard deviation above the mean

50. More than 2 standard deviations above the mean

Social Science   *Studies have shown that women are charged an average of $500 more than men for cars.* Assume a normal distribution of overcharges with a mean of $500 and a standard deviation of $65. Find the probability of a woman's paying the given additional amounts for a car.*

51. Less than $400

52. At least $700

53. Between $350 and $600

Business   *The table gives the annual revenue for Pepsi Co. and Coco-Cola Co. (in billions of U.S. dollars) for a 10-year period:†*

Year	Pepsi	Coca-Cola
1999	20.4	19.8
2000	20.4	20.5
2001	26.9	20.1
2002	25.1	19.6
2003	27.0	21.0
2004	29.3	22.0
2005	32.6	23.1
2006	35.1	24.1
2007	39.5	28.9
2008	43.3	31.9

54. What is the five-number summary for Pepsi?

55. What is the five-number summary for Coca-Cola?

56. Construct a boxplot for Pepsi.

57. Construct a boxplot for Coca-Cola.

58. Graph the boxplots for Pepsi and Coca-Cola on the same scale. Are the distributions similar? Which company has the higher median of sales over the 10-year period?

*"From repair shops to cleaners, women pay more," by Bob Dart, as appeared in *The Chicago Tribune*, May 27, 1993. Reprinted by permission of the author.

†www.morningstar.com.

Finance   *The following table shows U.S. federal government payments to selected states for child nutrition programs and food stamp programs (in millions of dollars):**

State	Child Nutrition	Food Stamp
Alabama	214	33
Alaska	33	9
Arizona	254	40
Arkansas	144	26
Colorado	109	28
Connecticut	86	20
Delaware	35	9
Florida	661	82
Georgia	473	68
Hawaii	40	11
Idaho	52	11
Illinois	449	95

59. What is the five-number summary for the child nutrition programs?

60. What is the five-number summary for the food stamp programs?

61. Construct a boxplot for the child nutrition programs data.

62. Construct a boxplot for the food stamp programs data.

63. Which program has higher variability?

✓Checkpoint Answers

1. (a) 43.45%   (b) 47.93%   (c) 26.42%

2. (a) 34.13%   (b) 49.25%

3. (a) 46.55%   (b) 32.82%   (c) 6.81%
(d) 68.26%, 95.46%, 99.74%;
almost all the data lies within 3 standard deviations of the mean.

4. (a) −4.8   (b) −1

5. .8607   **6.** .1469

7.

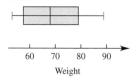

*The Statistical Abstract of the United States: 2009.

10.5 ▶ Normal Approximation to the Binomial Distribution

As we saw in Section 9.4, many practical experiments have only two possible outcomes, sometimes referred to as success or failure. Such experiments are called Bernoulli trials or Bernoulli processes. Examples of Bernoulli trials include flipping a coin (with heads being a success, for instance, and tails a failure) and testing a computer chip coming off the assembly line to see whether it is defective. A binomial experiment consists of repeated independent Bernoulli trials, such as flipping a coin 10 times or taking a random sample of 20 computer chips from the assembly line. In Section 9.4, we found the probability distribution for several binomial experiments, such as sampling five people with bachelor's degrees in education and counting how many are women. The probability distribution for a binomial experiment is known as a **binomial distribution**.

As another example, it is reported that 40% of registered vehicles in the United States are vans, pickup trucks, or sport utility vehicles (SUVs).* Suppose an auto insurance agent wants to verify this statistic and records the type of vehicle for 10 randomly selected drivers. The agent finds that 3 out of 10, or 30%, are vans, pickups, or SUVs. How likely is this result if the figure for all vehicles is truly 40%? We can answer that question with the binomial probability formula

$$\,_nC_x \cdot p^x(1 - p)^{n-x},$$

where n is the sample size (10 in this case); x is the number of vans, pickups, or SUVs (3 in this case); and p is the probability that a vehicle is a van, pickup, or SUV (.40 in this case). We obtain

$$P(x = 3) = \,_{10}C_3 \cdot (.40)^3(1 - .40)^7$$
$$= 120(.064)(.0279936)$$
$$\approx .2150.$$

The probability is over 20%, so this result is not unusual.

Suppose that the insurance agent takes a larger random sample, say, of 100 drivers. What is the probability that 30 or fewer vehicles are vans, pickups, or SUVs if the 40% figure is accurate? Calculating $P(x = 0) + P(x = 1) + \ldots + P(x = 30)$ is a formidable task. One solution is provided by graphing calculators or computers. There is, however, a low-tech method that has the advantage of connecting two different distributions: the normal and the binomial. The normal distribution is continuous, since the random variable can be any real number. The binomial distribution is *discrete*, because the random variable can take only integer values between 0 and n. Nevertheless, the normal distribution can be used to give a good approximation to binomial probability. We call this approximation the **normal approximation**.

In order to use the normal approximation, we first need to know the mean and standard deviation of the binomial distribution. Recall from Section 9.4 that,

---

The Statistical Abstract of the United States: 2009.

for the binomial distribution, $E(x) = np$. In Section 10.2, we referred to $E(x)$ as μ, and that notation will be used here. It is shown in more advanced courses in statistics that the standard deviation of the binomial distribution is given by $\sigma = \sqrt{np(1 - p)}$.

> ## Mean and Standard Deviation for the Binomial Distribution
>
> For the binomial distribution, the mean and standard deviation are respectively given by
>
> $$\mu = np \quad \text{and} \quad \sigma = \sqrt{np(1 - p)},$$
>
> where n is the number of trials and p is the probability of success on a single trial. ✓

✓ **Checkpoint 1**

Find μ and σ for a binomial distribution having $n = 120$ and $p = 1/6$.

Answer: See page 647.

Example 1 Suppose a fair coin is flipped 15 times.

(a) Find the mean and standard deviation for the number of heads.

Solution With $n = 15$ and $p = 1/2$, the mean is

$$\mu = np = 15\left(\frac{1}{2}\right) = 7.5.$$

The standard deviation is

$$\sigma = \sqrt{np(1 - p)} = \sqrt{15\left(\frac{1}{2}\right)\left(1 - \frac{1}{2}\right)}$$

$$= \sqrt{15\left(\frac{1}{2}\right)\left(\frac{1}{2}\right)} = \sqrt{3.75} \approx 1.94.$$

We expect, on average, to get 7.5 heads out of 15 tosses. Most of the time, the number of heads will be within three standard deviations of the mean, or between $7.5 - 3(1.94) = 1.68$ and $7.5 + 3(1.94) = 13.32$.

(b) Find the probability distribution for the number of heads, and draw a histogram of the probabilities.

Solution The probability distribution is found by putting $n = 15$ and $p = 1/2$ into the formula for binomial probability. For example, the probability of getting 9 heads is given by

$$P(x = 9) = {}_{15}C_9\left(\frac{1}{2}\right)^9\left(1 - \frac{1}{2}\right)^6 \approx .15274.$$

Probabilities for the other values of x between 0 and 15, as well as a histogram of the probabilities, are shown in Figure 10.23.

x	P(x)
0	.00003
1	.00046
2	.00320
3	.01389
4	.04166
5	.09164
6	.15274
7	.19638
8	.19638
9	.15274
10	.09164
11	.04166
12	.01389
13	.00320
14	.00046
15	.00003

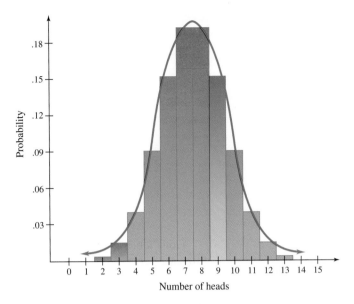

FIGURE 10.23

In Figure 10.23, we have superimposed the normal curve with $\mu = 7.5$ and $\sigma = 1.94$ over the histogram of the distribution. Notice how well the normal distribution fits the binomial distribution. This approximation was first discovered in 1718 by Abraham De Moivre (1667–1754) for the case $p = 1/2$. The result was generalized by the French mathematician Pierre-Simon Laplace (1749–1827) in a book published in 1812. As n becomes larger and larger, a histogram for the binomial distribution looks more and more like a normal curve. Figures 10.24(a) and (b), show histograms of the binomial distribution with $p = .3$, using $n = 8$ and $n = 50$, respectively.

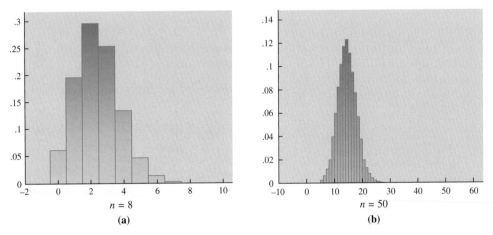

FIGURE 10.24

The probability of getting exactly 9 heads in the 15 tosses, or .15274, is the same as the area of the blue bar in Figure 10.23. As the graph suggests, the blue area is approximately equal to the area under the normal curve from $x = 8.5$ to $x = 9.5$. The normal curve is higher than the top of the bar in the left half, but lower in the right half.

To find the area under the normal curve from $x = 8.5$. to $x = 9.5$, first find z-scores, as in the previous section. Use the mean and the standard deviation for the distribution, which we have already calculated, to get z-scores for $x = 8.5$ and $x = 9.5$:

$$\text{For } x = 8.5, \qquad\qquad \text{For } x = 9.5,$$

$$z = \frac{8.5 - 7.5}{1.94} \qquad\qquad z = \frac{9.5 - 7.5}{1.94}$$

$$= \frac{1.00}{1.94} \qquad\qquad = \frac{2.00}{1.94}$$

$$z \approx .52. \qquad\qquad z \approx 1.03.$$

From Table 2, $z = .52$ gives an area of .1985, and $z = 1.03$ gives .3485. The difference between these two numbers is the desired result:

$$.3485 - .1985 = .1500.$$

This answer is not far from the more accurate answer of .15274 found earlier.

🛈 **CAUTION** The normal-curve approximation to a binomial distribution is quite accurate, _provided that n is large and p is not close to 0 or 1._ As a rule of thumb, the normal-curve approximation can be used as long as both np and $n(1 - p)$ are at least 5.

Example 2　**Business**　Consider the previously discussed sample of 100 vehicles selected at random, where 40% of the registered vehicles are vans, pickups, or SUVs.

(a) Use the normal distribution to approximate the probability that at least 51 vehicles are vans, pickups, or SUVs.

Solution　First find the mean and the standard deviation, using $n = 100$ and $p = .40$:

$$\mu = 100(.40) \qquad\qquad \sigma = \sqrt{100(.40)(1 - .40)}$$

$$= 40. \qquad\qquad = \sqrt{100(.40)(.60)}$$

$$\approx 4.90.$$

As the graph in Figure 10.25 shows, we need to find the area to the right of $x = 50.5$ (since we want 51 or more vehicles to be vans, pickups, or SUVs). The z-score corresponding to $x = 50.5$ is

$$z = \frac{50.5 - 40}{4.90} \approx 2.14.$$

From Table 2, $z = 2.14$ corresponds to an area of .4838, so

$$P(z > 2.14) = .5 - .4838 = .0162.$$

This is an extremely low probability. If an insurance agent obtained 51 vehicles that were vans, pickups, or SUVs in a sample of 100, she would suspect that either her sample is not truly random or the 40% figure is too low.

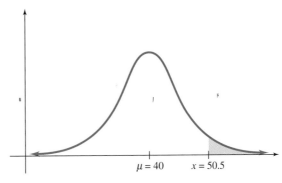

FIGURE 10.25

(b) Calculate the probability of finding between 41 and 48 vehicles that were vans, pickups, or SUVs in a random sample of 100.

Solution As Figure 10.26 shows, we need to find the area between $x = 40.5$, and $x = 48.5$:

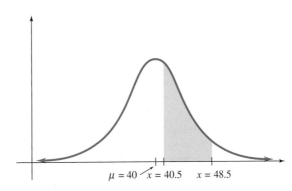

FIGURE 10.26

✓ **Checkpoint 3**

In December 2008, Michigan led the nation with the highest unemployment rate of 9.6%.* Find the approximate probability that in a random sample of 200 adults from Michigan during that month, the given numbers of people would be unemployed.

(a) Exactly 12

(b) 15 or fewer

(c) More than 10

Answers: See page 647.

*www.money.cnn.com.

$$\text{If } x = 40.5, \text{ then } z = \frac{40.5 - 40}{4.90} \approx .10.$$

$$\text{If } x = 48.5, \text{ then } z = \frac{48.5 - 40}{4.90} \approx 1.73.$$

Use Table 2 to find that $z = .10$ corresponds to an area of .0398 and $z = 1.73$ yields .4582. The final answer is the difference of these numbers:

$$P(.10 \leq z \leq 1.73) = .4582 - .0398 = .4184.$$

The probability of finding between 41 and 48 vehicles that are vans, pickups, or SUVs is approximately .4184. **3** ✓

10.5 ▸ Exercises

1. What must be known to find the mean and standard deviation of a binomial distribution?

2. What is the rule of thumb for using the normal distribution to approximate a binomial distribution?

Suppose 16 coins are tossed. Find the probability of getting each of the given results by using (a) the binomial probability formula and (b) the normal-curve approximation. (See Examples 1 and 2.)

3. Exactly 8 heads

4. Exactly 9 heads

5. More than 13 tails

6. Fewer than 6 tails

For the remaining exercises in this section, use the normal-curve approximation to the binomial distribution.

Suppose 1000 coins are tossed. Find the probability of getting each of the given results.

7. Exactly 500 heads

8. Exactly 510 heads

9. 475 or more heads

10. Fewer than 460 tails

A die is tossed 120 times. Find the probability of getting each of the given results.

11. Exactly twenty 5's

12. Exactly twenty-four 4's

13. More than seventeen 3's

14. Fewer than twenty-one 6's

15. A reader asked Mr. Statistics (a feature in *Fortune* magazine) about the game of 26 once played in the bars of Chicago.* In this game, the player chooses a number between 1 and 6 and then rolls a cup full of 10 dice 13 times. Out of the 130 numbers rolled, if the number chosen appears at least 26 times, the player wins. Calculate the probability of winning.

16. **Natural Science**　For certain bird species, with appropriate assumptions, the number of nests escaping predation has a binomial distribution.† Suppose the probability of success (that is, a nest's escaping predation) is .3. Find the probability that at least half of 26 nests escape predation.

17. **Natural Science**　Let us assume, under certain appropriate assumptions, that the probability of a young animal eating *x* units of food is binomially distributed, with *n* equal to the maximum number of food units the animal can acquire and *p* equal to the probability per time unit that an animal eats a unit of food. Suppose *n* = 120 and *p* = .6.
    (a) Find the probability that an animal consumes 80 units of food.
    (b) Suppose the animal must consume at least 70 units of food to survive. What is the probability that this happens?

18. **Finance**　In 2007–2008, 66% of all undergraduates received some type of financial aid.* Suppose 50 undergraduates are selected at random.
    (a) Find the probability that at least 35 received financial aid.
    (b) Find the probability that at most 25 received financial aid.

19. **Finance**　In 2007–2008, 27% of all undergraduates received a Federal Pell Grant.* If a random sample of 500 students is selected, find the probability that at least 150 students received a Pell Grant.

20. **Finance**　In 2007–2008, 34% of all undergraduates took out a Federal Stafford loan.* If a random sample of 250 students is selected, find the probability that at most 75 students took out a Federal Stafford loan.

21. **Health**　An article in the *New York Times* stated that 30% of Americans have trouble sleeping.† If 150 Americans are selected at random, find the probability that 40 or less have trouble sleeping.

22. **Health**　In Exercise 21, what is the probability that more than 55 have trouble sleeping?

23. **Natural Science**　A flu vaccine has a probability of 80% of preventing a person who is inoculated from getting the flu. A county health office inoculates 134 people. Find the probabilities of the given results.
    (a) Exactly 12 of the people inoculated get the flu.
    (b) No more than 12 of the people inoculated get the flu.
    (c) None of the people inoculated get the flu.

24. **Natural Science**　The probability that a male will be color blind is .042. Find the probabilities that, in a group of 53 men, the given conditions will be true.
    (a) Exactly 6 are color blind.
    (b) No more than 6 are color blind.
    (c) At least 1 is color blind.

Business　*In February 2008, the warranty company Square Trade estimated that 16.4% of Microsoft Xbox 360 video game systems were defective.‡*

25. If 700 systems are selected at random, find the probability that at least 100 are defective.

26. If 700 systems are selected at random, find the probability that no more than 85 are defective.

---

*Daniel Seligman and Patty De Llosa, "Ask Mr. Statistics," *Fortune*, May 1, 1995, p. 141.

†From G. deJong, *American Naturalist*, vol. 110.

*National Center for Education Statistics, www.nces.ed.gov.

†*The New York Times*, April 23, 2009.

‡www.squaretrade.com.

27. **Natural Science** The blood types B– and AB– are the rarest of the eight human blood types, representing 1.5% and .6% of the population, respectively.*
    (a) If the blood types of a random sample of 1000 blood donors are recorded, what is the probability that 10 or more of the samples are AB–?
    (b) If the blood types of a random sample of 1000 blood donors are recorded, what is the probability that 20 to 40, inclusive, of the samples are B–?
    (c) If a particular city had a blood drive in which 500 people gave blood and 3% of the donations were B–, would we have reason to believe that this town has a higher-than-normal number of donors who are B–? (*Hint*: Calculate the probability of 15 or more donors being B– for a random sample of 500, and then consider the probability obtained.)

Health *According to data from the American Heart Association, 49.7% of non-Hispanic white women and 42.1% of non-Hispanic black women have total cholesterol levels above 200 mg/dL.†*

28. If we select 500 non-Hispanic white women at random, what is the probability that at least 220 of the women will have a cholesterol level higher than 200 mg/dL?

29. If we select 500 non-Hispanic black women at random, what is the probability that at least 220 of the women will have a cholesterol level higher than 200 mg/dL?

30. **Health** According to *HealthDay News*, 5% of infants and young children suffer from food allergies.‡. If 250 infants

are selected at random, what is the probability that between 10 and 20 inclusive have a food allergy?

31. In the 1989 U.S. Open, four golfers each made a hole in one on the same par-3 hole on the same day. *Sports Illustrated* writer R. Reilly stated the probability of getting a hole in one for a given golf pro on a given par-3 hole to be 1/3709.*
    (a) For a specific par-3 hole, use the binomial distribution to find the probability that 4 or more of the 156 golf pros in the tournament field shoot a hole in one.†
    (b) For a specific par-3 hole, use the normal approximation to the binomial distribution to find the probability that 4 or more of the 156 golf pros in the tournament field shoot a hole in one. Why must we be very cautious when using this approximation for this application?
    (c) If the probability of a hole in one remains constant and is 1/3709 for any par-3 hole, find the probability that, in 20,000 attempts by golf pros, there will be 4 or more holes in one. Discuss whether this assumption is reasonable.

✓ **Checkpoint Answers**

1. $\mu = 20; \sigma = 4.08$
2. (a) .1985   (b) .0909
3. (a) .0215   (b) .1867   (c) .9901

---

*National Center for Statistics and Analysis.

†www.americanheart.org.

‡www.nlm.nih.gov/medlineplus/news/fullstory_81741.html.

---

*R. Reilly, "King of the Hill," *Sports Illustrated*, June 1989, pp. 20–25.

†Bonnie Litwiller and David Duncan, "The Probability of a Hole in One," *School Science and Mathematics* 91, no. 1, (January 1991): 30.

CHAPTER 10 ▶ Summary

KEY TERMS AND SYMBOLS

10.1 ▶ random sample
grouped frequency distribution
histogram
frequency polygon
stem-and-leaf-plot
uniform distribution
right-skewed distribution
left-skewed distribution
normal distribution

10.2 ▶ Σ, summation (sigma) notation
$\bar{x}$, sample mean
μ, population mean

(arithmetic) mean
median
statistic
mode

10.3 ▶ s^2, sample variance
s, sample standard deviation
σ, population standard deviation
range
deviations from the mean
variance
standard deviation

10.4 ▶ μ, mean of a continuous distribution
σ, standard deviation of a normal distribution
continuous distribution
normal curves
standard normal curve
z-score
boxplot
quartile

10.5 ▶ binomial distribution

CHAPTER 10 KEY CONCEPTS

To organize the data from a sample, we use a **grouped frequency distribution**—a set of intervals with their corresponding frequencies. The same information can be displayed with a **histogram**—a type of bar graph with a bar for each interval. Each bar has width 1 and height equal to the probability of the corresponding interval. A **stem-and-leaf plot** presents the individual data in a similar form, so it can be viewed as a bar graph as well. Another way to display this information is with a **frequency polygon**, which is formed by connecting the midpoints of consecutive bars of the histogram with straight-line segments.

The **mean** $\bar{x}$ of a frequency distribution is the expected value.

For n numbers $x_1, x_2, \ldots, x_n$,

$$\bar{x} = \frac{\sum x}{n}.$$

For a grouped distribution,

$$\bar{x} = \frac{\sum(xf)}{n}.$$

The **median** is the middle entry in a set of data arranged in either increasing or decreasing order.

The **mode** is the most frequent entry in a set of numbers.

The **range** of a distribution is the difference between the largest and smallest numbers in the distribution.

The **sample standard deviation** s is the square root of the sample **variance**.

For n numbers,

$$s = \sqrt{\frac{\sum x^2 - n\bar{x}^2}{n-1}}.$$

For a grouped distribution,

$$s = \sqrt{\frac{\sum fx^2 - n\bar{x}^2}{n-1}}.$$

A **normal distribution** is a continuous distribution with the following properties: The highest frequency is at the mean; the graph is symmetric about a vertical line through the mean; the total area under the curve, above the x-axis, is 1. If a normal distribution has mean μ and standard deviation σ, then the z-score for the number x is $z = \dfrac{x - \mu}{\sigma}$.

A **boxplot** organizes a list of data using the minimum and maximum values, the median, and the first and third quartiles to give a visual overview of the distribution.

The **area under a normal curve** between $x = a$ and $x = b$ gives the probability that an observed data value will be between a and b.

The **binomial distribution** is a distribution with the following properties: For n independent repeated trials, in which the probability of success in a single trial is p, the probability of x successes is $_nC_x p^x(1 - p)^{n-x}$. The mean is $\mu = np$, and the standard deviation is

$$\sigma = \sqrt{np(1 - p)}.$$

CHAPTER 10 REVIEW EXERCISES

1. Discuss some reasons for organizing data into a grouped frequency distribution.

2. What is the rule of thumb for an appropriate interval in a grouped frequency distribution?

In Exercises 3 and 4, (a) write a frequency distribution; (b) draw a histogram; and (c) draw a stem-and-leaf plot.

3. The following are scores on a 100-point final exam (use intervals of 40–49, 50–59, and so on):

68	45	71	77	82	94	89	63	99	55
76	77	82	92	77	76	53	84	91	81
71	69	42	88	91	84	77	84	89	91

4. The number of units carried in one semester by the students in a business mathematics class was as follows (use intervals of 9–10, 11–12, 13–14, and 15–16):

| 10 | 9 | 16 | 12 | 13 | 15 | 13 | 16 | 15 | 11 | 13 |
| 12 | 12 | 15 | 12 | 14 | 10 | 12 | 14 | 15 | 15 | 13 |

Find the mean for each of the given data sets.

5. The data in Exercise 3

6. The data in Exercise 4

7. The following table gives the frequency counts for 44 first-year college students' waist circumference in cm:

Interval	Frequency
60–69	10
70–79	24
80–89	6
90–99	3
100–109	1

8. The following table gives the frequency counts for 44 first-year college students' caloric intake on a random day:

Interval	Frequency
0–999	1
1000–1999	12
2000–2999	14
3000–3999	11
4000–4999	5
5000–5999	1

9. What do the mean, median, and mode of a distribution have in common? How do they differ? Describe each in a sentence or two.

Find the median and the mode (or modes) for each of the given data sets.

10. Ages (years) of senior citizens tested for low calcium levels:

78, 72, 72, 73, 73, 73, 65, 68, 89, 84, 71, 80

11. Ages (years) of senior citizens tested for low calcium levels:

68, 80, 76, 66, 72, 73, 72, 74, 72, 71, 67, 77, 70

The modal class is the interval containing the most data values. Find the modal class for the distributions of the given data sets.

12. The data in Exercise 7   **13.** The data in Exercise 8

For the given histograms, identify the shape of the distribution.

14.

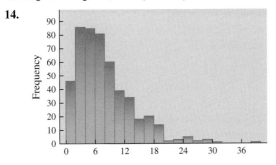

15.

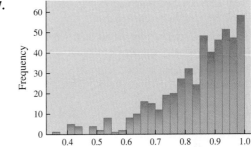

16.

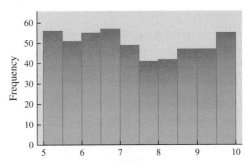

17.

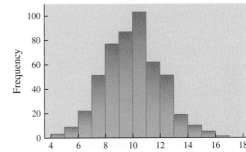

18. What is meant by the range of a distribution?

19. How are the variance and the standard deviation of a distribution related? What is measured by the standard deviation?

Find the range and standard deviation for each of the given distributions.

20. Number of days in a month of sunshine for a village:

14, 17, 18, 19, 30

21. Ages of drivers entering a fast-food restaurant:

26, 43, 17, 20, 25, 37, 54, 28, 20, 19

Find the standard deviation for the given data sets.

22. The data in Exercise 7

23. The data in Exercise 8

24. Describe the characteristics of a normal distribution.

25. What is meant by a skewed distribution?

Find the given areas under the standard normal curve.

26. Between $z = 0$ and $z = 1.35$

27. To the left of $z = .38$

28. Between $z = -1.88$ and $z = 2.41$

29. Between $z = 1.53$ and $z = 2.82$

30. Find a z-score such that 8% of the area under the curve is to the right of z.

31. Why is the normal distribution not a good approximation of a binomial distribution that has a value of p close to 0 or 1?

Social Science *The table gives the population (in thousands) of 18–24 year olds for the 50 U.S. states in 2004:**

456	126	598	206	87
74	157	997	1825	576
571	1260	531	828	2400
280	632	323	77	313
3596	316	589	1128	62
457	299	99	385	748
311	413	191	350	635
84	503	210	1185	173
1549	124	122	112	575
902	521	744	429	57

32. Using intervals that begin with 0–499, create a frequency distribution for the population data.

33. (a) Create a histogram for the population data.
(b) What is the shape of the distribution?

34. **Finance** The annual stock returns (percent) of Target Corporation are given in the following table:†

Year	2005	2006	2007	2008
Return	6.6	4.7	−11.7	−30.4

Find the mean and standard deviation of the return for the four-year period.

35. **Finance** The annual stock returns (percent) of Wal-Mart Stores, Inc., are given in the table:†

Year	2005	2006	2007	2008
Return	−10.3	.1	4.9	20.0

Find the mean and standard deviation of the return for the four-year period.

36. **Natural Science** The weight gains of two groups of 10 rats fed on two different experimental diets were as follows:

Weight Gains									
Diet A	1	0	3	7	1	1	5	4	1	4
Diet B	2	1	1	2	3	2	1	0	1	0

Compute the mean and standard deviation for each group, and compare them to answer the following questions:
(a) Which diet produced the greatest mean gain?
(b) Which diet produced the most consistent gain?

37. **Natural Science** Refer to the data in Exercise 36.
(a) Construct a boxplot for each set of diet data.
(b) Use the boxplots to compare weight gains for the two diets.

38. **Business** The table gives the frequency distribution for the 161 movies that earned $75 million or more dollars in gross domestic receipts from 2004–2008:*

Interval (in Millions of Dollars)	Frequency
75–149.999999	102
150–224.999999	34
225–299.999999	13
300–374.999999	8
375–449.999999	3
450–524.999999	0
525–599.999999	1

Calculate the mean and standard deviation for the data. (*Hint*: Round the midpoint to the nearest tenth.)

Business *The table gives the number of vehicles (in thousands) sold within the United States in March 2008 and March 2009 for 12 auto manufacturers:†*

Auto Manufacturer	March 2008 Sales	March 2009 Sales
General Motors Corp.	115	68
Ford Motor Corporation	73	46
Chrysler LLC	47	24
Toyota Motor Sales USA, Inc.	130	81
American Honda Motor Co., Inc.	82	55
Nissan North America, Inc.	66	43
Hyundai Motor America	31	32
Mazda Motors of America, Inc.	22	15
Mitsubishi Motors NA, Inc.	8	3
Kia Motors America, Inc.	14	12
Volkswagen of America, Inc.	19	13
Audi of America, Inc.	7	5

**State and Metropolitan Area Data Book*: 2006.
†www.morningstar.com.

*Based on data available at www.thebigmoney.com.
†http://online.wsj.com.

39. **(a)** Find the mean and standard deviation for each set of sales.

   (b) Which company is closest to the mean sales in March 2008? in March 2009?

40. Find the five-number summary for each set of sales.

41. **(a)** Construct boxplots for the two data sets on the same scale.

   (b) Does it appear that sales increased or decreased? Explain.

42. **Social Science** On standard IQ tests, the mean is 100, with a standard deviation of 15. The results are very close to fitting a normal curve. Suppose an IQ test is given to a very large group of people. Find the percentage of people whose IQ score is

   (a) more than 130;

   (b) less than 85;

   (c) between 85 and 115.

43. **Business** A machine that fills quart orange juice cartons is set to fill them with 32.1 oz. If the actual contents of the cartons vary normally, with a standard deviation of .1 oz, what percentage of the cartons contains less than a quart (32 oz)?

Social Science *The results of the 2007 National Survey on Drug Use and Health found that among young adults ages 18–25, in the last month, 16.4% had used marijuana; 1.7% had used cocaine; 6.0% had abused prescription drugs.* If we select 1000 young adults at random, approximate the probability of the given event.*

44. Less than 150 had used marijuana.

45. Between 12 and 25 had used cocaine.

46. More than 50 had abused prescription drugs.

* www.oas.samhsa.gov/nsduh/2k7nsduh/2k7Results.cfm#2.3.

CASE 10

Statistics in the Law: The *Castañeda* Decision

Statistical evidence is now routinely presented in both criminal and civil cases. In this application, we look at a famous case that established use of the binomial distribution and measurement by standard deviation as an accepted procedure.*

Defendants who are convicted in criminal cases sometimes appeal their conviction on the grounds that the jury which indicted or convicted them was drawn from a pool of jurors that does not represent the population of the district in which they live. These appeals almost always cite the Supreme Court's decision in *Castañeda v. Partida* [430 U.S. 482], a case that dealt with the selection of grand juries in the state of Texas. The decision summarizes the facts this way:

> After respondent, a Mexican-American, had been convicted of a crime in a Texas District Court and had exhausted his state remedies on his claim of discrimination in the selec-

*The *Castañeda* case and many other interesting applications of statistics in law are discussed in Michael O. Finkelstein and Bruce Levin, *Statistics for Lawyers*, New York, Springer-Verlag, 1990. U.S. Supreme Court decisions are online at http://www.findlaw.com/casecode/supreme.html, and most states now have important state court decisions online.

tion of the grand jury that had indicted him, he filed a habeas corpus petition in the Federal District Court, alleging a denial of due process and equal protection under the Fourteenth Amendment, because of gross underrepresentation of Mexican-Americans on the county grand juries.

The case went to the Appeals Court, which noted that "the county population was 79% Mexican-American, but, over an 11-year period, only 39% of those summoned for grand jury service were Mexican-American," and concluded that together with other testimony about the selection process, "the proof offered by respondent was sufficient to demonstrate a prima facie case of intentional discrimination in grand jury selection. . . ."

The state appealed to the Supreme Court, which then needed to decide whether the underrepresentation of Mexican-Americans on grand juries was indeed too extreme to be an effect of chance. To do so, they invoked the binomial distribution. Here is the argument:

> Given that 79.1% of the population is Mexican-American, the expected number of Mexican-Americans among the 870 persons summoned to serve as grand jurors over the 11-year period is approximately 688. The observed number is 339. Of course, in any given drawing some fluctuation from the expected number is predicted. The important point, however, is that the statistical model shows that the results of a random drawing are likely to fall in the vicinity of the expected value. . . .
>
> The measure of the predicted fluctuations from the expected value is the standard deviation, defined for the binomial distribution as the square root of the product of the total number in the sample (here 870) times the probability of selecting a Mexican-American (.791) times the probability of selecting a non-Mexican-American (.209). . . . Thus, in this case the standard deviation is approximately 12. As a general rule for such large samples, if the difference between the expected value and the observed number is greater than two or three standard deviations, then the hypothesis that the jury drawing was random would be suspect to a social scientist. The 11-year data here reflect a difference between the expected and observed number of Mexican-Americans of approximately 29 standard deviations. A detailed calculation reveals that the likelihood that such a substantial departure from the expected value would occur by chance is less than 1 in 10^{140}.

The Court decided that the statistical evidence supported the conclusion that jurors were not randomly selected, and that it was up to the state to show that its selection process did not discriminate against Mexican-Americans. The Court concluded the following:

> The proof offered by respondent was sufficient to demonstrate a prima facie case of discrimination in grand jury selection. Since the State failed to rebut the presumption

of purposeful discrimination by competent testimony, despite two opportunities to do so, we affirm the Court of Appeals' holding of a denial of equal protection of the law in the grand jury selection process in respondent's case.

EXERCISES

1. Check the Court's calculation of 29 standard deviations as the difference between the expected number of Mexican-Americans and the number actually chosen.

2. Where do you think the Court's figure of 1 in 10^{140} came from?

3. The *Castañeda* decison also presents data from a $2\frac{1}{2}$-year period during which the state district judge supervised the selection process. During this period, 220 persons were called to serve as grand jurors, and only 100 of these were Mexican-American.
   (a) Considering the 220 jurors as a random selection from a large population, what is the expected number of Mexican-Americans, given the 79.1% population figure?
   (b) If we model the drawing of jurors as a sequence of 220 independent Bernoulli trials, what is the standard deviation of the number of Mexican-Americans?
   (c) About how many standard deviations is the actual number of Mexican-Americans drawn (100) from the expected number that you calculated in part (a)?
   (d) What does the normal-distribution table at the back of the book (Table 2) tell you about this result?

4. The following information is from a case brought by Hy-Vee stores before the Iowa Supreme Court, appealing a ruling by the Iowa Civil Rights Commission in favor of a female employee of one of its grocery stores:

   > In 1985, there were 112 managerial positions in the ten Hy-Vee stores located in Cedar Rapids. Only 6 of these managers were women. During that same year there were 294 employees; 206 were men and 88 were women.

   (a) How far from the expected number of women in management was the actual number, assuming that gender had nothing to do with promotion? Measure the difference in standard deviations.
   (b) Does this look like evidence of purposeful discrimination?

Graphing Calculators

▶ Basics

Instructions on using your graphing calculator are readily available in:

the instruction book for your calculator; and
the web site for this book (www.pearsonhighered.com/mwal0e).

In addition, you may purchase the *Graphing Calculator and Excel Spreadsheet Manual,* written specifically to accompany this textbook. It is described in the Student Supplement section of the Preface and is available at your bookstore or online at www.pearsonstore.com or at www.coursesmart.com. It is also available in MyMathLab.

▶ Programs

The following programs are available for TI and most Casio graphing calculators. You can download them from www.pearsonhighered.com/mwal0e, and use the appropriate USB cable and software to install them in your calculator.

> *General*

1. Fraction Conversion for Casio

> *Chapter 1: Algebra and Equations*

2. Quadratic Formula for TI-83

> *Chapter 5: Mathematics of Finance*

3. Present and Future Value of an Annuity

4. Loan Payment

5. Loan Balance after *n* Payments

6. Amortization Table for TI

> *Chapter 6: Systems of Linear Equations and Matrices*

7. RREF Program for Casio 9750GA+, 9850, and 9860G

> *Chapter 7: Linear Programming*

8. Simplex Method

9. Two-Stage Method

> *Chapter 13: Integral Calculus*

10. Rectangle Approximation of $\displaystyle\int_a^b f(x)\, dx$ (using left endpoints)

Programs 1, 2, 6 and 7 are built into most calculators other than those mentioned. Programs 3–5 are part of the TVM Solver on TI and most Casio models, although some students may find the versions here easier to use. Programs 8–10 are not built into any calculator.

Tables

Table 1 Formulas from Geometry

CIRCLE

Area: $A = \pi r^2$

Circumference: $C = 2\pi r$

RECTANGLE

Area: $A = lw$

Perimeter: $P = 2l + 2w$

PARALLELOGRAM

Area: $A = bh$

Perimeter: $P = 2a + 2b$

TRIANGLE

Area: $A = \dfrac{1}{2}bh$

SPHERE

Volume: $V = \dfrac{4}{3}\pi r^3$

Surface area: $A = 4\pi r^2$

RECTANGULAR BOX

Volume: $V = lwh$

Surface area: $A = 2lh + 2wh + 2lw$

CIRCULAR CYLINDER

Volume: $V = \pi r^2 h$

Surface area: $A = 2\pi r^2 + 2\pi rh$

TRIANGULAR CYLINDER

Volume: $V = \dfrac{1}{2}bhl$

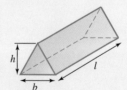

CONE

Volume: $V = \dfrac{1}{3}\pi r^2 h$

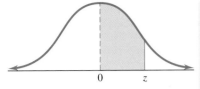

Table 2 Areas under the Normal Curve
The column under A gives the proportion of the area under the entire curve that is between $z = 0$ and a positive value of z.

z	A	z	A	z	A	z	A
.00	.0000	.48	.1844	.96	.3315	1.44	.4251
.01	.0040	.49	.1879	.97	.3340	1.45	.4265
.02	.0080	.50	.1915	.98	.3365	1.46	.4279
.03	.0120	.51	.1950	.99	.3389	1.47	.4292
.04	.0160	.52	.1985	1.00	.3413	1.48	.4306
.05	.0199	.53	.2019	1.01	.3438	1.49	.4319
.06	.0239	.54	.2054	1.02	.3461	1.50	.4332
.07	.0279	.55	.2088	1.03	.3485	1.51	.4345
.08	.0319	.56	.2123	1.04	.3508	1.52	.4357
.09	.0359	.57	.2157	1.05	.3531	1.53	.4370
.10	.0398	.58	.2190	1.06	.3554	1.54	.4382
.11	.0438	.59	.2224	1.07	.3577	1.55	.4394
.12	.0478	.60	.2258	1.08	.3599	1.56	.4406
.13	.0517	.61	.2291	1.09	.3621	1.57	.4418
.14	.0557	.62	.2324	1.10	.3643	1.58	.4430
.15	.0596	.63	.2357	1.11	.3665	1.59	.4441
.16	.0636	.64	.2389	1.12	.3686	1.60	.4452
.17	.0675	.65	.2422	1.13	.3708	1.61	.4463
.18	.0714	.66	.2454	1.14	.3729	1.62	.4474
.19	.0754	.67	.2486	1.15	.3749	1.63	.4485
.20	.0793	.68	.2518	1.16	.3770	1.64	.4495
.21	.0832	.69	.2549	1.17	.3790	1.65	.4505
.22	.0871	.70	.2580	1.18	.3810	1.66	.4515
.23	.0910	.71	.2612	1.19	.3830	1.67	.4525
.24	.0948	.72	.2642	1.20	.3849	1.68	.4535
.25	.0987	.73	.2673	1.21	.3869	1.69	.4545
.26	.1026	.74	.2704	1.22	.3888	1.70	.4554
.27	.1064	.75	.2734	1.23	.3907	1.71	.4564
.28	.1103	.76	.2764	1.24	.3925	1.72	.4573
.29	.1141	.77	.2794	1.25	.3944	1.73	.4582
.30	.1179	.78	.2823	1.26	.3962	1.74	.4591
.31	.1217	.79	.2852	1.27	.3980	1.75	.4599
.32	.1255	.80	.2881	1.28	.3997	1.76	.4608
.33	.1293	.81	.2910	1.29	.4015	1.77	.4616
.34	.1331	.82	.2939	1.30	.4032	1.78	.4625
.35	.1368	.83	.2967	1.31	.4049	1.79	.4633
.36	.1406	.84	.2996	1.32	.4066	1.80	.4641
.37	.1443	.85	.3023	1.33	.4082	1.81	.4649
.38	.1480	.86	.3051	1.34	.4099	1.82	.4656
.39	.1517	.87	.3079	1.35	.4115	1.83	.4664
.40	.1554	.88	.3106	1.36	.4131	1.84	.4671
.41	.1591	.89	.3133	1.37	.4147	1.85	.4678
.42	.1628	.90	.3159	1.38	.4162	1.86	.4686
.43	.1664	.91	.3186	1.39	.4177	1.87	.4693
.44	.1700	.92	.3212	1.40	.4192	1.88	.4700
.45	.1736	.93	.3238	1.41	.4207	1.89	.4706
.46	.1772	.94	.3264	1.42	.4222	1.90	.4713
.47	.1808	.95	.3289	1.43	.4236	1.91	.4719

(continued)

Table 2 (*continued*)

z	A	z	A	z	A	z	A
1.92	.4726	2.42	.4922	2.92	.4983	3.42	.4997
1.93	.4732	2.43	.4925	2.93	.4983	3.43	.4997
1.94	.4738	2.44	.4927	2.94	.4984	3.44	.4997
1.95	.4744	2.45	.4929	2.95	.4984	3.45	.4997
1.96	.4750	2.46	.4931	2.96	.4985	3.46	.4997
1.97	.4756	2.47	.4932	2.97	.4985	3.47	.4997
1.98	.4762	2.48	.4934	2.98	.4986	3.48	.4998
1.99	.4767	2.49	.4936	2.99	.4986	3.49	.4998
2.00	.4773	2.50	.4938	3.00	.4987	3.50	.4998
2.01	.4778	2.51	.4940	3.01	.4987	3.51	.4998
2.02	.4783	2.52	.4941	3.02	.4987	3.52	.4998
2.03	.4788	2.53	.4943	3.03	.4988	3.53	.4998
2.04	.4793	2.54	.4945	3.04	.4988	3.54	.4998
2.05	.4798	2.55	.4946	3.05	.4989	3.55	.4998
2.06	.4803	2.56	.4948	3.06	.4989	3.56	.4998
2.07	.4808	2.57	.4949	3.07	.4989	3.57	.4998
2.08	.4812	2.58	.4951	3.08	.4990	3.58	.4998
2.09	.4817	2.59	.4952	3.09	.4990	3.59	.4998
2.10	.4821	2.60	.4953	3.10	.4990	3.60	.4998
2.11	.4826	2.61	.4955	3.11	.4991	3.61	.4999
2.12	.4830	2.62	.4956	3.12	.4991	3.62	.4999
2.13	.4834	2.63	.4957	3.13	.4991	3.63	.4999
2.14	.4838	2.64	.4959	3.14	.4992	3.64	.4999
2.15	.4842	2.65	.4960	3.15	.4992	3.65	.4999
2.16	.4846	2.66	.4961	3.16	.4992	3.66	.4999
2.17	.4850	2.67	.4962	3.17	.4992	3.67	.4999
2.18	.4854	2.68	.4963	3.18	.4993	3.68	.4999
2.19	.4857	2.69	.4964	3.19	.4993	3.69	.4999
2.20	.4861	2.70	.4965	3.20	.4993	3.70	.4999
2.21	.4865	2.71	.4966	3.21	.4993	3.71	.4999
2.22	.4868	2.72	.4967	3.22	.4994	3.72	.4999
2.23	.4871	2.73	.4968	3.23	.4994	3.73	.4999
2.24	.4875	2.74	.4969	3.24	.4994	3.74	.4999
2.25	.4878	2.75	.4970	3.25	.4994	3.75	.4999
2.26	.4881	2.76	.4971	3.26	.4994	3.76	.4999
2.27	.4884	2.77	.4972	3.27	.4995	3.77	.4999
2.28	.4887	2.78	.4973	3.28	.4995	3.78	.4999
2.29	.4890	2.79	.4974	3.29	.4995	3.79	.4999
2.30	.4893	2.80	.4974	3.30	.4995	3.80	.4999
2.31	.4896	2.81	.4975	3.31	.4995	3.81	.4999
2.32	.4898	2.82	.4976	3.32	.4996	3.82	.4999
2.33	.4901	2.83	.4977	3.33	.4996	3.83	.4999
2.34	.4904	2.84	.4977	3.34	.4996	3.84	.4999
2.35	.4906	2.85	.4978	3.35	.4996	3.85	.4999
2.36	.4909	2.86	.4979	3.36	.4996	3.86	.4999
2.37	.4911	2.87	.4980	3.37	.4996	3.87	.5000
2.38	.4913	2.88	.4980	3.38	.4996	3.88	.5000
2.39	.4916	2.89	.4981	3.39	.4997	3.89	.5000
2.40	.4918	2.90	.4981	3.40	.4997		
2.41	.4920	2.91	.4982	3.41	.4997		

Table 3 Integrals
(C is an arbitrary constant.)

---

1. $\int x^n \, dx = \dfrac{1}{n+1} x^{n+1} + C \qquad (n \neq -1)$

2. $\int e^{kx} \, dx = \dfrac{1}{k} e^{kx} + C$

3. $\int \dfrac{a}{x} \, dx = a \ln|x| + C$

4. $\int \ln|ax| \, dx = x(\ln|ax| - 1) + C$

5. $\int \dfrac{1}{\sqrt{x^2 + a^2}} \, dx = \ln\left|x + \sqrt{x^2 + a^2}\right| + C$

6. $\int \dfrac{1}{\sqrt{x^2 - a^2}} \, dx = \ln\left|x + \sqrt{x^2 - a^2}\right| + C$

7. $\int \dfrac{1}{a^2 - x^2} \, dx = \dfrac{1}{2a} \cdot \ln\left|\dfrac{a + x}{a - x}\right| + C \qquad (a \neq 0)$

8. $\int \dfrac{1}{x^2 - a^2} \, dx = \dfrac{1}{2a} \cdot \ln\left|\dfrac{x - a}{x + a}\right| + C \qquad (a \neq 0)$

9. $\int \dfrac{1}{x\sqrt{a^2 - x^2}} \, dx = -\dfrac{1}{a} \cdot \ln\left|\dfrac{a + \sqrt{a^2 - x^2}}{x}\right| + C \qquad (a \neq 0)$

10. $\int \dfrac{1}{x\sqrt{a^2 + x^2}} \, dx = -\dfrac{1}{a} \cdot \ln\left|\dfrac{a + \sqrt{a^2 + x^2}}{x}\right| + C \qquad (a \neq 0)$

11. $\int \dfrac{x}{ax + b} \, dx = \dfrac{x}{a} - \dfrac{b}{a^2} \cdot \ln|ax + b| + C \qquad (a \neq 0)$

12. $\int \dfrac{x}{(ax + b)^2} \, dx = \dfrac{b}{a^2(ax + b)} + \dfrac{1}{a^2} \cdot \ln|ax + b| + C \qquad (a \neq 0)$

13. $\int \dfrac{1}{x(ax + b)} \, dx = \dfrac{1}{b} \cdot \ln\left|\dfrac{x}{ax + b}\right| + C \qquad (b \neq 0)$

14. $\int \dfrac{1}{x(ax + b)^2} \, dx = \dfrac{1}{b(ax + b)} + \dfrac{1}{b^2} \cdot \ln\left|\dfrac{x}{ax + b}\right| \qquad (b \neq 0)$

15. $\int \sqrt{x^2 + a^2} \, dx = \dfrac{x}{2} \sqrt{x^2 + a^2} + \dfrac{a^2}{2} \cdot \ln\left|x + \sqrt{x^2 + a^2}\right| + C$

16. $\int x^n \cdot \ln|x| \, dx = x^{n+1} \left[\dfrac{\ln|x|}{n+1} - \dfrac{1}{(n+1)^2}\right] + C \qquad (n \neq -1)$

17. $\int x^n e^{ax} \, dx = \dfrac{x^n e^{ax}}{a} - \dfrac{n}{a} \cdot \int x^{n-1} e^{ax} \, dx + C \qquad (a \neq 0)$

CHAPTER 8

Section 8.1 (Page 473)

1. False   **3.** True   **5.** True   **7.** True   **9.** False
11. Answers vary.   **13.** $\subseteq$ **15.** $\not\subseteq$ **17.** $\subseteq$ **19.** $\subseteq$
21. 8   **23.** 128   **25.** $\{x|x \text{ is an integer} \leq 0 \text{ or} \geq 8\}$
27. Answers vary.   **29.** $\cap$ **31.** $\cap$ **33.** $\cup$ **35.** $\cup$
37. $\{b, 1, 3\}$ **39.** $\{d, e, f, 4, 5, 6\}$ **41.** $\{e, 4, 6\}$
43. $\{a, b, c, d, 1, 2, 3, 5\}$ **45.** All students not taking this course.
47. All students taking both accounting and philosophy.   **49.** C
and D, A and E, C and E, D and E **51.** $\{$Allstate, Microsoft$\}$
53. $\{$Allstate, Microsoft$\}$ **55.** $M \cap E$ is the set of all male
employed applicants.   **57.** $M' \cup S'$ is the set of all female or married applicants.   **59.** $\{$Internet$\}$ **61.** $\{$Comcast Cable Communications, Time Warner Cable$\}$ **63.** $\{$Comcast, Time Warner, Cox, Charter, Cablevision$\}$ **65.** $\{$Comcast, Time Warner$\}$
67. $\{s, d, c\}$ **69.** $\{g\}$

Section 8.2 (Page 482)

1.   **3.**

5. 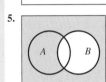   **7.** $\varnothing$ **9.** 8

11. 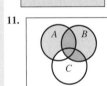   **13.**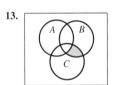

15.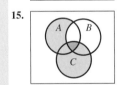

17. 3.2%   **19. (a)** 105   **(b)** 39   **(c)** 15   **(d)** 3
21. (a) 227   **(b)** 182   **(c)** 27   **23. (a)** 54   **(b)** 17   **(c)** 10
(d) 7   **(e)** 15   **(f)** 3   **(g)** 12   **(h)** 1   **25. (a)** 1018   **(b)** 732
(c) 2567   **(d)** 3058   **27. (a)** 945,000   **(b)** 3000
(c) 36,000   **(d)** 984,000   **(e)** 179,000   **29.** Answers vary.
31. 9   **33.** 27
35. 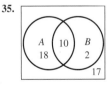   **37.**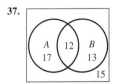

39. 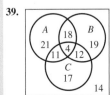   **41.**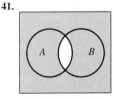

43.

45. The complement of A intersect B equals the union of the complement of A and the complement of B.   **47.** A union (B intersect C) equals (A union B) intersect (A union C).

Section 8.3 (Page 493)

1. Answers vary.   **3.** $\{$January, February, March, $\dots$, December$\}$
5. $\{0, 1, 2, \dots, 80\}$ **7.** $\{$go ahead, cancel$\}$ **9.** $\{Q_1, Q_2, Q_3, Q_4\}$
11. Answers vary.   **13.** No   **15.** Yes   **17.** No
19. $S = \{$C&K, C&L, C&J, C&T, C&N, K&L, K&J, K&T, K&N, L&J, L&T, L&N, J&T, J&N, T&N$\}$
(a) $\{$C&T, K&T, L&T, J&T, T&N$\}$ **(b)** $\{$C&J, C&N, J&N$\}$
21. $S = \{$forest sage & rag painting, forest sage & colorwash, evergreen & rag painting, evergreen & colorwash, opaque & rag painting, opaque & colorwash$\}$ **(a)** $\dfrac{1}{2}$ **(b)** $\dfrac{2}{3}$
23. $S = \{$10′ & beige, 10′ & forest green, 10′ & rust, 12′ & beige, 12′ & forest green, 12′ & rust$\}$ **(a)** $\dfrac{1}{6}$ **(b)** $\dfrac{1}{2}$ **(c)** $\dfrac{1}{3}$ **25.** $\dfrac{1}{2}$
27. $\dfrac{1}{3}$ **29.** $\dfrac{5}{6}$ **31.** $\dfrac{1}{2}$ **33.** $\dfrac{1}{8}$ **35.** $\dfrac{3}{4}$
37. $\dfrac{159}{5471} \approx .029$ **39. (a)** $\dfrac{215}{1168} \approx .184$ **(b)** $\dfrac{545}{1168} \approx .467$
(c) $\dfrac{302}{1168} \approx .259$ **41. (a)** The person smokes or has a family history of heart disease.   **(b)** The person does not smoke and has a family history of heart disease.   **(c)** The person does not have a family history of heart disease or is not overweight.   **43.** Possible
45. Not possible   **47.** Not possible

Section 8.4 (Page 502)

1. $\dfrac{20}{38} = \dfrac{10}{19}$ **3.** $\dfrac{28}{38} = \dfrac{14}{19}$ **5.** $\dfrac{5}{38}$ **7.** $\dfrac{12}{38} = \dfrac{6}{19}$
9. (a) $\dfrac{5}{36}$ **(b)** $\dfrac{1}{9}$ **(c)** $\dfrac{1}{12}$ **(d)** 0   **11. (a)** $\dfrac{5}{18}$ **(b)** $\dfrac{5}{12}$ **(c)** $\dfrac{1}{3}$
13. $\dfrac{1}{3}$ **15. (a)** $\dfrac{1}{2}$ **(b)** $\dfrac{2}{5}$ **(c)** $\dfrac{3}{10}$ **17. (a)** .62   **(b)** .32
(c) .11   **(d)** .81   **19. (a)** .196   **(b)** .08   **(c)** .804   **(d)** .987
21. (a) .42   **(b)** .893   **(c)** .107   **23.** 1:5   **25.** 2:1
27. (a) 1:4   **(b)** 8:7   **(c)** 4:11   **29.** 2:7   **31.** 21:79
33. 7:93   **35.** $\dfrac{2}{7}$ **37.** $\dfrac{1}{10}$ **39.** 1:9   **41. (a)** .2778
(b) .4167   **43. (a)** .15625   **(b)** .3125   **45.** .300   **47.** .966
49. .595   **51.** .808   **53.** .377   **55.** .833   **57.** .841
59. .453   **61. (a)** .961   **(b)** .491   **(c)** .509   **(d)** .505   **(e)** .004
(f) .544   **63. (a)** $\dfrac{1}{4}$ **(b)** $\dfrac{1}{2}$ **(c)** $\dfrac{1}{4}$ **65. (a)** .828   **(b)** .339
(c) .083   **67.** .020   **69.** .557

Section 8.5 (Page 517)

1. $\dfrac{1}{3}$ **3.** 1   **5.** $\dfrac{1}{6}$ **7.** $\dfrac{4}{17}$ **9.** .012   **11.** Answers vary.
13. Answers vary.   **15.** No   **17.** Yes   **19.** No, yes
21. $\dfrac{3}{7} = .43$ **23.** .271   **25. (a)** .158   **(b)** .001   **(c)** .008

(d) .440   **27.** .374   **29.** .522   **31.** .30   **33.** Answers vary.
35. .049   **37.** .534   **39.** .143   **41.** Dependent   **43.** .05
45. .25   **47.** .933   **49.** .245   **51.** .493   **53.** .159
55. .0457   **57.** .999985   **59. (a)** 3 backups   **(b)** Answers
vary.   **61.** Dependent or "No"

Section 8.6 (Page 524)

1. $\frac{1}{3}$ **3.** .0488   **5.** .5122   **7.** .4706   **9.** .571
11. .259   **13.** .372   **15.** .143   **17.** .478   **19.** (c)
21. .481   **23.** .919   **25.** .367   **27. (a)** .4738   **(b)** .1665
29. .011   **31.** .354   **33.** .871   **35.** .713

Chapter 8 Review (Page 527)

1. False   **3.** False   **5.** True   **7.** True   **9.** {New Year's
Day, Martin Luther King Jr.'s Birthday, Presidents' Day, Memorial Day,
Independence Day, Labor Day, Columbus Day, Veterans' Day,
Thanksgiving, Christmas}   **11.** {1, 2, 3, 4}   **13.** $\{B_1, B_2, B_3, B_6, B_{12}\}$
15. {A, C, E}   **17.** $\{A, B_3, B_6, B_{12}, C, D, E\}$
19. Female students older than 22   **21.** Females or students with a
GPA > 3.5   **23.** Non-finance majors who are 22 or younger
25. 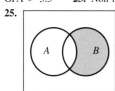   **27.**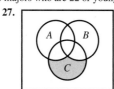

29. 100   **31.** {1, 2, 3, 4, 5, 6}   **33.** {(red, 10), (red, 20),
(red, 30), (blue, 10), (blue, 20), (blue, 30), (green, 10), (green, 20),
(green, 30)}   **35.** No. Not equal probabilities for each genre.
37. No   **39.** $E \cup F$ **41.** Answers vary.   **43.** Answers vary.
45. .1910   **47.** .014   **49.** .196   **51.** .130   **53.** .276
55.

	N_2	T_2
N_1	N_1N_2	N_1T_2
T_1	T_1N_2	T_1T_2

57. $\frac{1}{2}$ **59.** $\frac{5}{36} \approx .139$ **61.** $\frac{5}{18} \approx .278$ **63.** $\frac{1}{3}$

65. .79   **67.** .66   **69. (a)** .7   **(b)** $\frac{2}{15} \approx .1333$

71. Answers vary.   **73.** $\frac{3}{22}$ **75.** $\frac{2}{3}$ **77. (a)** .271   **(b)** .379
(c) .625   **(d)** .342   **(e)** .690   **(f)** .514   **(g)** No. Answers vary.

Additional Probability Review (Page 530)

1. (a) .88   **(b)** .30   **(c)** .70   **3. (a)** .0962   **(b)** .0595
(c) .8168   **5. (a)** 0   **(b)** $\frac{1}{3}$ **(c)** 1   **7.** .358   **9.** .144
11. No   **13.** $\frac{1}{6}$ **15.** 82.4%   **17.** .196   **19.** .270
21. .286   **23.** 127:73   **25.** .525   **27.** .176

Case 8 Exercises (Page 533)

1. .001   **3.** .331

CHAPTER 9

Section 9.1 (Page 542)

1.

Number of boys	0	1	2	3	4
P(x)	.063	.25	.375	.25	.063

3.

Number of Queens	0	1	2	3
P(x)	.7826	.2042	.0130	.0002

5.

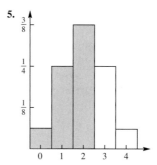

7.

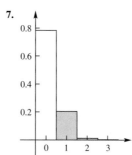

9. 4   **11.** 5.4   **13.** 2.7   **15.** 2.5   **17.** $-\frac{1}{19} \approx -.05$
19. −$.50   **21.** −$.97   **23.** −$41.75   **25.** 3.4278
27. No, cannot have a probability <0.   **29.** Yes, cannot have a
probability <0.   **31.** .15   **33.** .25   **35.** Many correct
answers, including .15, .15.   **37.** $4550   **39.** .477
41.

Account Number	*Expected Value*	*Existing Volume + Expected Value of Potential*	*Class*
3	2000	22,000	C
4	1000	51,000	B
5	25,000	30,000	C
6	60,000	60,000	A
7	16,000	46,000	B

43. (a) $68.51, $72.84   **(b)** Amoxicillin   **45. (a)** £550,000
(b) £618,000

Section 9.2 (Page 557)

1. 12   **3.** 56   **5.** 8   **7.** 24   **9.** 84   **11.** 1716
13. 6,375,600   **15.** 240,240   **17.** 8568   **19.** 40,116,600
21. $\frac{24}{0}$ is undefined.   **23. (a)** 8   **(b)** 64   **25.** 576
27. 1 billion in theory; however, some numbers will never be used (such
as those beginning 000); yes.   **29.** 1 billion   **31.** 120
33. (a) 160; 8,000,000   **(b)** Some, such as 800, 900, etc., are reserved.
35. 1600   **37.** Answers vary.   **39.** 95,040   **41.** 12,144
43. 863,040   **45.** 272   **47. (a)** 210   **(b)** 210   **49.** 330
51. Answers vary.   **53. (a)** 9   **(b)** 6   **(c)** 3, yes **55. (a)** 8568
(b) 21   **(c)** 3465   **(d)** 8547   **57. (a)** 210   **(b)** 7980
59. (a) 1,120,529,256   **(b)** 806,781,064,320   **61.** 81
63. Not possible, 4 initials   **65. (a)** 10   **(b)** 0   **(c)** 1   **(d)** 10
(e) 30   **(f)** 15   **(g)** 0   **67.** 3,247,943,160   **69.** 5.524×10^{26}
71. (a) 2520   **(b)** 840   **(c)** 5040   **73. (a)** 479,001,600   **(b)** 6
(c) 27,720

Section 9.3 (Page 565)

1. .422 **3.** $\frac{5}{8}$ **5.** $\frac{5}{28}$ **7.** .00005 **9.** .0163

11. .5630 **13.** 1326 **15.** .851 **17.** .765 **19.** .941
21. Answers vary. **23.** .1396 **25. (a)** 8.9×10^{-10}
(b) 1.2×10^{-12} **27.** 2.62×10^{-17} **29. (a)** .0322
(b) .2418 **(c)** .7582 **31. (a)** .0015 **(b)** .0033 **(c)** .3576

33. $1 - \frac{_{365}P_{100}}{(365)^{100}} \approx 1$ **35.** .0031 **37.** .3083

39. We obtained the following answers—yours should be similar:
(a) .0399 **(b)** .5191 **(c)** .0226

Section 9.4 (Page 572)

1. .200 **3.** .000006 **5.** .999994 **7.** .3010 **9.** .1216

11. .8784 **13.** $\frac{1}{32}$ **15.** $\frac{13}{16}$ **17.** Answers vary.

19. .1222 **21.** .0719 **23.** 68 **25.** .0608 **27.** .9903
29. .247 **31.** .193 **33.** .350 **35.** 3.85 **37.** .9747
39. Lower **41. (a)** .9995 **(b)** Answers vary.
43. (a) 1 chance in 1024 **(b)** 1 chance in 1.1×10^{12} **(c)** 1 chance
in 2.6×10^{6} **(d)** Answers vary.

Section 9.5 (Page 582)

1. Yes **3.** Yes **5.** No **7.** No **9.** No **11.** No

13. Not a transition diagram **15.** $\begin{bmatrix} .6 & .20 & .20 \\ .9 & .02 & .08 \\ .4 & 0 & .6 \end{bmatrix}$ **17.** Yes

19. Yes **21.** No **23.** $\begin{bmatrix} \frac{19}{64}, \frac{45}{64} \end{bmatrix}$ **25.** $\begin{bmatrix} \frac{3}{11}, \frac{8}{11} \end{bmatrix}$

27. $[.4633, .1683, .3684]$ **29.** $[.4872, .2583, .2545]$

31. $A^2 = \begin{bmatrix} .23 & .21 & .24 & .17 & .15 \\ .26 & .18 & .26 & .16 & .14 \\ .23 & .18 & .24 & .19 & .16 \\ .19 & .19 & .27 & .18 & .17 \\ .17 & .2 & .26 & .19 & .18 \end{bmatrix}$

$A^3 = \begin{bmatrix} .226 & .192 & .249 & .177 & .156 \\ .222 & .196 & .252 & .174 & .156 \\ .219 & .189 & .256 & .177 & .159 \\ .213 & .192 & .252 & .181 & .162 \\ .213 & .189 & .252 & .183 & .163 \end{bmatrix}$

$A^4 = \begin{bmatrix} .2205 & .1916 & .2523 & .1774 & .1582 \\ .2206 & .1922 & .2512 & .1778 & .1582 \\ .2182 & .1920 & .2525 & .1781 & .1592 \\ .2183 & .1909 & .2526 & .1787 & .1595 \\ .2176 & .1906 & .2533 & .1787 & .1598 \end{bmatrix}$

$A^5 = \begin{bmatrix} .21932 & .19167 & .25227 & .17795 & .15879 \\ .21956 & .19152 & .25226 & .17794 & .15872 \\ .21905 & .19152 & .25227 & .17818 & .15898 \\ .21880 & .19144 & .25251 & .17817 & .15908 \\ .21857 & .19148 & .25253 & .17824 & .15918 \end{bmatrix}$; .17794

33. (a) $\begin{bmatrix} .9 & .10 \\ .3 & .70 \end{bmatrix}$ **(b)** $[.51, .49]$ **(c)** $[.75, .25]$

35. $[.802, .198]$ **37.** $\begin{bmatrix} \frac{1}{4}, \frac{1}{2}, \frac{1}{4} \end{bmatrix}$ **39. (a)** $[.576, .421, .004]$

(b) $[.473, .526, .002]$ **41. (a)** $[42{,}500 \quad 5000 \quad 2500]$
(b) $[37{,}125 \quad 8750 \quad 4125]$ **(c)** $[33{,}281 \quad 11{,}513 \quad 5206]$

(d) $[.475 \quad .373 \quad .152]$ **43. (a)** .157 **(b)** .494
45. (a) $\begin{array}{c} \\ 0 \\ 1 \\ 2 \end{array} \begin{array}{ccc} 0 & 1 & 2 \\ \left[.4 \right. & .3 & .3 \\ .4 & .3 & .3 \\ \left. 0 \right. & .5 & .5 \end{array}$ **(b)** $\begin{array}{c} \\ 0 \\ 1 \\ 2 \end{array} \begin{array}{ccc} 0 & 1 & 2 \\ \left[.28 \right. & .36 & .36 \\ .28 & .36 & .36 \\ \left. .2 \right. & .4 & .4 \end{array}$
(c) .36 **47.** $[0 \quad 0 \quad .102273 \quad .897727]$

Section 9.6 (Page 588)

1. (a) Coast **(b)** Highway **(c)** Highway; $38,000 **(d)** Coast
3. (a) Do not upgrade. **(b)** Upgrade. **(c)** Do not upgrade;
$10,060.

5. (a)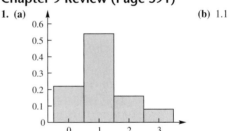

	Fails	Doesn't Fail
Overhaul	−$8600	−$2600
Don't Overhaul	−$6000	$0

(b) Don't overhaul the machine.

7. (a)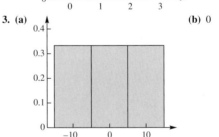

	No Rain	Rain
Rent tent	$2500	$1500
Do not rent tent	$3000	$0

(b) Rent tent because expected value is $2100.
9. Environment, 15.3

Chapter 9 Review (Page 591)

1. (a)

[histogram: values approx 0.22, 0.54, 0.16, 0.08 over x = 0,1,2,3]

(b) 1.1

3. (a)

[histogram: three bars of height ≈ 0.34 over −10, 0, 10]

(b) 0

5. 2.7382

7. (a)

x	0	1	2	3
$P(x)$	.292	.525	.175	.008

(b) .889
9. Under, $E(x) = -33$; exactly 7, $E(x) = -$1.00$; over,
$E(x) = -$.33$ **11.** 1.25 **13.** 40,320 **15.** 220
17. 427,518,000 **19. (a)** 14,905,800 **(b)** 14,905,800
21. Answers vary. **23.** .059 **25.** .995 **27.** .018

29. .218 **31. (a)** $1, n, \frac{n(n-1)}{2}, 1$

(b) $_nC_0 + {}_nC_1 + {}_nC_2 + \cdots + {}_nC_n$ **(c)** Answers vary.
33. .956 **35.** 4.68
37. (a)

x	0	1	2	3	4	5
$P(x)$	.4437	.3915	.1382	.0244	.0022	.0001

(b) .7504 **39.** No **41.** Yes **43. (a)** $[.1515, .5635, .2850]$
(b) $[.1526, .5183, .3290]$ **(c)** $[.1509, .4697, .3795]$
45. (a) Active learning **(b)** Active learning **(c)** Lecture, 17.5
(d) Active learning, 48 **47. (c)**

Case 9 Exercises (Page 596)

1. $+.2031$

3.

x	$P(x)$
0	.30832
1	.43273
2	.21264
3	.04325
4	.00306

5. $+.1947$

CHAPTER 10

Section 10.1 (Page 604)

1. (a) and (b)

Interval	Frequency
14–17	2
18–21	11
22–25	12
26–29	11
30–33	7
34–37	5
38–41	1
42–45	1

(c) and (d)

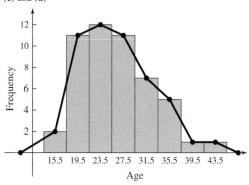

3. (a) and (b)

Interval	Frequency
0–4	1
5–9	4
10–14	4
15–19	3
20–24	5
25–29	8
30–34	9
35–39	8
40–44	3
45–49	5

(c) and (d)

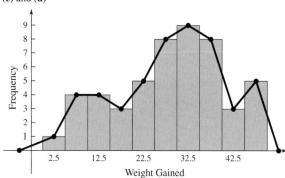

5.

Interval	Frequency
0–24	6
25–49	8
50–74	2
75–99	5
100–124	2
125–149	2
150–174	3
175–199	1
200–224	0
225–249	1

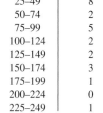

7.

Interval	Frequency
0–49	1
50–99	10
100–149	6
150–199	5
200–249	3
250–299	1
300–349	1
350–399	1
400–449	1
450–499	0
500–549	1

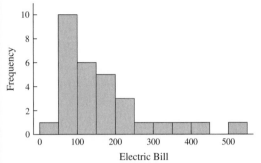

9.
Interval	Frequency
40–44	1
45–49	2
50–54	6
55–59	9
60–64	6
65–69	4
70–74	2

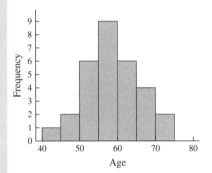

11.
Stem	Leaves
1	55889
2	00000011223444444
2	55566677788899
3	00112334
3	55678
4	4

Units: 4|4 = 44 years

13.
Stem	Leaves
0	0
0	5578
1	0013
1	569
2	00022
2	55556889
3	000112223
3	55555679
4	012
4	55799

Units: 4|9 = 49 pounds

15.
Stem	Leaves
0	11122233344
0	555558889
1	0003
1	56678
2	3

Units: 2|3 = 230 thousand

17.
Stem	Leaves
0	3
0	5556778889
1	011223
1	56899
2	003
2	5
3	1
3	7
4	0
4	
5	2

Units: 5|2 = 520 dollars

19.
Stem	Leaves
7	99
8	000011122333444
8	55666667777777888889999999
9	000001111

Units: 9|1 = 91%

21. Uniform   **23.** Left skewed   **25.** Right skewed
27. (a) Normal (b) 3 (c) 40s   **29.** (a) Right skewed
(b) 8 (c) 5

Section 10.2 (Page 614)

1. $27,955   **3.** 4.8   **5.** 10.3   **7.** 21.2   **9.** 14.8
11. $33,679   **13.** 98.5   **15.** 2   **17.** 65, 71   **19.** No mode
21. Answers vary.   **23.** $\bar{x}$ = 3150 grams, 3000–3499
25. (a) 57.5 (b) 60.5 (c) 37   **27.** (a) $435.333 million
(b) $427 million   **29.** (a) $5310.78 million; $4684.9 million
(b) 2004   **31.** $\bar{x}$ = 49.6, median = 48.5   **33.** right skewed,
median = $175   **35.** Right skewed, median = 13%

Section 10.3 (Page 624)

1. Answers vary.   **3.** 12; 4.8   **5.** 1731; 728.6   **7.** 1061;
430.8   **9.** 336; 132.7   **11.** 45.2   **13.** $\bar{x}$ = 5.0876, s = .1087
15. $\frac{3}{4}$ **17.** $\frac{5}{9}$ **19.** 93.75%   **21.** 11.1%
23. $\bar{x}$ = $252.8 million; s = $20.7 million
25. $\bar{x}$ = $1449.3 million; s = $76.7 million
27. (a) s^2 = 14.8, s = 3.8 (b) 10   **29.** (a) $\bar{x}$ = 127.71 days,
s = 30.16 days (b) All (c) Answers vary.
31. (a) $\frac{1}{3}$, 2, $-\frac{1}{3}$, 0, $\frac{5}{3}$, $\frac{7}{3}$, 1, $\frac{4}{3}$, $\frac{7}{3}$, $\frac{2}{3}$ (b) 2.1, 2.6, 1.5,
2.6, 2.5, .6, 1, 2.1, .6, 1.2 (c) 1.13 (d) 1.68 (e) −2.15, 4.41; the
process is out of control.   **33.** $\bar{x}$ = 80.17, s = 12.2
35. Answers vary.

Section 10.4 (Page 638)

1. The mean   **3.** Answers vary.   **5.** 45.99%   **7.** 16.64%
9. 7.7%   **11.** 47.35%   **13.** 91.20%   **15.** 1.64 or 1.65
17. −1.04   **19.** .5; .5   **21.** .889; .997   **23.** .3821   **25.** .5762
27. .2776   **29.** .0062   **31.** .4452   **33.** .9370   **35.** .0179
37. .0726   **39.** 45.2 mph   **41.** 24.17%   **43.** Answers vary.
45. 665 units   **47.** 190 units   **49.** 15.87%   **51.** .0618
53. .9278
55. Min = 19.6, Q_1 = 20.1, Q_2 = 21.5, Q_3 = 24.1, max = 31.9

Index of Applications

Subject Index

Mathematical Ideas
Eleventh Edition

by Charles D. Miller, Vern E. Heeren, and John Hornsby

INTRODUCTION TO LOGIC

The 1959 Oscar-nominated animated short *Donald in Mathmagic Land* was the first Disney cartoon televised in color. After nearly 50 years, it has proved to be a classic, rendering mathematical topics such as geometry, mathematics in music, games, and nature, and the amazing Golden Section in a way that anyone can understand. In one segment, Donald Duck, dressed as Alice from Lewis Carroll's *Through the Looking Glass*, is attacked by a "none-too-friendly group of chess pieces."

Logic (the subject of this chapter) and chess have been paired for centuries. Most scholars agree that chess dates back at least 1500 years, coming from Northern India and Afghanistan following trade routes through Persia. One does not have to have a high I.Q. to excel at chess. In fact, recent studies indicate that chess strategy might rely more on brain activity not usually associated with general intelligence. Good chess players rely on memory, imagination, determination, and inspiration. They are pattern thinkers that use long-established sets of consequences and probabilities resulting from countless hours of studying and playing. In the end, logic does not necessarily dictate the final outcome of any chess game, for if it did, humans would not stand a chance when playing faceless, number-crunching computers.

Sources: www.imdb.com, Walter A. Smart.

Statements and Quantifiers

Statements • Negations • Symbols • Quantifiers • Sets of Numbers

Gottfried Leibniz (1646–1716) was a wide-ranging philosopher and a universalist who tried to patch up Catholic–Protestant conflicts. He promoted cultural exchange between Europe and the East. Chinese ideograms led him to search for a universal symbolism. He was an early inventor of **symbolic logic.**

Statements   This section introduces the study of *symbolic logic,* which uses letters to represent statements, and symbols for words such as *and, or, not.* One of the main applications of logic is in the study of the *truth value* (that is, the truth or falsity) of statements with many parts. The truth value of these statements depends on the components of which they are comprised.

Many kinds of sentences occur in ordinary language, including factual statements, opinions, commands, and questions. Symbolic logic discusses only the first type of sentence, the kind that involves facts. A **statement** is defined as a declarative sentence that is either true or false, but not both simultaneously. For example, both of the following are statements:

$$\left.\begin{array}{l}\text{Electronic mail provides a means of communication.}\\11+6=12.\end{array}\right\} \text{Statements}$$

Each one is either true or false. However, based on this definition, the following sentences are not statements:

Access the file.

Is this a great time, or what?

Luis Pujols is a better baseball player than Johnny Damon.

This sentence is false.

These sentences cannot be identified as being either true or false. The first sentence is a command, and the second is a question. The third is an opinion. "This sentence is false" is a paradox; if we assume it is true, then it is false, and if we assume it is false, then it is true.

A **compound statement** may be formed by combining two or more statements. The statements making up a compound statement are called **component statements.** Various **logical connectives,** or simply **connectives,** can be used in forming compound statements. Words such as *and, or, not,* and *if . . . then* are examples of connectives. (While a statement such as "Today is not Tuesday" does not consist of two component statements, for convenience it is considered compound, because its truth value is determined by noting the truth value of a different statement, "Today is Tuesday.")

EXAMPLE 1   Deciding Whether a Statement Is Compound

Decide whether each statement is compound.

(a) Shakespeare wrote sonnets, and the poem exhibits iambic pentameter.
(b) You can pay me now, or you can pay me later.
(c) If he said it, then it must be true.
(d) My pistol was made by Smith and Wesson.

SOLUTION

(a) This statement is compound, because it is made up of the component statements "Shakespeare wrote sonnets" and "the poem exhibits iambic pentameter." The connective is *and.*

(b) The connective here is *or*. The statement is compound.

(c) The connective here is *if . . . then,* discussed in more detail in a later section. The statement is compound.

(d) While the word "and" is used in this statement, it is not used as a *logical* connective, because it is part of the name of the manufacturer. The statement is not compound. ▨

Negations　The sentence "Greg Chustz has a red truck" is a statement; the **negation** of this statement is "Greg Chustz does not have a red truck." The negation of a true statement is false, and the negation of a false statement is true.

EXAMPLE 2　Forming Negations

Form the negation of each statement.

(a) That state has a governor.　　(b) The sun is not a star.

SOLUTION

(a) To negate this statement, we introduce *not* into the sentence: "That state does not have a governor."

(b) The negation is "The sun is a star." ▨

One way to detect incorrect negations is to check truth values. A negation must have the opposite truth value from the original statement.

The next example uses some of the inequality symbols in Table 1.

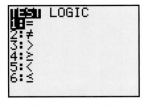

The TEST menu of the TI-83/84 Plus calculator allows the user to test the truth or falsity of statements involving $=$, $\neq$, $>$, $\geq$, $<$, and $\leq$. If a statement is true, it returns a 1; if false, it returns a 0.

TABLE 1

Symbolism	Meaning	Examples	
$a < b$	a is less than b	$4 < 9$	$\frac{1}{2} < \frac{3}{4}$
$a > b$	a is greater than b	$6 > 2$	$-5 > -11$
$a \leq b$	a is less than or equal to b	$8 \leq 10$	$3 \leq 3$
$a \geq b$	a is greater than or equal to b	$-2 \geq -3$	$-5 \geq -5$

EXAMPLE 3　Negating Inequalities

Give a negation of each inequality. Do *not* use a slash symbol.

(a) $p < 9$　　(b) $7x + 11y \geq 77$

SOLUTION

(a) The negation of "p is less than 9" is "p is *not* less than 9." Because we cannot use "not," which would require writing $p \not< 9$, phrase the negation as "p is greater than or equal to 9," or $p \geq 9$.

(b) The negation, with no slash, is $7x + 11y < 77$. ▨

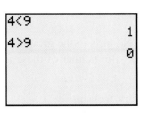

$4 < 9$ is true, as indicated by the 1.
$4 > 9$ is false, as indicated by the 0.

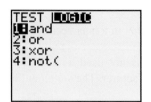

The LOGIC menu of the TI-83/84 Plus calculator allows the user to test truth or falsity of statements involving *and, or, exclusive or* (see Exercise 77 in the next section), and *not*.

Symbols

To simplify work with logic, we use symbols. Statements are represented with letters, such as *p, q,* or *r,* while several symbols for connectives are shown in Table 2. The table also names the type of statement having the given connective.

TABLE 2

Connective	Symbol	Type of Statement
and	$\wedge$	Conjunction
or	$\vee$	Disjunction
not	$\sim$	Negation

The symbol $\sim$ represents the connective *not.* If *p* represents the statement "George W. Bush was president in 2005" then $\sim p$ represents "George W. Bush was not president in 2005."

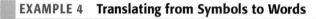

EXAMPLE 4 Translating from Symbols to Words

Let *p* represent "It is 80° today," and let *q* represent "It is Tuesday." Write each symbolic statement in words.

(a) $p \vee q$ **(b)** $\sim p \wedge q$ **(c)** $\sim(p \vee q)$ **(d)** $\sim(p \wedge q)$

SOLUTION

(a) From the table, $\vee$ symbolizes *or*; thus, $p \vee q$ represents

It is 80° today or it is Tuesday.

(b) It is not 80° today and it is Tuesday.
(c) It is not the case that it is 80° today or it is Tuesday.
(d) It is not the case that it is 80° today and it is Tuesday.

The statement in Example 4(c) usually is translated as "Neither *p* nor *q.*"

Aristotle, the first to systematize the logic we use in everyday life, appears above in a detail from the painting *The School of Athens,* by Raphael. He is shown debating a point with his teacher **Plato.**

Quantifiers

The words *all, each, every,* and *no(ne)* are called **universal quantifiers,** while words and phrases such as *some, there exists,* and *(for) at least one* are called **existential quantifiers.** Quantifiers are used extensively in mathematics to indicate *how many* cases of a particular situation exist. Be careful when forming the negation of a statement involving quantifiers.

The negation of a statement must be false if the given statement is true and must be true if the given statement is false, in all possible cases. Consider the statement

All girls in the group are named Mary.

Many people would write the negation of this statement as "No girls in the group are named Mary" or "All girls in the group are not named Mary." But neither of these is correct. To see why, look at the three groups below:

Group I: Mary Lynn Brumfield, Mary Smith, Mary Jackson

Group II: Mary Johnson, Lynne Olinde, Margaret Westmoreland

Group III: Donna Garbarino, Paula Story, Rhonda Alessi, Kim Falgout.

These groups contain all possibilities that need to be considered. In Group I, *all* girls are named Mary; in Group II, *some* girls are named Mary (and some are not); in Group III, *no* girls are named Mary. Look at the truth values in Table 3 and keep in mind that "some" means "at least one (and possibly all)."

TABLE 3 Truth Value as Applied to:

	Group I	Group II	Group III
(1) All girls in the group are named Mary. (Given)	T	F	F
(2) No girls in the group are named Mary. (Possible negation)	F	F	T
(3) All girls in the group are not named Mary. (Possible negation)	F	F	T
(4) Some girls in the group are not named Mary. (Possible negation)	F	T	T

The negation of the given statement (1) must have opposite truth values in *all* cases. It can be seen that statements (2) and (3) do not satisfy this condition (for Group II), but statement (4) does. It may be concluded that the correct negation for "All girls in the group are named Mary" is "Some girls in the group are not named Mary." Other ways of stating the negation are

Not all girls in the group are named Mary.

It is not the case that all girls in the group are named Mary.

At least one girl in the group is not named Mary.

Table 4 can be used to generalize the method of finding the negation of a statement involving quantifiers.

TABLE 4 Negations of Quantified Statements

Statement	Negation
All do.	Some do not. (Equivalently: Not all do.)
Some do.	None do. (Equivalently: All do not.)

The negation of the negation of a statement is simply the statement itself. For instance, the negations of the statements in the Negation column are simply the corresponding original statements in the Statement column. As an example, the negation of "Some do not" is "All do."

EXAMPLE 5 Forming Negations of Quantified Statements

Form the negation of each statement.

(a) Some cats have fleas.   **(b)** Some cats do not have fleas.

(c) No cats have fleas.

SOLUTION

(a) Because *some* means "at least one," the statement "Some cats have fleas" is really the same as "At least one cat has fleas." The negation of this is "No cat has fleas."

(b) The statement "Some cats do not have fleas" claims that at least one cat, somewhere, does not have fleas. The negation of this is "All cats have fleas."

(c) The negation is "Some cats have fleas." ⟵   *Avoid the incorrect answer "All cats have fleas."* ◼

Sets of Numbers
Earlier we introduced sets of numbers that are studied in algebra, and they are repeated here.

The 1997 film *Smilla's Sense of Snow* stars Julia Ormond as a brilliant young scientist who has been displaced from her beloved native Greenland. She has a passion for snow and mathematics. In a conversation, she speaks of her love of **numbers:**

To me, the number system is like human life. First you have the natural numbers, the ones that are whole and positive, like the numbers of a small child. Consciousness expands and a child discovers longing. Do you know the mathematical expression for longing? Negative numbers, the formalization of the feeling that you're missing something. Then the child discovers the in-between spaces, between stones, between people, between numbers, and that produces fractions. But it's like a kind of madness, because it doesn't even stop there. It never stops. There are numbers that we can't even begin to comprehend. Mathematics is a vast, open landscape. You head towards the horizon which is always receding, like Greenland.

Sets of Numbers

Natural or Counting numbers $\{1, 2, 3, 4, \ldots\}$

Whole numbers $\{0, 1, 2, 3, 4, \ldots\}$

Integers $\{\ldots, -3, -2, -1, 0, 1, 2, 3, \ldots\}$

Rational numbers $\left\{\frac{p}{q} \mid p \text{ and } q \text{ are integers, and } q \neq 0\right\}$
(Some examples of rational numbers are $\frac{3}{5}$, $-\frac{7}{5}$, 5, and 0. Any rational number may be expressed as a terminating decimal number, such as .25 or a repeating decimal number, such as .666. . . .)

Real numbers $\{x \mid x \text{ is a number that can be written as a decimal}\}$

Irrational numbers $\{x \mid x \text{ is a real number and } x \text{ cannot be written as a quotient of integers}\}$
(Some examples of irrational numbers are $\sqrt{2}$, $\sqrt[3]{4}$, and π. Decimal representations of irrational numbers never terminate and never repeat.)

EXAMPLE 6   Deciding Whether Quantified Statements Are True or False

Decide whether each of the following statements about sets of numbers involving a quantifier is *true* or *false*.

(a) There exists a whole number that is not a natural number.
(b) Every integer is a natural number.
(c) Every natural number is a rational number.
(d) There exists an irrational number that is not real.

SOLUTION

(a) Because there is such a whole number (it is 0), this statement is true.

(b) This statement is false, because we can find at least one integer that is not a natural number. For example, -1 is an integer but is not a natural number.

(c) Because every natural number can be written as a fraction with denominator 1, this statement is true.

(d) In order to be an irrational number, a number must first be real. Therefore, because we cannot give an irrational number that is not real, this statement is false. (Had we been able to find at least one, the statement would have then been true.) ◼

3.1 EXERCISES

Decide whether each is a statement or is not a statement.

1. September 11, 2001, was a Tuesday.

2. The ZIP code for Manistee, MI, is 49660.

3. Listen, my children, and you shall hear of the midnight ride of Paul Revere.

4. Yield to oncoming traffic.

5. $5 + 8 \neq 13$ and $4 - 3 = 12$

6. $5 + 8 \neq 12$ or $4 - 3 = 5$

7. Some numbers are negative.

8. James Garfield was president of the United States in 1881.

9. Accidents are the main cause of deaths of children under the age of 7.

10. *Shrek 2* was the top-grossing movie of 2004.

11. Where are you going today?

12. Behave yourself and sit down.

13. Kevin "Catfish" McCarthy once took a prolonged continuous shower for 340 hours, 40 minutes.

14. One gallon of milk weighs more than 4 pounds.

Decide whether each statement is compound.

15. I read the *Arizona Republic*, and I read the *Sacramento Bee*.

16. My brother got married in Amsterdam.

17. Tomorrow is Wednesday.

18. Mamie Zwettler is younger than 18 years of age, and so is her friend Emma Lister.

19. Jay Beckenstein's wife loves Ben and Jerry's ice cream.

20. The sign on the back of the car read "Alaska or bust!"

21. If Jane Fleming sells her quota, then Pam Snow will be happy.

22. If Tom is a politician, then Jack is a crook.

Write a negation for each statement.

23. Her aunt's name is Hildegard.

24. The flowers are to be watered.

25. Every dog has its day.

26. No rain fell in southern California today.

27. Some books are longer than this book.

28. All students present will get another chance.

29. No computer repairman can play poker.

30. Some people have all the luck.

31. Everybody loves somebody sometime.

32. Everyone loves a winner.

Give a negation of each inequality. Do not use a slash symbol.

33. $x > 12$

34. $x < -6$

35. $x \geq 5$

36. $x \leq 19$

37. Try to negate the sentence "The exact number of words in this sentence is ten" and see what happens. Explain the problem that arises.

38. Explain why the negation of "$x > 5$" is not "$x < 5$."

Let p represent the statement "She has green eyes" and let q represent the statement "He is 56 years old." Translate each symbolic compound statement into words.

39. $\sim p$

40. $\sim q$

41. $p \wedge q$

42. $p \vee q$

43. $\sim p \vee q$

44. $p \wedge \sim q$

45. $\sim p \vee \sim q$

46. $\sim p \wedge \sim q$

47. $\sim (\sim p \wedge q)$

48. $\sim (p \vee \sim q)$

Let p represent the statement "Chris collects DVDs" and let q represent the statement "Jack is an English major." Convert each compound statement into symbols.

49. Chris collects DVDs and Jack is not an English major.

50. Chris does not collect DVDs or Jack is not an English major.

51. Chris does not collect DVDs or Jack is an English major.

52. Jack is an English major and Chris does not collect DVDs.

53. Neither Chris collects DVDs nor Jack is an English major.

54. Either Jack is an English major or Chris collects DVDs, and it is not the case that both Jack is an English major and Chris collects DVDs.

55. Incorrect use of quantifiers often is heard in everyday language. Suppose you hear that a local electronics chain is having a 40% off sale, and the radio advertisement states "All items are not available in all stores." Do you think that, literally translated, the ad really means what it says? What do you think is really meant? Explain your answer.

56. Repeat Exercise 55 for the following: "All people don't have the time to devote to maintaining their vehicles properly."

Refer to the groups of art labeled A, B, *and* C, *and identify by letter the group or groups that are satisfied by the given statements involving quantifiers.*

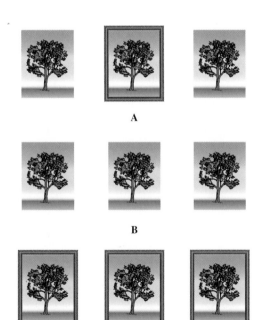

A

B

C

57. All pictures have frames.

58. No picture has a frame.

59. At least one picture does not have a frame.

60. Not every picture has a frame.

61. At least one picture has a frame.

62. No picture does not have a frame.

63. All pictures do not have frames.

64. Not every picture does not have a frame.

Decide whether each statement in Exercises 65–74 involving a quantifier is true *or* false.

65. Every whole number is an integer.

66. Every natural number is an integer.

67. There exists a rational number that is not an integer.

68. There exists an integer that is not a natural number.

69. All rational numbers are real numbers.

70. All irrational numbers are real numbers.

71. Some rational numbers are not integers.

72. Some whole numbers are not rational numbers.

73. Each whole number is a positive number.

74. Each rational number is a positive number.

75. Explain the difference between the following statements:

All students did not pass the test.

Not all students passed the test.

76. The statement "For some real number x, $x^2 \geq 0$" is true. However, your friend does not understand why, because he claims that $x^2 \geq 0$ for *all* real numbers x (and not *some*). How would you explain his misconception to him?

77. Write the following statement using "every": There is no one here who has not done that at one time or another.

78. Only one of the following statements is true. Which one is it?
A. For some real number x, $x \not< 0$.
B. For all real numbers x, $x^3 > 0$.
C. For all real numbers x less than 0, x^2 is also less than 0.
D. For some real number x, $x^2 < 0$.

Truth Tables and Equivalent Statements

**Conjunctions • Disjunctions • Negations • Mathematical Statements
• Truth Tables • Alternative Method for Constructing Truth Tables
• Equivalent Statements and De Morgan's Laws**

Conjunctions   The truth values of component statements are used to find the truth values of compound statements. To begin, let us decide on the truth values of the **conjunction** *p and q*, symbolized $p \wedge q$. In everyday language, the connective *and* implies the idea of "both." The statement

Monday immediately follows Sunday and March immediately follows February

is true, because each component statement is true. On the other hand, the statement

Monday immediately follows Sunday and March immediately follows January

is false, even though part of the statement (Monday immediately follows Sunday) is true. For the conjunction $p \wedge q$ to be true, both *p* and *q* must be true. This result is summarized by a table, called a **truth table,** which shows all four of the possible combinations of truth values for the conjunction *p and q*. The truth table for *conjunction* is shown here.

Truth Table for the Conjunction *p and q*		
	p and q	
p	*q*	$p \wedge q$
T	T	T
T	F	F
F	T	F
F	F	F

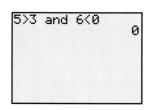

The calculator returns a "0" for
$5 > 3$ *and* $6 < 0$, indicating that
the statement is false.

EXAMPLE 1   Finding the Truth Value of a Conjunction

Let *p* represent "$5 > 3$" and let *q* represent "$6 < 0$." Find the truth value of $p \wedge q$.

SOLUTION

Here *p* is true and *q* is false. Looking in the second row of the conjunction truth table shows that $p \wedge q$ is false. ∎

In some cases, the logical connective *but* is used in compound statements:

He wants to go to the mountains but she wants to go to the beach.

Here, *but* is used in place of *and* to give a different sort of emphasis to the statement. In such a case, we consider the statement as we would consider the conjunction using the word *and*. The truth table for the conjunction, given above, would apply.

Disjunctions   In ordinary language, the word *or* can be ambiguous. The expression "this or that" can mean either "this or that or both," or "this or that but not both." For example, the statement

I will paint the wall or I will paint the ceiling

probably has the following meaning: "I will paint the wall or I will paint the ceiling or I will paint both." On the other hand, the statement

I will drive the Saturn or the BMW to the store

probably means "I will drive the Saturn, or I will drive the BMW, but I will not drive both."

The symbol $\vee$ normally represents the first *or* described. That is,

$p \vee q$ means   "*p* or *q* or both."

With this meaning of *or*, $p \vee q$ is called the *inclusive disjunction*, or just the **disjunction** of *p* and *q*. In everyday language, the disjunction implies the idea of "either." For example, the disjunction

I have a quarter or I have a dime

is true whenever I have either a quarter, a dime, or both. The only way this disjunction could be false would be if I had neither coin. A disjunction is false only if both component statements are false. The truth table for *disjunction* follows.

```
5>3 or 6<0
                    1
```

The calculator returns a "1" for $5 > 3$ *or* $6 < 0$, indicating that the statement is true.

Truth Table for the Disjunction *p* or *q*

	p or *q*	
p	*q*	*p* ∨ *q*
T	T	T
T	F	T
F	T	T
F	F	F

EXAMPLE 2   Finding the Truth Value of a Disjunction

Let *p* represent "$5 > 3$" and let *q* represent "$6 < 0$." Find the truth value of $p \vee q$.

SOLUTION

Here, as in Example 1, *p* is true and *q* is false. The second row of the disjunction truth table shows that $p \vee q$ is true.   ▪

TABLE 5

Statement	Reason That It Is True
$8 \geq 8$	$8 = 8$
$3 \geq 1$	$3 > 1$
$-5 \leq -3$	$-5 < -3$
$-4 \leq -4$	$-4 = -4$

The symbol $\geq$ is read "is greater than or equal to," while $\leq$ is read "is less than or equal to." If *a* and *b* are real numbers, then $a \leq b$ is true if $a < b$ or $a = b$. Table 5 in the margin shows several statements and the reasons they are true.

Negations The **negation** of a statement p, symbolized $\sim p$, must have the opposite truth value from the statement p itself. This leads to the truth table for the negation, shown here.

Truth Table for the Negation not p

	not p
p	$\sim p$
T	F
F	T

EXAMPLE 3 Finding the Truth Value of a Compound Statement

Suppose p is false, q is true, and r is false. What is the truth value of the compound statement $\sim p \wedge (q \vee \sim r)$?

SOLUTION

Here parentheses are used to group q and $\sim r$ together. Work first inside the parentheses. Because r is false, $\sim r$ will be true. Because $\sim r$ is true and q is true, find the truth value of $q \vee \sim r$ by looking in the first row of the *or* truth table. This row gives the result T. Because p is false, $\sim p$ is true, and the final truth value of $\sim p \wedge (q \vee \sim r)$ is found in the top row of the *and* truth table. From the *and* truth table, when $\sim p$ is true, and $q \vee \sim r$ is true, the statement $\sim p \wedge (q \vee \sim r)$ is true.

The preceding paragraph may be interpreted using a short-cut symbolic method. This method involves replacing the statements with their truth values, letting T represent a true statement and F represent a false statement:

$$\sim p \wedge (q \vee \sim r)$$
$$\sim F \wedge (T \vee \sim F)$$

Work within parentheses first. → $\text{T} \wedge (\text{T} \vee \text{T})$ $\sim$F gives T.

$\text{T} \wedge \text{T}$ T $\vee$ T gives T.

T.   T $\wedge$ T gives T.

The T in the final row indicates that the compound statement is true. ∎

Mathematical Statements

We can use truth tables to determine the truth values of compound mathematical statements.

EXAMPLE 4 Deciding Whether a Compound Mathematical Statement Is True or False

Let p represent the statement $3 > 2$, q represent $5 < 4$, and r represent $3 < 8$. Decide whether each statement is *true* or *false*.

(a) $\sim p \wedge \sim q$ **(b)** $\sim (p \wedge q)$ **(c)** $(\sim p \wedge r) \vee (\sim q \wedge \sim p)$

```
not(3>2) and not
(5<4)
                0
not((3>2) and (5
<4))
                1
```

Example 4(a) explains why $\sim (3 > 2) \wedge [\sim (5 < 4)]$ is false. The calculator returns a 0. For a true statement such as $\sim [(3 > 2) \wedge (5 < 4)]$, it returns a 1.

SOLUTION

(a) Because p is true, $\sim p$ is false. By the *and* truth table, if one part of an "and" statement is false, the entire statement is false. This makes $\sim p \wedge \sim q$ false.

(b) For $\sim(p \wedge q)$, first work within the parentheses. Because p is true and q is false, $p \wedge q$ is false by the *and* truth table. Next, apply the negation. The negation of a false statement is true, making $\sim(p \wedge q)$ a true statement.

(c) Here p is true, q is false, and r is true. This makes $\sim p$ false and $\sim q$ true. By the *and* truth table, $\sim p \wedge r$ is false, and $\sim q \wedge \sim p$ is also false. Finally,

$$(\sim p \wedge r) \vee (\sim q \wedge \sim p)$$
$$\downarrow \qquad\qquad \downarrow$$
$$\text{F} \quad \vee \quad \text{F},$$

which is false by the *or* truth table. (Alternatively, see Example 8(b).) ■

For Further Thought

Beauty or the Beast?

Raymond Smullyan is one of today's foremost writers of logic puzzles. This multitalented professor of mathematics and philosophy at City University of New York has written several books on recreational logic, including *The Lady or the Tiger?, What Is the Name of This Book?,* and *Alice in Puzzleland.* The title of the first of these is taken from the classic Frank Stockton short story, in which a prisoner must make a choice between two doors: behind one is a beautiful lady, and behind the other is a hungry tiger.

For Group Discussion or Individual Investigation

Smullyan proposes the following: What if each door has a sign, and the man knows that only one sign is true?

The sign on Door 1 reads:

> IN THIS ROOM THERE IS A LADY AND IN THE OTHER ROOM THERE IS A TIGER.

The sign on Door 2 reads:

> IN ONE OF THESE ROOMS THERE IS A LADY AND IN ONE OF THESE ROOMS THERE IS A TIGER.

With this information, the man is able to choose the correct door. Can you? (The answer is on page 110.)

When a quantifier is used with a conjunction or a disjunction, we must be careful in determining the truth value, as shown in the following example.

EXAMPLE 5 Deciding Whether a Quantified Mathematical Statement Is True or False

Decide whether each statement is *true* or *false.*

(a) For some real number x, $x < 5$ and $x > 2$.

(b) For every real number x, $x > 0$ or $x < 1$.

(c) For all real numbers x, $x^2 > 0$.

SOLUTION

(a) Replacing x with 3 (as an example) gives $3 < 5$ and $3 > 2$. Because both $3 < 5$ and $3 > 2$ are true statements, the given statement is true by the *and* truth table. (Remember: *some* means "at least one.")

(b) No matter which real number might be tried as a replacement for x, at least one of the statements $x > 0$ and $x < 1$ will be true. Because an "or" statement is true if one or both component statements are true, the entire statement as given is true.

(c) Because the quantifier is a universal quantifier, we need only find one case in which the inequality is false to make the entire statement false. Can we find a real number whose square is not positive (that is, not greater than 0)? Yes, we can—0 itself is a real number (and the *only* real number) whose square is not positive. Therefore, this statement is false. ∎

George Boole (1815–1864) grew up in poverty. His father, a London tradesman, gave him his first mathematics lessons and taught him to make optical instruments. Boole was largely self-educated. At 16 he worked in an elementary school and by age 20 had opened his own school. He studied mathematics in his spare time. He died of lung disease at age 49.

Boole's ideas have been used in the design of computers and telephone systems.

Truth Tables

In the preceding examples, the truth value for a given statement was found by going back to the basic truth tables. In the long run, it is easier to first create a complete truth table for the given statement itself. Then final truth values can be read directly from this table.

In this book we use the following standard format for listing the possible truth values in compound statements involving two component statements.

p	q	Compound Statement
T	T	
T	F	
F	T	
F	F	

EXAMPLE 6   Constructing a Truth Table

Consider the statement $(\sim p \wedge q) \vee \sim q$.

(a) Construct a truth table.

(b) Suppose both p and q are true. Find the truth value of this statement.

SOLUTION

(a) Begin by listing all possible combinations of truth values for p and q, as above. Then list the truth values of $\sim p$, which are the opposite of those of p.

p	q	$\sim p$
T	T	F
T	F	F
F	T	T
F	F	T

Use only the "$\sim p$" column and the "q" column, along with the *and* truth table, to find the truth values of $\sim p \wedge q$. List them in a separate column, as shown on the next page.

p	q	$\sim p$	$\sim p \wedge q$
T	T	F	F
T	F	F	F
F	T	T	T
F	F	T	F

Next include a column for $\sim q$.

p	q	$\sim p$	$\sim p \wedge q$	$\sim q$
T	T	F	F	F
T	F	F	F	T
F	T	T	T	F
F	F	T	F	T

Finally, make a column for the entire compound statement. To find the truth values, use *or* to combine $\sim p \wedge q$ with $\sim q$.

p	q	$\sim p$	$\sim p \wedge q$	$\sim q$	$(\sim p \wedge q) \vee \sim q$
T	T	F	F	F	F
T	F	F	F	T	T
F	T	T	T	F	T
F	F	T	F	T	T

(b) Look in the first row of the final truth table above, where both p and q have truth value T. Read across the row to find that the compound statement is false. ▪

EXAMPLE 7 Constructing a Truth Table

Construct the truth table for $p \wedge (\sim p \vee \sim q)$.

SOLUTION

Proceed as shown.

p	q	$\sim p$	$\sim q$	$\sim p \vee \sim q$	$p \wedge (\sim p \vee \sim q)$
T	T	F	F	F	F
T	F	F	T	T	T
F	T	T	F	T	F
F	F	T	T	T	F

▪

Answer to the Problem of *The Lady or the Tiger?*

The lady is behind Door 2. Suppose that the sign on Door 1 is true. Then the sign on Door 2 would also be true, but this is impossible. So the sign on Door 2 must be true, and the sign on Door 1 must be false. Because the sign on Door 1 says the lady is in Room 1, and this is false, the lady must be behind Door 2.

Emilie, Marquise du Châtelet
(1706–1749) participated in the scientific activity of the generation after Newton and Leibniz. Educated in science, music, and literature, she was studying mathematics at the time (1733) she began a long intellectual relationship with the philosopher **François Voltaire** (1694–1778). She and Voltaire competed independently in 1738 for a prize offered by the French Academy on the subject of fire. Although du Châtelet did not win, her dissertation was published by the academy in 1744. During the last four years of her life she translated Newton's *Principia* from Latin into French—the only French translation to date.

If a compound statement involves three component statements p, q, and r, we will use the following standard format in setting up the truth table.

p	q	r	Compound Statement
T	T	T	
T	T	F	
T	F	T	
T	F	F	
F	T	T	
F	T	F	
F	F	T	
F	F	F	

EXAMPLE 8 Constructing a Truth Table

Consider the statement $(\sim p \wedge r) \vee (\sim q \wedge \sim p)$.

(a) Construct a truth table.
(b) Suppose p is true, q is false, and r is true. Find the truth value of this statement.

SOLUTION

(a) This statement has three component statements, p, q, and r. The truth table thus requires eight rows to list all possible combinations of truth values of p, q, and r. The final truth table, however, can be found in much the same way as the ones above.

p	q	r	$\sim p$	$\sim p \wedge r$	$\sim q$	$\sim q \wedge \sim p$	$(\sim p \wedge r) \vee (\sim q \wedge \sim p)$
T	T	T	F	F	F	F	F
T	T	F	F	F	F	F	F
T	F	T	F	F	T	F	F
T	F	F	F	F	T	F	F
F	T	T	T	T	F	F	T
F	T	F	T	F	F	F	F
F	F	T	T	T	T	T	T
F	F	F	T	F	T	T	T

(b) By the third row of the truth table in part (a), the compound statement is false. (This is an alternative method for working part (c) of Example 4.) ∎

PROBLEM-SOLVING HINT   One strategy for problem solving is to notice a pattern and use inductive reasoning. This strategy is applied in the next example.

TABLE 6

Number of Statements	Number of Rows
1	$2 = 2^1$
2	$4 = 2^2$
3	$8 = 2^3$

EXAMPLE 9   Using Inductive Reasoning

If n is a counting number, and a logical statement is composed of n component statements, how many rows will appear in the truth table for the compound statement?

SOLUTION

To answer this question, we examine some of the earlier truth tables in this section. The truth table for the negation has one statement and two rows. The truth tables for the conjunction and the disjunction have two component statements, and each has four rows. The truth table in Example 8(a) has three component statements and eight rows. Summarizing these in Table 6 seen in the margin reveals a pattern encountered earlier. Inductive reasoning leads us to the conjecture that if a logical statement is composed of n component statements, it will have 2^n rows. This can be proved using more advanced concepts. ■

The result of Example 9 is reminiscent of the formula for the number of subsets of a set having n elements.

Number of Rows in a Truth Table

A logical statement having n component statements will have 2^n rows in its truth table.

Alternative Method for Constructing Truth Tables   After making a reasonable number of truth tables, some people prefer the shortcut method shown in Example 10, which repeats Examples 6 and 8.

EXAMPLE 10   Constructing Truth Tables

Construct the truth table for each statement.

(a) $(\sim p \wedge q) \vee \sim q$ **(b)** $(\sim p \wedge r) \vee (\sim q \wedge \sim p)$

SOLUTION

(a) Start by inserting truth values for $\sim p$ and for q.

p	q	$(\sim p$	$\wedge$	$q)$	$\vee$	$\sim q$
T	T	F				T
T	F	F				F
F	T	T				T
F	F	T				F

Next, use the *and* truth table to obtain the truth values for $\sim p \wedge q$.

p	q	$(\sim p$	$\wedge$	$q)$	$\vee$	$\sim q$
T	T	F	F			T
T	F	F	F			F
F	T	T	T			T
F	F	T	F			F

Now disregard the two preliminary columns of truth values for $\sim p$ and for q, and insert truth values for $\sim q$. Finally, use the *or* truth table.

p	q	$(\sim p \wedge q) \vee \sim q$	
T	T	F	F
T	F	F	T
F	T	T	F
F	F	F	T

p	q	$(\sim p \wedge q) \vee \sim q$		
T	T	F	F F
T	F	F	T T
F	T	T	T F
F	F	F	T T

These steps can be summarized as follows.

p	q	$(\sim p$	$\wedge$	$q)$	$\vee$	$\sim p$
T	T	F	F	T	F	F
T	F	F	F	F	T	T
F	T	T	T	T	T	F
F	F	T	F	F	T	T
		①	②	①	④	③

The circled numbers indicate the order in which the various columns of the truth table were found.

(b) Work as follows.

p	q	r	$(\sim p$	$\wedge$	$r)$	$\vee$	$(\sim q$	$\wedge$	$\sim p)$
T	T	T	F	F	T	F	F	F	F
T	T	F	F	F	F	F	F	F	F
T	F	T	F	F	T	F	T	F	F
T	F	F	F	F	F	F	T	F	F
F	T	T	T	T	T	T	F	F	T
F	T	F	T	F	F	F	F	F	T
F	F	T	T	T	T	T	T	T	T
F	F	F	T	F	F	T	T	T	T
			①	②	①	⑤	③	④	③

The circled numbers indicate the order.

Equivalent Statements and De Morgan's Laws

One application of truth tables is to show that two statements are equivalent. Two statements are **equivalent** if they have the same truth value in *every* possible situation. The columns of each truth table that were the last to be completed will be the same for equivalent statements.

EXAMPLE 11 Deciding Whether Two Statements Are Equivalent

Are the following statements equivalent?

$$\sim p \wedge \sim q \quad \text{and} \quad \sim (p \vee q)$$

SOLUTION

Construct a truth table for each statement.

p	q	$\sim p \wedge \sim q$
T	T	F
T	F	F
F	T	F
F	F	T

p	q	$\sim(p \vee q)$
T	T	F
T	F	F
F	T	F
F	F	T

Because the truth values are the same in all cases, as shown in the columns in color, the statements $\sim p \wedge \sim q$ and $\sim(p \vee q)$ are equivalent. Equivalence is written with a three-bar symbol, $\equiv$. Using this symbol, $\sim p \wedge \sim q \equiv \sim(p \vee q)$. ∎

In the same way, the statements $\sim p \vee \sim q$ and $\sim(p \wedge q)$ are equivalent. We call these equivalences *De Morgan's laws*.

De Morgan's Laws

For any statements p and q,

$$\sim(p \vee q) \equiv \sim p \wedge \sim q \quad \text{and} \quad \sim(p \wedge q) \equiv \sim p \vee \sim q.$$

(Compare the logic statements of De Morgan's laws with the set versions.) De Morgan's laws can be used to find the negations of certain compound statements.

EXAMPLE 12   Applying De Morgan's Laws

Find a negation of each statement by applying De Morgan's laws.

(a) I got an A or I got a B.   **(b)** She won't try and he will succeed.
(c) $\sim p \vee (q \wedge \sim p)$

SOLUTION

(a) If p represents "I got an A" and q represents "I got a B," then the compound statement is symbolized $p \vee q$. The negation of $p \vee q$ is $\sim(p \vee q)$; by one of De Morgan's laws, this is equivalent to

$$\sim p \wedge \sim q,$$

or, in words,

> I didn't get an A and I didn't get a B.

This negation is reasonable—the original statement says that I got either an A or a B; the negation says that I didn't get *either* grade.

(b) From one of De Morgan's laws, $\sim(p \wedge q) \equiv \sim p \vee \sim q$, so the negation becomes

> She will try or he won't succeed.

(c) Negate both component statements and change $\vee$ to $\wedge$.

$$\sim[\sim p \vee (q \wedge \sim p)] \equiv p \wedge \sim(q \wedge \sim p)$$

Now apply De Morgan's law again.

$$p \land \sim(q \land \sim p) \equiv p \land (\sim q \lor \sim(\sim p))$$
$$\equiv p \land (\sim q \lor p)$$

A truth table will show that the statements

$$\sim p \lor (q \land \sim p) \quad \text{and} \quad p \land (\sim q \lor p)$$

are negations.

3.2 EXERCISES

Use the concepts introduced in this section to answer Exercises 1–6.

1. If q is false, what must be the truth value of the statement $(p \land \sim q) \land q$?

2. If q is true, what must be the truth value of the statement $q \lor (q \land \sim p)$?

3. If the statement $p \land q$ is true, and p is true, then q must be _____.

4. If the statement $p \lor q$ is false, and p is false, then q must be _____.

5. If $\sim(p \lor q)$ is true, what must be the truth values of the component statements?

6. If $\sim(p \land q)$ is false, what must be the truth values of the component statements?

Let p represent a false statement and let q represent a true statement. Find the truth value of the given compound statement.

7. $\sim p$

8. $\sim q$

9. $p \lor q$

10. $p \land q$

11. $p \lor \sim q$

12. $\sim p \land q$

13. $\sim p \lor \sim q$

14. $p \land \sim q$

15. $\sim(p \land \sim q)$

16. $\sim(\sim p \lor \sim q)$

17. $\sim[\sim p \land (\sim q \lor p)]$

18. $\sim[(\sim p \land \sim q) \lor \sim q]$

19. Is the statement $5 \geq 2$ a conjunction or a disjunction? Why?

20. Why is the statement $7 \geq 3$ true? Why is $9 \geq 9$ true?

Let p represent a true statement, and q and r represent false statements. Find the truth value of the given compound statement.

21. $(p \land r) \lor \sim q$

22. $(q \lor \sim r) \land p$

23. $p \land (q \lor r)$

24. $(\sim p \land q) \lor \sim r$

25. $\sim(p \land q) \land (r \lor \sim q)$

26. $(\sim r \land \sim q) \lor (\sim r \land q)$

27. $\sim[(\sim p \land q) \lor r]$

28. $\sim[r \lor (\sim q \land \sim p)]$

29. $\sim[\sim q \lor (r \land \sim p)]$

30. What is the only possible case in which the statement $(p \land \sim q) \land \sim r$ is true?

Let p represent the statement $15 < 8$, let q represent the statement $9 \not> 4$, and let r represent the statement $18 \leq 18$. Find the truth value of the given compound statement.

31. $p \land r$

32. $p \lor \sim q$

33. $\sim q \lor \sim r$

34. $\sim p \land \sim r$

35. $(p \land q) \lor r$

36. $\sim p \lor (\sim r \lor \sim q)$

37. $(\sim r \land q) \lor \sim p$

38. $\sim(p \lor \sim q) \lor \sim r$

Give the number of rows in the truth table for each compound statement.

39. $p \lor \sim r$

40. $p \land (r \land \sim s)$

41. $(\sim p \land q) \lor (\sim r \lor \sim s) \land r$

42. $[(p \lor q) \land (r \land s)] \land (t \lor \sim p)$

43. $[(\sim p \wedge \sim q) \wedge (\sim r \wedge s \wedge \sim t)] \wedge (\sim u \vee \sim v)$

44. $[(\sim p \wedge \sim q) \vee (\sim r \vee \sim s)]$
$\vee [(\sim m \wedge \sim n) \wedge (u \wedge \sim v)]$

45. If the truth table for a certain compound statement has 128 rows, how many distinct component statements does it have?

46. Is it possible for the truth table of a compound statement to have exactly 54 rows? Why or why not?

Construct a truth table for each compound statement.

47. $\sim p \wedge q$

48. $\sim p \vee \sim q$

49. $\sim (p \wedge q)$

50. $p \vee \sim q$

51. $(q \vee \sim p) \vee \sim q$

52. $(p \wedge \sim q) \wedge p$

53. $\sim q \wedge (\sim p \vee q)$

54. $\sim p \vee (\sim q \wedge \sim p)$

55. $(p \vee \sim q) \wedge (p \wedge q)$

56. $(\sim p \wedge \sim q) \vee (\sim p \vee q)$

57. $(\sim p \wedge q) \wedge r$

58. $r \vee (p \wedge \sim q)$

59. $(\sim p \wedge \sim q) \vee (\sim r \vee \sim p)$

60. $(\sim r \vee \sim p) \wedge (\sim p \vee \sim q)$

61. $\sim (\sim p \wedge \sim q) \vee (\sim r \vee \sim s)$

62. $(\sim r \vee s) \wedge (\sim p \wedge q)$

Use one of De Morgan's laws to write the negation of each statement.

63. You can pay me now or you can pay me later.

64. I am not going or she is going.

65. It is summer and there is no snow.

66. $\frac{1}{2}$ is a positive number and -9 is less than zero.

67. I said yes but she said no.

68. Fellman Chutz tried to sell the wine, but he was unable to do so.

69. $5 - 1 = 4$ and $9 + 12 \neq 7$

70. $3 < 10$ or $7 \neq 2$

71. Dasher or Blitzen will lead Santa's sleigh next Christmas.

72. The lawyer and the client appeared in court.

Identify each statement as true *or* false.

73. For every real number x, $x < 13$ or $x > 6$.

74. For every real number x, $x > 9$ or $x < 9$.

75. For some integer n, $n \geq 4$ and $n \leq 4$.

76. There exists an integer n such that $n > 0$ and $n < 0$.

77. Complete the truth table for *exclusive disjunction*. The symbol $\underline{\vee}$ represents "one or the other is true, but not both."

78. Attorneys sometimes use the phase "and/or." This phrase corresponds to which usage of the word *or*: inclusive or exclusive disjunction?

p	q	$p \underline{\vee} q$
T	T	
T	F	
F	T	
F	F	

Exclusive disjunction

Decide whether each compound statement is true *or* false. *Remember that* $\vee$ *is the* exclusive disjunction; *that is, assume* "either *p* or *q* is true, but not both."

79. $3 + 1 = 4 \vee 2 + 5 = 7$

80. $3 + 1 = 4 \vee 2 + 5 = 10$

81. $3 + 1 = 6 \vee 2 + 5 = 7$

82. $3 + 1 = 12 \vee 2 + 5 = 10$

3.3 | The Conditional and Circuits

Conditionals • Negation of a Conditional • Circuits

K E V I N · C O S T N E R

FIELD OF DREAMS

 In his April 21, 1989, five-star review of *Field of Dreams*, the *Chicago Sun-Times* movie critic Roger Ebert gave an explanation of why the movie has become an American classic.

There is a speech in this movie about baseball that is so simple and true that it is heartbreaking. And the whole attitude toward the players reflects that attitude. Why do they come back from the great beyond and play in this cornfield? Not to make any kind of vast, earthshattering statement, but simply to hit a few and field a few, and remind us of a good and innocent time.

Conditionals

"If you build it, he will come."
          —The Voice in the movie *Field of Dreams*

Ray Kinsella, an Iowa farmer in the movie *Field of Dreams*, heard a voice from the sky. Ray interpreted it as a promise that if he would build a baseball field in his cornfield, then the ghost of Shoeless Joe Jackson (a baseball star in the early days of the twentieth century) would come to play on it. The promise came in the form of a conditional statement. A **conditional** statement is a compound statement that uses the connective *if . . . then.* For example, here are a few conditional statements:

> *If* I read for too long, *then* I get a headache.
>
> *If* looks could kill, *then* I would be dead.
>
> *If* he doesn't get back soon, *then* you should go look for him.

In each of these conditional statements, the component coming after the word *if* gives a condition (but not necessarily the only condition) under which the statement coming after *then* will be true. For example, "If it is over 90°, then I'll go to the mountains" tells one possible condition under which I will go to the mountains—if the temperature is over 90°. The conditional is written with an arrow, so "if *p*, then *q*" is symbolized

$$p \rightarrow q.$$

We read $p \rightarrow q$ as "*p* implies *q*" or "if *p*, then *q*." In the conditional $p \rightarrow q$, the statement *p* is the **antecedent,** while *q* is the **consequent.**

The conditional connective may not always be explicitly stated. That is, it may be "hidden" in an everyday expression. For example, the statement

> Big girls don't cry

can be written in *if . . . then* form as

> If you're a big girl, then you don't cry.

As another example, the statement

> It is difficult to study when you are distracted

can be written

> If you are distracted, then it is difficult to study.

In the quote from the movie *Field of Dreams*, the word "then" is not stated but understood to be there from the context of the statement. In that statement, "you build it" is the antecedent, and "he will come" is the consequent.

$\frac{2}{3}$ $8 > 5$ $\neq$ $|x|$

5.1×10^{-3}

$-2 + 8 = 6$ $\leq$ π

$ax + b = c$ (x, y)

x^2 Δ $y = -3$

The importance of **symbols** was emphasized by the American philosopher-logician **Charles Sanders Peirce** (1839–1914), who asserted the nature of humans as symbol-using or sign-using organisms. Symbolic notation is half of mathematics, Bertrand Russell once said.

The conditional truth table is a little harder to define than the tables in the previous section. To see how to define the conditional truth table, let us analyze a statement made by a politician, Senator Shootie Gosserand:

> If I am elected, then taxes will go down.

As before, there are four possible combinations of truth values for the two component statements. Let p represent "I am elected," and let q represent "Taxes will go down."

As we analyze the four possibilities, it is helpful to think in terms of the following: "Did Senator Gosserand lie?" If she lied, then the conditional statement is considered false; if she did not lie, then the conditional statement is considered true.

Possibility	Elected?	Taxes Go Down?	
1	Yes	Yes	p is T, q is T
2	Yes	No	p is T, q is F
3	No	Yes	p is F, q is T
4	No	No	p is F, q is F

The four possibilities are as follows:

1. In the first case assume that the senator was elected and taxes did go down (p is T, q is T). The senator told the truth, so place T in the first row of the truth table. (We do not claim that taxes went down *because* she was elected; it is possible that she had nothing to do with it at all.)

2. In the second case assume that the senator was elected and taxes did not go down (p is T, q is F). Then the senator did not tell the truth (that is, she lied). So we put F in the second row of the truth table.

3. In the third case assume that the senator was defeated, but taxes went down anyway (p is F, q is T). The senator did not lie; she only promised a tax reduction if she were elected. She said nothing about what would happen if she were not elected. In fact, her campaign promise gives no information about what would happen if she lost. Because we cannot say that the senator lied, place T in the third row of the truth table.

4. In the last case assume that the senator was defeated and taxes did not go down (p is F, q is F). We cannot blame her, because she only promised to reduce taxes if elected. Thus, T goes in the last row of the truth table.

The completed truth table for the conditional is defined as follows.

Truth Table for the Conditional If p, then q

If p, then q		
p	q	$p \rightarrow q$
T	T	T
T	F	F
F	T	T
F	F	T

It must be emphasized that the use of the conditional connective in no way implies a cause-and-effect relationship. Any two statements may have an arrow placed between them to create a compound statement. For example,

If I pass mathematics, then the sun will rise the next day

is true, because the consequent is true. (See the special characteristics following Example 1.) There is, however, no cause-and-effect connection between my passing mathematics and the sun's rising. The sun will rise no matter what grade I get.

EXAMPLE 1 Finding the Truth Value of a Conditional

Given that p, q, and r are all false, find the truth value of the statement

$$(p \rightarrow \sim q) \rightarrow (\sim r \rightarrow q).$$

SOLUTION

Using the short-cut method explained in Example 3 of the previous section, we can replace p, q, and r with F (since each is false) and proceed as before, using the negation and conditional truth tables as necessary.

$$
\begin{array}{rcll}
(p \rightarrow \sim q) & \rightarrow & (\sim r \rightarrow q) & \\
(F \rightarrow \sim F) & \rightarrow & (\sim F \rightarrow F) & \\
(F \rightarrow T) & \rightarrow & (T \rightarrow F) & \text{Use the negation truth table.} \\
T & \rightarrow & F & \text{Use the conditional truth table.} \\
& F &
\end{array}
$$

The statement $(p \rightarrow \sim q) \rightarrow (\sim r \rightarrow q)$ is false when p, q, and r are all false. ■

The following observations come from the truth table for $p \rightarrow q$.

Special Characteristics of Conditional Statements

1. $p \rightarrow q$ is false only when the antecedent is *true* and the consequent is *false*.
2. If the antecedent is *false*, then $p \rightarrow q$ is automatically *true*.
3. If the consequent is *true*, then $p \rightarrow q$ is automatically *true*.

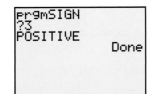

Conditional statements are useful in writing programs. The short program in the first two screens determines whether a number is positive. Notice the lines that begin with *If* and *Then*.

EXAMPLE 2 Determining Whether a Conditional Is True or False

Write *true* or *false* for each statement. Here T represents a true statement, and F represents a false statement.

(a) $T \rightarrow (6 = 3)$ **(b)** $(5 < 2) \rightarrow F$ **(c)** $(3 \neq 2 + 1) \rightarrow T$

SOLUTION

(a) Because the antecedent is true, while the consequent, $6 = 3$, is false, the given statement is false by the first point mentioned above.
(b) The antecedent is false, so the given statement is true by the second observation.
(c) The consequent is true, making the statement true by the third characteristic of conditional statements. ■

Truth tables for compound statements involving conditionals are found using the techniques described in the previous section.

EXAMPLE 3   Constructing Truth Tables

Construct a truth table for each statement.

(a) $(\sim p \rightarrow \sim q) \rightarrow (\sim p \wedge q)$ **(b)** $(p \rightarrow q) \rightarrow (\sim p \vee q)$

SOLUTION

(a) First insert the truth values of $\sim p$ and of $\sim q$. Then find the truth values of $\sim p \rightarrow \sim q$.

p	q	$\sim p$	$\sim q$	$\sim p \rightarrow \sim q$
T	T	F	F	T
T	F	F	T	T
F	T	T	F	F
F	F	T	T	T

Next use $\sim p$ and q to find the truth values of $\sim p \wedge q$.

p	q	$\sim p$	$\sim q$	$\sim p \rightarrow \sim q$	$\sim p \wedge q$
T	T	F	F	T	F
T	F	F	T	T	F
F	T	T	F	F	T
F	F	T	T	T	F

Now find the truth values of $(\sim p \rightarrow \sim q) \rightarrow (\sim p \wedge q)$.

p	q	$\sim p$	$\sim q$	$\sim p \rightarrow \sim q$	$\sim p \wedge q$	$(\sim p \rightarrow \sim q) \rightarrow (\sim p \wedge q)$
T	T	F	F	T	F	F
T	F	F	T	T	F	F
F	T	T	F	F	T	T
F	F	T	T	T	F	F

(b) For $(p \rightarrow q) \rightarrow (\sim p \vee q)$, go through steps similar to the ones above.

p	q	$p \rightarrow q$	$\sim p$	$\sim p \vee q$	$(p \rightarrow q) \rightarrow (\sim p \vee q)$
T	T	T	F	T	T
T	F	F	F	F	T
F	T	T	T	T	T
F	F	T	T	T	T

As the truth table in Example 3(b) shows, the statement $(p \rightarrow q) \rightarrow (\sim p \vee q)$ is always true, no matter what the truth values of the components. Such a statement is called a **tautology.** Other examples of tautologies (as can be checked by forming truth tables) include $p \lor \sim p, p \rightarrow p, (\sim p \lor \sim q) \rightarrow \sim (q \land p)$, and so on. By the way, the truth tables in Example 3 also could have been found by the alternative method shown in the previous section.

Negation of a Conditional Suppose that someone makes the conditional statement

"If it rains, then I take my umbrella."

When will the person have lied to you? The only case in which you would have been misled is when it rains *and* the person does *not* take the umbrella. Letting p represent "it rains" and q represent "I take my umbrella," you might suspect that the symbolic statement

$$p \land \sim q$$

is a candidate for the negation of $p \rightarrow q$. That is,

$$\sim (p \rightarrow q) \equiv p \land \sim q.$$

This is indeed the case, as the next truth table indicates.

p	q	$p \rightarrow q$	$\sim(p \rightarrow q)$	$\sim q$	$p \land \sim q$
T	T	T	F	F	F
T	F	F	T	T	T
F	T	T	F	F	F
F	F	T	F	T	F

$$\equiv$$

Negation of $p \rightarrow q$

The negation of $p \rightarrow q$ is $p \land \sim q$.

Because

$$\sim (p \rightarrow q) \equiv p \land \sim q,$$

by negating each expression we have

$$\sim [\sim (p \rightarrow q)] \equiv \sim (p \land \sim q).$$

The left side of the above equivalence is $p \rightarrow q$, and one of De Morgan's laws can be applied to the right side:

$$p \rightarrow q \equiv \sim p \lor \sim (\sim q)$$
$$p \rightarrow q \equiv \sim p \lor q.$$

This final row indicates that a conditional may be written as a disjunction.

Writing a Conditional as an "or" Statement

$p \rightarrow q$ is equivalent to $\sim p \vee q$.

EXAMPLE 4 Determining Negations

Determine the negation of each statement.

(a) If you build it, he will come. **(b)** All dogs have fleas.

SOLUTION

Do not try to negate a conditional with another conditional.

(a) If b represents "you build it" and q represents "he will come," then the given statement can be symbolized by $b \rightarrow q$. The negation of $b \rightarrow q$, as shown earlier, is $b \wedge \sim q$, so the negation of the statement is

You build it and he will not come.

(b) First, we must restate the given statement in *if . . . then* form:

If it is a dog, then it has fleas.

Based on our earlier discussion, the negation is

It is a dog and it does not have fleas. ▪

As seen in Example 4, the negation of a conditional statement is written as a conjunction.

EXAMPLE 5 Determining Statements Equivalent to Conditionals

Write each conditional as an equivalent statement without using *if . . . then*.

(a) If the Cubs win the pennant, then Gwen will be happy.
(b) If it's Borden's, it's got to be good.

SOLUTION

(a) Because the conditional $p \rightarrow q$ is equivalent to $\sim p \vee q$, let p represent "The Cubs win the pennant" and q represent "Gwen will be happy." Restate the conditional as

The Cubs do not win the pennant or Gwen will be happy.

(b) If p represents "it's Borden's" and if q represents "it's got to be good," the conditional may be restated as

It's not Borden's or it's got to be good. ▪

FIGURE 1

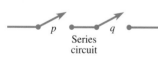

FIGURE 2

Circuits One of the first nonmathematical applications of symbolic logic was seen in the master's thesis of Claude Shannon in 1937. Shannon showed how logic could be used to design electrical circuits. His work was immediately used by computer designers. Then in the developmental stage, computers could be simplified and built for less money using the ideas of Shannon.

To see how Shannon's ideas work, look at the electrical switch shown in Figure 1. We assume that current will flow through this switch when it is closed and not when it is open.

Figure 2 shows two switches connected in *series;* in such a circuit, current will flow only when both switches are closed. Note how closely a series circuit

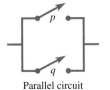

Parallel circuit

FIGURE 3

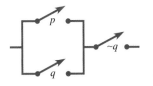

FIGURE 4

corresponds to the conjunction $p \wedge q$. We know that $p \wedge q$ is true only when both p and q are true.

A circuit corresponding to the disjunction $p \vee q$ can be found by drawing a *parallel* circuit, as in Figure 3. Here, current flows if either p *or* q is closed or if both p *and* q are closed.

The circuit in Figure 4 corresponds to the statement $(p \vee q) \wedge \sim q$, which is a compound statement involving both a conjunction and a disjunction.

Simplifying an electrical circuit depends on the idea of equivalent statements from Section 3.2. Recall that two statements are equivalent if they have the same truth table final column. The symbol $\equiv$ is used to indicate that the two statements are equivalent. Some equivalent statements are shown in the following box.

Equivalent Statements Used to Simplify Circuits	
$p \vee (q \wedge r) \equiv (p \vee q) \wedge (p \vee r)$	$p \vee p \equiv p$
$p \wedge (q \vee r) \equiv (p \wedge q) \vee (p \wedge r)$	$p \wedge p \equiv p$
$p \rightarrow q \equiv \sim q \rightarrow \sim p$	$\sim(p \wedge q) \equiv \sim p \vee \sim q$
$p \rightarrow q \equiv \sim p \vee q$	$\sim(p \vee q) \equiv \sim p \wedge \sim q$

If T represents any true statement and F represents any false statement, then

$$p \vee T \equiv T \qquad p \vee \sim p \equiv T$$
$$p \wedge F \equiv F \qquad p \wedge \sim p \equiv F.$$

Circuits can be used as models of compound statements, with a closed switch corresponding to T, while an open switch corresponds to F. The method for simplifying circuits is explained in the following example.

EXAMPLE 6   Simplifying a Circuit

Simplify the circuit of Figure 5.

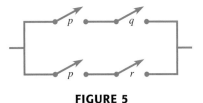

FIGURE 5

SOLUTION

At the top of Figure 5, p and q are connected in series, and at the bottom, p and r are connected in series. These are interpreted as the compound statements $p \wedge q$ and $p \wedge r$, respectively. These two conjunctions are connected in parallel, as indicated by the figure treated as a whole. Write the disjunction of the two conjunctions:

$$(p \wedge q) \vee (p \wedge r).$$

FIGURE 6

(Think of the two switches labeled "*p*" as being controlled by the same lever.) By one of the pairs of equivalent statements in the preceding box,

$$(p \land q) \lor (p \land r) \equiv p \land (q \lor r),$$

which has the circuit of Figure 6. This circuit is logically equivalent to the one in Figure 5, and yet it contains only three switches instead of four—which might well lead to a large savings in manufacturing costs. ■

EXAMPLE 7 Drawing a Circuit for a Conditional Statement

Draw a circuit for $p \to (q \land \sim r)$.

SOLUTION

From the list of equivalent statements in the box, $p \to q$ is equivalent to $\sim p \lor q$. This equivalence gives $p \to (q \land \sim r) \equiv \sim p \lor (q \land \sim r)$, which has the circuit diagram in Figure 7. ■

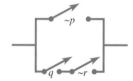

FIGURE 7

3.3 EXERCISES

Rewrite each statement using the if . . . then *connective. Rearrange the wording or add words as necessary.*

1. You can believe it if you see it on the Internet.

2. It must be alive if it is breathing.

3. Garrett Olinde's area code is 225.

4. Lorri Morgan visits Hawaii every summer.

5. All Marines love boot camp.

6. Every picture tells a story.

7. No koalas live in Iowa.

8. No guinea pigs are scholars.

9. An opium eater cannot have self-command.

10. Running Bear loves Little White Dove.

Decide whether each statement is true *or* false.

11. If the consequent of a conditional statement is true, the conditional statement is true.

12. If the antecedent of a conditional statement is false, the conditional statement is true.

13. If p is true, then $\sim p \to (q \lor r)$ is true.

14. If q is true, then $(p \land q) \to q$ is true.

15. The statements "If it flies, then it's a bird" and "It does not fly or it's a bird" are logically equivalent.

16. The negation of "If pigs fly, I'll believe it" is "If pigs don't fly, I won't believe it."

17. Given that $\sim p$ is false and q is false, the conditional $p \to q$ is true.

18. Given that $\sim p$ is true and q is false, the conditional $p \to q$ is true.

19. In a few sentences, explain how to determine the truth value of a conditional statement.

20. Explain why the statement "If $3 = 5$, then $4 = 6$" is true.

Tell whether each conditional is true (T) *or* false (F).

21. $T \rightarrow (6 < 3)$

22. $F \rightarrow (4 \neq 7)$

23. $F \rightarrow (3 \neq 3)$

24. $(6 \geq 6) \rightarrow F$

25. $(4^2 \neq 16) \rightarrow (4 - 4 = 8)$

26. $(4 = 11 - 7) \rightarrow (8 > 0)$

Let s represent "She has a ferret for a pet," *let p represent* "he trains dogs," *and let m represent* "they raise alpacas." *Express each compound statement in words.*

27. $\sim m \rightarrow p$

28. $p \rightarrow \sim m$

29. $s \rightarrow (m \wedge p)$

30. $(s \wedge p) \rightarrow m$

31. $\sim p \rightarrow (\sim m \vee s)$

32. $(\sim s \vee \sim m) \rightarrow \sim p$

Let b represent "I ride my bike," *let r represent* "it rains," *and let p represent* "the concert is cancelled." *Write each compound statement in symbols.*

33. If I ride my bike, then the concert is cancelled.

34. If it rains, then I ride my bike.

35. If the concert is cancelled, then it does not rain.

36. If I do not ride my bike, then it does not rain.

37. The concert is cancelled, and if it rains then I do not ride my bike.

38. I ride my bike, or if the concert is cancelled then it rains.

39. It rains if the concert is cancelled.

40. I'll ride my bike if it doesn't rain.

Find the truth value of each statement. Assume that p and r are false, and q is true.

41. $\sim r \rightarrow q$

42. $\sim p \rightarrow \sim r$

43. $q \rightarrow p$

44. $\sim r \rightarrow p$

45. $p \rightarrow q$

46. $\sim q \rightarrow r$

47. $\sim p \rightarrow (q \wedge r)$

48. $(\sim r \vee p) \rightarrow p$

49. $\sim q \rightarrow (p \wedge r)$

50. $(\sim p \wedge \sim q) \rightarrow (p \wedge \sim r)$

51. $(p \rightarrow \sim q) \rightarrow (\sim p \wedge \sim r)$

52. $(p \rightarrow \sim q) \wedge (p \rightarrow r)$

53. Explain why, if we know that p is true, we also know that

$$[r \vee (p \vee s)] \rightarrow (p \vee q)$$

is true, even if we are not given the truth values of q, r, and s.

54. Construct a true statement involving a conditional, a conjunction, a disjunction, and a negation (not necessarily in that order), that consists of component statements p, q, and r, with all of these component statements false.

Construct a truth table for each statement. Identify any tautologies.

55. $\sim q \rightarrow p$

56. $p \rightarrow \sim q$

57. $(\sim p \rightarrow q) \rightarrow p$

58. $(\sim q \rightarrow \sim p) \rightarrow \sim q$

59. $(p \vee q) \rightarrow (q \vee p)$

60. $(p \wedge q) \rightarrow (p \vee q)$

61. $(\sim p \rightarrow \sim q) \rightarrow (p \wedge q)$

62. $r \rightarrow (p \wedge \sim q)$

63. $[(r \vee p) \wedge \sim q] \rightarrow p$

64. $[(r \wedge p) \wedge (p \wedge q)] \rightarrow p$

65. $(\sim r \rightarrow s) \vee (p \rightarrow \sim q)$

66. $(\sim p \wedge \sim q) \rightarrow (s \rightarrow r)$

67. What is the minimum number of Fs that must appear in the final column of a truth table for us to be assured that the statement is not a tautology?

68. If all truth values in the final column of a truth table are F, how can we easily transform the statement into a tautology?

Write the negation of each statement. Remember that the negation of $p \rightarrow q$ *is* $p \wedge \sim q$.

69. If that is an authentic Persian rug, I'll be surprised.

70. If Ella reaches that note, she will shatter glass.

71. If the English measures are not converted to metric measures, then the spacecraft will crash on the surface of Saturn.

72. If you say "I do," then you'll be happy for the rest of your life.

73. "If you want to be happy for the rest of your life, never make a pretty woman your wife." *Jimmy Soul*

74. If loving you is wrong, I don't want to be right.

Write each statement as an equivalent statement that does not use the if . . . then *connective. Remember that* $p \rightarrow q$ *is equivalent to* $\sim p \vee q$.

75. If you give your plants tender, loving care, they flourish.

76. If the check is in the mail, I'll be surprised.

77. If she doesn't, he will.

78. If I say "black", she says "white."

79. All residents of Oregon City are residents of Oregon.

80. All men were once boys.

Use truth tables to decide which of the pairs of statements are equivalent.

81. $p \rightarrow q$; $\sim p \vee q$

82. $\sim(p \rightarrow q)$; $p \wedge \sim q$

83. $p \rightarrow q$; $\sim q \rightarrow \sim p$

84. $q \rightarrow p$; $\sim p \rightarrow \sim q$

85. $p \rightarrow \sim q$; $\sim p \vee \sim q$

86. $p \rightarrow q$; $q \rightarrow p$

87. $p \wedge \sim q$; $\sim q \rightarrow \sim p$

88. $\sim p \wedge q$; $\sim p \rightarrow q$

89. $q \rightarrow \sim p$; $p \rightarrow \sim q$

90. Explain why the circuit shown will always have exactly one open switch. What does this circuit simplify to?

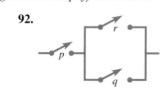

Write a logical statement representing each of the following circuits. Simplify each circuit when possible.

91.

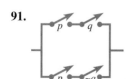

92.

93.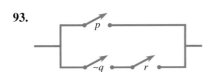

94.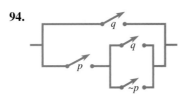

95.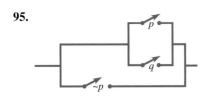

96.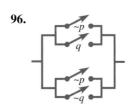

Draw circuits representing the following statements as they are given. Simplify if possible.

97. $p \wedge (q \vee \sim p)$

98. $(\sim p \wedge \sim q) \wedge \sim r$

99. $(p \vee q) \wedge (\sim p \wedge \sim q)$

100. $(\sim q \wedge \sim p) \vee (\sim p \vee q)$

101. $[(p \vee q) \wedge r] \wedge \sim p$

102. $[(\sim p \wedge \sim r) \vee \sim q] \wedge (\sim p \wedge r)$

103. $\sim q \rightarrow (\sim p \rightarrow q)$

104. $\sim p \rightarrow (\sim p \vee \sim q)$

105. Refer to Figures 5 and 6 in Example 6. Suppose the cost of the use of one switch for an hour is $.06. By using the circuit in Figure 6 rather than the circuit in Figure 5, what is the savings for a year of 365 days, assuming that the circuit is in continuous use?

3.4 More on the Conditional

Converse, Inverse, and Contrapositive • Alternative Forms of "If p, then q" • Biconditionals • Summary of Truth Tables

Converse, Inverse, and Contrapositive Many mathematical properties and theorems are stated in *if . . . then* form. Because of their usefulness, we expand our consideration of statements of the form $p \rightarrow q$. Any conditional statement is made up of an antecedent and a consequent. If they are interchanged, negated, or both, a new conditional statement is formed. Suppose that we begin with the given conditional statement

If you stay, then I go,

and interchange the antecedent ("you stay") and the consequent ("I go"). We obtain the new conditional statement

If I go, then you stay.

This new conditional is called the **converse** of the given statement.

Alfred North Whitehead
(1861–1947) and Bertrand Russell worked together on *Principia Mathematica*. During that time, Whitehead was teaching mathematics at Cambridge University and had written *Universal Algebra*. In 1910 he went to the University of London, exploring not only the philosophical basis of science but also the "aims of education" (as he called one of his books). It was as a philosopher that he was invited to Harvard University in 1924. Whitehead died at the age of 86 in Cambridge, Massachusetts.

By negating both the antecedent and the consequent, we obtain the **inverse** of the given statement:

$$\text{If you do not stay, then I do not go.}$$

If the antecedent and the consequent are both interchanged *and* negated, the **contrapositive** of the given statement is formed:

$$\text{If I do not go, then you do not stay.}$$

These three related statements for the conditional $p \rightarrow q$ are summarized below. (Notice that the inverse is the contrapositive of the converse.)

Related Conditional Statements		
Conditional Statement	$p \rightarrow q$	(If p, then q.)
Converse	$q \rightarrow p$	(If q, then p.)
Inverse	$\sim p \rightarrow \sim q$	(If not p, then not q.)
Contrapositive	$\sim q \rightarrow \sim p$	(If not q, then not p.)

EXAMPLE 1 Determining Related Conditional Statements

Given the conditional statement

$$\text{If I live in Miami, then I live in Florida,}$$

determine each of the following:

(a) the converse
(b) the inverse
(c) the contrapositive

SOLUTION

(a) Let p represent "I live in Miami" and q represent "I live in Florida." Then the given statement may be written $p \rightarrow q$. The converse, $q \rightarrow p$, is

$$\text{If I live in Florida, then I live in Miami.}$$

Notice that for this statement, the converse is not necessarily true, even though the given statement is true.

(b) The inverse of $p \rightarrow q$ is $\sim p \rightarrow \sim q$. For the given conditional statement, the inverse is

$$\text{If I don't live in Miami, then I don't live in Florida,}$$

which is again not necessarily true.

(c) The contrapositive, $\sim q \rightarrow \sim p$, is

$$\text{If I don't live in Florida, then I don't live in Miami.}$$

The contrapositive, like the given conditional statement, is true. ▪

Bertrand Russell (1872–1970) was a student of Whitehead's before they wrote the *Principia*. Like his teacher, Russell turned toward philosophy. His works include a critique of Leibniz, analyses of mind and of matter, and a history of Western thought.

Russell became a public figure because of his involvement in social issues. Deeply aware of human loneliness, he was "passionately desirous of finding ways of diminishing this tragic isolation." During World War I he was an antiwar crusader, and he was imprisoned briefly. Again in the 1960s he championed peace. He wrote many books on social issues, winning the Nobel Prize for Literature in 1950.

Example 1 shows that the converse and inverse of a true statement need not be true. They *can* be true, but they need not be. The relationships between the truth values of the conditional statement, converse, inverse, and contrapositive are shown in the truth table that follows.

		Conditional	Converse	Inverse	Contrapositive
p	q	$p \rightarrow q$	$q \rightarrow p$	$\sim p \rightarrow \sim q$	$\sim q \rightarrow \sim p$
T	T	T	T	T	T
T	F	F	T	T	F
F	T	T	F	F	T
F	F	T	T	T	T

Equivalent: Conditional ↔ Contrapositive. *Equivalent:* Converse ↔ Inverse.

As this truth table shows, a conditional statement and its contrapositive always have the same truth values, making it possible to replace any statement with its contrapositive without affecting the logical meaning. Also, the converse and inverse always have the same truth values.

This discussion is summarized as follows.

> **Equivalences**
>
> A conditional statement and its contrapositive are equivalent, and the converse and the inverse are equivalent.

EXAMPLE 2 Determining Related Conditional Statements

For the conditional statement $\sim p \rightarrow q$, write each of the following.
(a) the converse **(b)** the inverse **(c)** the contrapositive

SOLUTION

(a) The converse of $\sim p \rightarrow q$ is $q \rightarrow \sim p$.
(b) The inverse is $\sim(\sim p) \rightarrow \sim q$, which simplifies to $p \rightarrow \sim q$.
(c) The contrapositive is $\sim q \rightarrow \sim(\sim p)$, which simplifies to $\sim q \rightarrow p$. ∎

Alternative Forms of "If p, then q"
The conditional statement "if p, then q" can be stated in several other ways in English. For example,

> If you go to the shopping center, then you will find a place to park

can also be written

> Going to the shopping center is *sufficient* for finding a place to park.

According to this statement, going to the shopping center is enough to guarantee finding a place to park. Going to other places, such as schools or office buildings, *might* also guarantee a place to park, but at least we *know* that going to the shopping center does.

In a speech during the 2004 presidential race, **John Kerry** made the following statement:

Mark my words. If I am elected president and there still has not been sufficient progress rapidly in these next months on these issues, then I will lead.

This promise involves a conditional, a conjunction, and a negation.

Thus, $p \rightarrow q$ can be written "p is sufficient for q." Knowing that p has occurred is sufficient to guarantee that q will also occur. On the other hand,

Turning on the set is necessary for watching television (∗)

has a different meaning. Here, we are saying that one condition that is necessary for watching television is that you turn on the set. This may not be enough; the set might be broken, for example. The statement labeled (∗) could be written as

If you watch television, then you turned on the set.

As this example suggests, $p \rightarrow q$ is the same as "q is necessary for p." In other words, if q doesn't happen, then neither will p. Notice how this idea is closely related to the idea of equivalence between a conditional statement and its contrapositive.

Common Translations of $p \rightarrow q$

The conditional $p \rightarrow q$ can be translated in any of the following ways,

If p, then q.	p is sufficient for q.
If p, q.	q is necessary for p.
p implies q.	All p are q.
p only if q.	q if p.

The translation of $p \rightarrow q$ into these various word forms does not in any way depend on the truth or falsity of $p \rightarrow q$.

For example, the statement

If you are 18, then you can vote

can be written in any of the following alternative ways:

You can vote if you are 18.

You are 18 only if you can vote.

Being able to vote is necessary for you to be 18.

Being 18 is sufficient for being able to vote.

All 18-year-olds can vote.

Being 18 implies that you can vote.

EXAMPLE 3 Rewording Conditional Statements

Write each statement in the form "if p, then q."

(a) You'll be sorry if I go.
(b) Today is Friday only if yesterday was Thursday.
(c) All nurses wear white shoes.

SOLUTION

(a) If I go, then you'll be sorry.
(b) If today is Friday, then yesterday was Thursday.
(c) If you are a nurse, then you wear white shoes.

For Further Thought

A Word to the Wise Is Sufficient

How many times have you heard a wise saying like "A stitch in time saves nine," "A rolling stone gathers no moss," or "Birds of a feather flock together"? In many cases, such proverbial advice can be restated as a conditional in *if . . . then* form. For example, these three statements can be restated as follows:

"If you make a stitch in time, then it will save you nine (stitches)."

"If a stone rolls, then it gathers no moss."

"If they are birds of a feather, then they flock together."

For Group Discussion or Individual Investigation

1. Think of some wise sayings that have been around for a long time, and state them in *if . . . then* form.
2. You have probably heard the saying "All that glitters is not gold." Do you think that what is said here is actually what is meant? If not, restate it as you think it should be stated. (*Hint:* Write the original statement in *if . . . then* form.)

Principia Mathematica, the title chosen by Whitehead and Russell, was a deliberate reference to *Philosophiae naturalis principia mathematica,* or "mathematical principles of the philosophy of nature," Isaac Newton's epochal work of 1687. Newton's Principia pictured a kind of "clockwork universe" that ran via his Law of Gravitation. Newton independently invented the calculus, unaware that Leibniz had published his own formulation of it earlier. A controversy over their priority continued into the eighteenth century.

EXAMPLE 4 Translating from Words to Symbols

Let p represent "A triangle is equilateral," and let q represent "A triangle has three sides of equal length." Write each of the following in symbols.

(a) A triangle is equilateral if it has three sides of equal length.
(b) A triangle is equilateral only if it has three sides of equal length.

SOLUTION

(a) $q \to p$ **(b)** $p \to q$

Biconditionals The compound statement *p if and only if q* (often abbreviated *p iff q*) is called a **biconditional.** It is symbolized $p \leftrightarrow q$, and is interpreted as the conjunction of the two conditionals $p \to q$ and $q \to p$. Using symbols, this conjunction is written

$$(q \to p) \wedge (p \to q)$$

so that, by definition, $\quad p \leftrightarrow q \equiv (q \to p) \wedge (p \to q).$

The truth table for the biconditional $p \leftrightarrow q$ can be determined using this definition.

Truth Table for the Biconditional *p* if and only if *q*

	p if and only if *q*	
p	*q*	$p \leftrightarrow q$
T	T	T
T	F	F
F	T	F
F	F	T

From the truth table, we see that a biconditional is true when both component statements have the same truth value. It is false when they have different truth values.

> ### EXAMPLE 5 Determining Whether Biconditionals Are True or False
>
> Determine whether each biconditional statement is *true* or *false*.
>
> **(a)** $6 + 9 = 15$ if and only if $12 + 4 = 16$ **(b)** $6 = 5$ if and only if $12 \neq 12$
> **(c)** $5 + 2 = 10$ if and only if $17 + 19 = 36$
>
> **SOLUTION**
>
> **(a)** Both $6 + 9 = 15$ and $12 + 4 = 16$ are true. By the truth table for the biconditional, this biconditional is true.
> **(b)** Both component statements are false, so by the last line of the truth table for the biconditional, this biconditional statement is true.
> **(c)** Because the first component ($5 + 2 = 10$) is false, and the second is true, this biconditional statement is false. ◼

Summary of Truth Tables
In this section and in the previous two sections, truth tables have been derived for several important types of compound statements. The summary that follows describes how these truth tables may be remembered.

> ### Summary of Basic Truth Tables
>
> **1.** $\sim p$, the **negation** of p, has truth value opposite of p.
> **2.** $p \wedge q$, the **conjunction,** is true only when both p and q are true.
> **3.** $p \vee q$, the **disjunction,** is false only when both p and q are false.
> **4.** $p \rightarrow q$, the **conditional,** is false only when p is true and q is false.
> **5.** $p \leftrightarrow q$, the **biconditional,** is true only when p and q have the same truth value.

3.4 EXERCISES

For each given conditional statement (or statement that can be written as a conditional), write **(a)** *the converse,* **(b)** *the inverse, and* **(c)** *the contrapositive in* if . . . then *form. In some of the exercises, it may be helpful to first restate the given statement in* if . . . then *form.*

1. If beauty were a minute, then you would be an hour.

2. If you lead, then I will follow.

3. If it ain't broke, don't fix it.

4. If I had a nickel for each time that happened, I would be rich.

5. Walking in front of a moving car is dangerous to your health.

6. Milk contains calcium.

7. Birds of a feather flock together.

8. A rolling stone gathers no moss.

9. If you build it, he will come.

10. Where there's smoke, there's fire.

11. $p \rightarrow \sim q$ **12.** $\sim p \rightarrow q$

13. $\sim p \rightarrow \sim q$ **14.** $\sim q \rightarrow \sim p$

15. $p \rightarrow (q \vee r)$ (*Hint:* Use one of De Morgan's laws as necessary.)

16. $(r \lor \sim q) \rightarrow p$ (*Hint:* Use one of De Morgan's laws as necessary.)

17. Discuss the equivalences that exist among a given conditional statement, its converse, its inverse, and its contrapositive.

18. State the contrapositive of "If the square of a natural number is even, then the natural number is even." The two statements must have the same truth value. Use several examples and inductive reasoning to decide whether both are true or both are false.

Write each statement in the form "if p, then q."

19. If it is muddy, I'll wear my galoshes.

20. If I finish studying, I'll go to the party.

21. "18 is positive" implies that $18 + 1$ is positive.

22. "Today is Tuesday" implies that yesterday was Monday.

23. All integers are rational numbers.

24. All whole numbers are integers.

25. Doing crossword puzzles is sufficient for driving me crazy.

26. Being in Baton Rouge is sufficient for being in Louisiana.

27. A day's growth of beard is necessary for Gerald Guidroz to shave.

28. Being an environmentalist is necessary for being elected.

29. I can go from Park Place to Baltic Avenue only if I pass GO.

30. The principal will hire more teachers only if the school board approves.

31. No whole numbers are not integers.

32. No integers are irrational numbers.

33. The Orioles will win the pennant when their pitching improves.

34. Rush will be a liberal when pigs fly.

35. A rectangle is a parallelogram with a right angle.

36. A parallelogram is a four-sided figure with opposite sides parallel.

37. A triangle with two sides of the same length is isosceles.

38. A square is a rectangle with two adjacent sides equal.

39. The square of a two-digit number whose units digit is 5 will end in 25.

40. An integer whose units digit is 0 or 5 is divisible by 5.

41. One of the following statements is not equivalent to all the others. Which one is it?
A. r only if s. **B.** r implies s.
C. If r, then s. **D.** r is necessary for s.

42. Many students have difficulty interpreting *necessary* and *sufficient*. Use the statement "Being in Quebec is sufficient for being in North America" to explain why "p is sufficient for q" translates as "if p, then q."

43. Use the statement "To be an integer, it is necessary that a number be rational" to explain why "p is necessary for q" translates as "if q, then p."

44. Explain why the statement "A week has eight days if and only if October has forty days" is true.

October						
SUNDAY	MONDAY	TUESDAY	WEDNESDAY	THURSDAY	FRIDAY	SATURDAY
1	2	3	4	5	6	7
8	9	10	11	12	13	14
15	16	17	18	19	20	21
22	23	24	25	26	27	28
29	30	31				

Identify each statement as true *or* false.

45. $5 = 9 - 4$ if and only if $8 + 2 = 10$.

46. $3 + 1 \neq 6$ if and only if $8 \neq 8$.

47. $8 + 7 \neq 15$ if and only if $3 \times 5 \neq 9$.

48. $6 \times 2 = 14$ if and only if $9 + 7 \neq 16$.

49. Bill Clinton was president if and only if Jimmy Carter was not president.

50. Burger King sells Big Macs if and only if Apple manufactures Ipods.

Two statements that can both be true about the same object are **consistent.** *For example, "It is brown" and "It weighs 50 pounds" are consistent statements. Statements that cannot both be true about the same object are called* **contrary;** *"It is a Dodge" and "It is a Toyota" are contrary. In Exercises 51–56, label each pair of statements as either* contrary *or* consistent.

51. Elvis is alive. Elvis is dead.

52. George W. Bush is a Democrat. George W. Bush is a Republican.

53. That animal has four legs. That same animal is a dog.

54. That book is nonfiction. That book costs more than $100.

55. This number is an integer. This same number is irrational.

56. This number is positive. This same number is a natural number.

57. Make up two statements that are consistent.

58. Make up two statements that are contrary.

3.5 Analyzing Arguments with Euler Diagrams

Logical Arguments • Arguments with Universal Quantifiers • Arguments with Existential Quantifiers

Leonhard Euler (1707–1783) won the academy prize and edged out du Châtelet and Voltaire. That was a minor achievement, as was the invention of "Euler circles" (which antedated Venn diagrams). Euler was the most prolific mathematician of his generation despite blindness that forced him to dictate from memory.

Logical Arguments With inductive reasoning we observe patterns to solve problems. Now, in this section and the next, we study how deductive reasoning may be used to determine whether logical arguments are valid or invalid. A logical argument is made up of **premises** (assumptions, laws, rules, widely held ideas, or observations) and a **conclusion.** Together, the premises and the conclusion make up the argument. Also recall that *deductive* reasoning involves drawing specific conclusions from given general premises. When reasoning from the premises of an argument to obtain a conclusion, we want the argument to be valid.

Valid and Invalid Arguments

An argument is **valid** if the fact that all the premises are true forces the conclusion to be true. An argument that is not valid is **invalid.** It is called a **fallacy.**

It is very important to note that "valid" and "true" are not the same—an argument can be valid even though the conclusion is false. (See Example 4.)

Arguments with Universal Quantifiers Several techniques can be used to check whether an argument is valid. One of these is the visual technique based on **Euler diagrams,** as shown in Examples 1–4.

▎**EXAMPLE 1** **Using an Euler Diagram to Determine Validity**

Is the following argument valid?

> All dogs are animals.
> Puddles is a dog.
> Puddles is an animal.

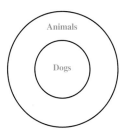

FIGURE 8

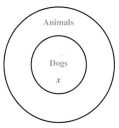

x represents Puddles.

FIGURE 9

SOLUTION

Here we use the common method of placing one premise over another, with the conclusion below a line. To begin, draw regions to represent the first premise. One is the region for "animals." Because all dogs are animals, the region for "dogs" goes inside the region for "animals," as in Figure 8.

The second premise, "Puddles is a dog," suggests that "Puddles" would go inside the region representing "dogs." Let *x* represent "Puddles." Figure 9 shows that "Puddles" is also inside the region for "animals." If both premises are true, the conclusion that Puddles is an animal must be true also. The argument is valid. ▪

EXAMPLE 2 Using an Euler Diagram to Determine Validity

Is the following argument valid?

> All rainy days are cloudy.
>
> Today is not cloudy.
> _____
> Today is not rainy.

SOLUTION

In Figure 10, the region for "rainy days" is drawn entirely inside the region for "cloudy days." Since "Today is *not* cloudy," place an *x* for "today" *outside* the region for "cloudy days." See Figure 11. Placing the *x* outside the region for "cloudy days" forces it also to be outside the region for "rainy days." Thus, if the first two premises are true, then it is also true that today is not rainy. The argument is valid.

 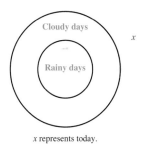

x represents today.

FIGURE 10   **FIGURE 11** ▪

EXAMPLE 3 Using an Euler Diagram to Determine Validity

Is the following argument valid?

> All banana trees have green leaves.
>
> That plant has green leaves.
> _____
> That plant is a banana tree.

FIGURE 12

SOLUTION

The region for "banana trees" goes entirely inside the region for "things that have green leaves." See Figure 12. There is a choice for locating the *x* that represents "that plant." The *x* must go inside the region for "things that have green leaves," but can go either inside or outside the region for "banana trees." Even if the premises are true, we are not forced to accept the conclusion as true. This argument is invalid; it is a fallacy. ▪

As mentioned earlier, the validity of an argument is not the same as the truth of its conclusion. The argument in Example 3 was invalid, but the conclusion "That plant is a banana tree" may or may not be true. We cannot be sure.

EXAMPLE 4   Using an Euler Diagram to Determine Validity

Is the following argument valid?

> All expensive things are desirable.
> All desirable things make you feel good.
> All things that make you feel good make you live longer.
> All expensive things make you live longer.

SOLUTION

A diagram for the argument is given in Figure 13.

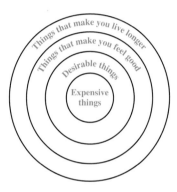

FIGURE 13

FIGURE 14

If each premise is true, then the conclusion must be true because the region for "expensive things" lies completely within the region for "things that make you live longer." Thus, the argument is valid. (This argument is an example of the fact that a *valid* argument need *not* have a true conclusion.) ▪

Arguments with Existential Quantifiers

EXAMPLE 5   Using an Euler Diagram to Determine Validity

Is the following argument valid?

> Some students go to the beach for Spring Break.
> I am a student.
> I go to the beach for Spring Break.

SOLUTION

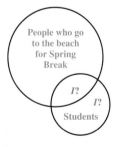

FIGURE 15

The first premise is sketched in Figure 14. As the sketch shows, some (but not necessarily *all*) students go to the beach. There are two possibilities for *I*, as shown in Figure 15.

One possibility is that *I* go to the beach; the other is that *I* don't. Since the truth of the premises does not force the conclusion to be true, the argument is invalid. ▪

3.5 EXERCISES

Decide whether each argument is valid *or* invalid.

1. All amusement parks have thrill rides.
Great America is an amusement park.

Great America has thrill rides.

2. All disc jockeys play music.
Phlash Phelps is a disc jockey.

Phlash Phelps plays music.

3. All politicians lie, cheat, and steal.
That man lies, cheats, and steals.

That man is a politician.

4. All Southerners speak with an accent.
Bill Leonard speaks with an accent.

Bill Leonard is a Southerner.

5. All dogs love to bury bones.
Py does not love to bury bones.

Py is not a dog.

6. All handymen use cell phones.
Lee Guidroz does not use a cell phone.

Lee Guidroz is not a handyman.

7. All residents of Minnesota know how to live in freezing temperatures.
Wendy Rockswold knows how to live in freezing temperatures.

Wendy Rockswold lives in Minnesota.

8. All people who apply for a loan must pay for a title search.
Hilary Langlois paid for a title search.

Hilary Langlois applied for a loan.

9. Some dinosaurs were plant eaters.
Danny was a plant eater.

Danny was a dinosaur.

10. Some philosophers are absent minded.
Loretta Ramagos is a philosopher.

Loretta Ramagos is absent minded.

11. Some nurses wear blue uniforms.
Dee Boyle is a nurse.

Dee Boyle wears a blue uniform.

12. Some trucks have sound systems.
Some trucks have gun racks.

Some trucks with sound systems have gun racks.

13. Refer to Example 3. If the second premise and the conclusion were interchanged, would the argument then be valid?

14. Refer to Example 4. Give a different conclusion than the one given there so that the argument is still valid.

Construct a valid argument based on the Euler diagram shown.

15.

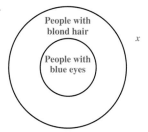

x represents Dinya Norris.

16.

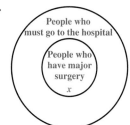

x represents Marty McDonald.

As mentioned in the text, an argument can have a true conclusion yet be invalid. In these exercises, each argument has a true conclusion. Identify each argument as valid *or* invalid.

17. All birds fly.
All planes fly.

A bird is not a plane.

18. All cars have tires.
All tires are rubber.

All cars have rubber.

19. All chickens have beaks.
All hens are chickens.

All hens have beaks.

20. All chickens have beaks.
All birds have beaks.

All chickens are birds.

21. Little Rock is northeast of Texarkana.
Little Rock is northeast of Austin.

Texarkana is northeast of Austin.

22. Veracruz is south of Tampico.
Tampico is south of Monterrey.

Veracruz is south of Monterrey.

23. No whole numbers are negative.
−4 is negative.

−4 is not a whole number.

24. A scalene triangle has a longest side.
A scalene triangle has a largest angle.

The largest angle in a scalene triangle
is opposite the longest side.

In Exercises 25–30, the premises marked A, B, *and* C *are followed by several possible conclusions. Take each conclusion in turn, and check whether the resulting argument is* valid *or* invalid.

A. *All people who drive contribute to air pollution.*
B. *All people who contribute to air pollution make life a little worse.*
C. *Some people who live in a suburb make life a little worse.*

25. Some people who live in a suburb contribute to air pollution.

26. Some people who live in a suburb drive.

27. Suburban residents never drive.

28. Some people who contribute to air pollution live in a suburb.

29. Some people who make life a little worse live in a suburb.

30. All people who drive make life a little worse.

31. Find examples of arguments on television commercials. Check them for validity.

32. Find examples of arguments in magazine ads. Check them for validity.

EXTENSION

Logic Problems and Sudoku

• How to Solve Logic Problems • How to Solve Sudoku

Some people find that logic problems, which appear in periodicals such as *Official's Logic Problems, World-Class Logic Problems* and *England's Best Logic Problems* (both PennyPress), and *Logic Puzzles* (Dell), provide hours of enjoyment. They are based on deductive reasoning, and players answer questions based on clues given. The following explanation on solving such problems appeared in the May 2004 issue of *England's Best Logic Problems.*

How to Solve Logic Problems Solving logic problems is entertaining and challenging. All the information you need to solve a logic problem is given in the introduction and clues, and in illustrations, when provided. If you've never solved a logic problem before, our sample should help you get started. Fill in the Sample Solving

Chart as you follow our explanation. We use a "•" to signify "Yes" and an "X" to signify "No."

Sample Logic Problem

Five couples were married last week, each on a different weekday. From the information provided, determine the woman (one is Cathy) and man (one is Paul) who make up each couple, as well as the day on which each couple was married.

1. Anne was married on Monday, but not to Wally.

2. Stan's wedding was on Wednesday. Rob was married on Friday, but not to Ida.

3. Vern (who married Fran) was married the day after Eve.

Sample Solving Chart:	PAUL	ROB	STAN	VERN	WALLY	MONDAY	TUESDAY	WEDNESDAY	THURSDAY	FRIDAY
ANNE										
CATHY										
EVE										
FRAN										
IDA										
MONDAY										
TUESDAY										
WEDNESDAY										
THURSDAY										
FRIDAY										

1

	PAUL	ROB	STAN	VERN	WALLY	MONDAY	TUESDAY	WEDNESDAY	THURSDAY	FRIDAY
ANNE	X	X			X	•	X	X	X	X
CATHY						X				
EVE						X				
FRAN						X				
IDA		X				X				X
MONDAY		X	X							
TUESDAY		X	X							
WEDNESDAY	X	X	•	X	X					
THURSDAY		X	X							
FRIDAY	X	•	X	X	X					

Explanation

Anne was married Mon. (1), so put a "•" at the intersection of Anne and Mon. Put "X"s in all the other days in Anne's row and all the other names in the Mon. column. (Whenever you establish a relationship, as we did here, be sure to place "X"s at the intersections of all relationships that become impossible as a result.) Anne wasn't married to Wally (1), so put an "X" at the intersection of Anne and Wally. Stan's wedding was Wed. (2), so put a "•" at the intersection of Stan and Wed. (Don't forget the "X"s.) Stan didn't marry Anne, who was married Mon., so put an "X" at the intersection of Anne and Stan. Rob was married Fri., but not to Ida (2), so put a "•" at the intersection of Rob and Fri., and "X"s at the intersections of Rob and Ida and Ida and Fri. Rob also didn't marry Anne, who was married Mon., so put an "X" at the intersection of Anne and Rob. Now your chart should look like chart 1.

Vern married Fran (3), so put a "•" at the intersection of Vern and Fran. This leaves Anne's only possible husband as Paul, so put a "•" at the intersection of Anne and Paul and Paul and Mon. Vern and Fran's wedding was the day after Eve's (3), which wasn't Mon. [Anne], so Vern's wasn't Tue. It must have been Thu. [see chart], so Eve's was Wed. (3). Put "•"s at the intersections of Vern and Thu., Fran and Thu., and Eve and Wed. Now your chart should look like chart 2.

(continued)

2	PAUL	ROB	STAN	VERN	WALLY	MONDAY	TUESDAY	WEDNESDAY	THURSDAY	FRIDAY
ANNE	•	×	×	×	×	•	×	×	×	×
CATHY	×		×		×		×	×		
EVE	×			×		×	×	•	×	×
FRAN	×	×	×	•	×	×	×	×	•	×
IDA	×	×		×		×		×	×	×
MONDAY	•	×	×	×	×					
TUESDAY	×	×	×	×						
WEDNESDAY	×	×	•	×						
THURSDAY	×	×	×	•	×					
FRIDAY	×	•	×	×	×					

3	PAUL	ROB	STAN	VERN	WALLY	MONDAY	TUESDAY	WEDNESDAY	THURSDAY	FRIDAY
ANNE	•	×	×	×	×	•	×	×	×	×
CATHY	×	•	×	×	×	×	×	×	×	•
EVE	×	×	•	×	×	×	×	•	×	×
FRAN	×	×	×	•	×	×	×	×	•	×
IDA	×	×	×	×	•	×	•	×	×	×
MONDAY	•	×	×	×	×					
TUESDAY	×	×	×	×	•					
WEDNESDAY	×	×	•	×	×					
THURSDAY	×	×	×	•	×					
FRIDAY	×	•	×	×	×					

The chart shows that Cathy was married Fri., Ida was married Tue., and Wally was married Tue. Ida married Wally, and Cathy's wedding was Fri., so she married Rob. After this information is filled in, Eve could only have married Stan. You've completed the puzzle, and your chart should now look like chart 3.

In summary: Anne and Paul, Mon.; Cathy and Rob, Fri.; Eve and Stan, Wed.; Fran and Vern, Thu.; Ida and Wally, Tue.

In some problems, it may be necessary to make a logical guess based on facts you've established. When you do, always look for clues or other facts that disprove it. If you find that your guess is incorrect, eliminate it as a possibility.

How to Solve Sudoku

Sudoku is a simple game that has gained great popularity in the United States during the past few years. It is believed that the game originated as Number Place in the United States over 25 years ago, but gained in popularity only after it became a sensation in Japan, where it was renamed Sudoku, meaning "single number." (*Source*: *Sudoku #13*, 2005, Platinum Magazine Group.) Today it can be found in daily newspapers, on day-by-day calendars, and in periodical publications on newsstands.

There is only one rule in Sudoku: "Fill in the grid so that every row, every column, and every 3 × 3 box contains the digits 1 through 9." This involves scanning the given digits, marking up the grid, and analyzing. Here is a Sudoku in its original (given) form and in its final (solved) form.

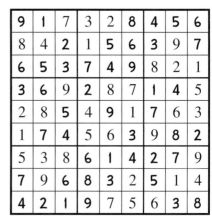

		7	3	2				
8	4		1				9	
						8	2	1
		9		8	7			5
2	8		4		1		6	3
1			5	6		9		
5	3	8						9
	9				2		1	4
				7	5	6		

Given Form

9	1	7	3	2	8	4	5	6
8	4	2	1	5	6	3	9	7
6	5	3	7	4	9	8	2	1
3	6	9	2	8	7	1	4	5
2	8	5	4	9	1	7	6	3
1	7	4	5	6	3	9	8	2
5	3	8	6	1	4	2	7	9
7	9	6	8	3	2	5	1	4
4	2	1	9	7	5	6	3	8

Solved Form

You can find Sudoku puzzles and solving strategies online at www.sudoku.org.

EXTENSION EXERCISES

Follow the guidelines to solve each logic problem, which appeared in the Spring 2004 issue of England's Best Logic Problems, *published by PennyPress.*

1. *A Moving Story*   On the first day of her visit to Russia, British chess prodigy Queenie King, aged 14, played and defeated the adult champions from four different cities. From the clues below, can you work out the full name of her opponent in each game and the city from which he came?

clues below, can you work out the name of the fellow-archaeologist making each offer, which university he is from, what is to be excavated, and where it is?

	Boris	Ivan	Piotr	Yuri	Bishopnik	Knightovich	Pawnchev	Rookov	Corki	Gorki	Porki	Yorki
First												
Second												
Third												
Fourth												
Corki												
Gorki												
Porki												
Yorki												
Bishopnik												
Knightovich												
Pawnchev												
Rookov												

	Universities								*Locations*			
	Arizona	Berlin	Miami	New York	Fort	Pyramid	Temple	Villa	China	Egypt	Peru	Scotland
Prof. Azimovic												
Prof. Katsouris												
Prof. Partington												
Prof. Voelkner												
China												
Egypt												
Peru												
Scotland												
Fort												
Pyramid												
Temple												
Villa												

Clues:

(a) Boris was from the famous city of Gorki, while the other champions came from cities not so well known.

(b) Mr Rookov, Queenie's second opponent, was not the man from the city of Yorki, centre of the Russian chocolate industry.

(c) Piotr, who was the first Russian to play—and be beaten by—Queenie wasn't Mr Pawnchev.

(d) Mr Bishopnik played Queenie immediately after Ivan and immediately before the man from Corki.

2. *Dig This!*   Professor Rosetta Stone, the eminent British archaeologist, is considering offers to participate in four different "digs" next year. From the

Clues:

(a) Professor Azimovic wants Rosetta to join him for an expedition into the wild highlands of Peru.

(b) The University of New York expedition is being mounted to excavate the site of a two thousand year old temple.

(c) Professor Katsouris isn't organising the expedition that is going to excavate an ancient fort.

(d) The site in the Takla Makan desert of China to be investigated by the University of Arizona expedition is not that of a villa.

(e) Professor Voelkner of the University of Berlin has no connection to the projected expedition to excavate a newly discovered pyramid in Egypt's Nile delta.

3. *Is That a Folk Song?* The traditional answer to the above question, when applied to something that may or may not be a folk song, is "Well, I never heard a cow sing it." None of the singers in this problem are cows, and they only sing folk songs. From the clues below, can you identify each male singer and his female partner, the name they perform under, and the type of folk songs they sing? (*Note*: The only vowels are A, E, I, O, and U.)

4. *Monsieur le Duc* In the 1930s, the Duc de Bauch made a number of profitable business partnerships. The Duc went into business with four heiresses, each of whom had inherited a business from her father. From the clues given below, can you work out each heiress' name, where her family money came from, and the city and year in which she partnered with the Duc?

Clues:

(a) Although he was born in Munich, Hans Gruber and his partner only sing traditional English folk songs.

(b) Nancy O'Hara is the Rose half of Rose and Thorn.

(c) One of the men whose surname begins with a vowel sings with Carol Dodds, while the other performs traditional American material with partner Jane Kenny.

(d) Peter Owen and his partner—who resemble each other not at all—perform as the Starr Twins; Ben Ashby isn't one of the Merlyns.

(e) The male half of the duo who perform folk-type songs of their own composition has a first name with one more letter than that of Sue Rogers' partner.

Clues:

(a) Neither the banking heiress who partnered with the Duc de Bauch in 1938 nor Horatia Hampton, whose father was an oil millionaire, had ever been to Athens.

(b) One partnership was formed in Berlin in 1936.

(c) The Monte Carlo business arrangement was formed earlier than the one with Mabelle Oakland.

(d) The family of Regina Stamford, the Duc's 1934 partner, had no major involvement in the automobile industry.

(e) Drusilla Camden joined forces with the Duc in Paris.

Solve each Sudoku, which appeared in *Sudoku #13*, 2005, *Platinum Magazine Group*. (They are categorized according to difficulty level.)

5. *Very Easy*

	2	6		9			3	
	4		8				1	7
8				5	2	4		
	8	1	3					9
2	9						8	4
3					7	1	6	
		9	1	3				5
5	3				6		7	
	6			7		8	4	

6. *Very Easy*

		3				5	8	
8		2			7	6		
7	9		5	6			3	1
	7		3		1	9		
		8				7		
		5	9		2		6	
6	4			5	3		1	2
		1	4			3		9
	2	7				4		

7. *Easy*

2				8			1	
			5	9		4		7
		9			2			
	4	7			8	1		6
6								3
5		1	6			2	4	
			8			3		
7		2		3	5			
	6			2				4

8. *Easy*

			2	5			6	
7			6		4	5		8
	6	5			7			
		7				3		9
8								2
9		3				4		
		8				9	2	
2		8	9		5			7
	4				3	2		

9. *Medium*

1						3	4	
5			8					
	6		2			8		5
4			7			6		
	7			8			2	
		5			3			1
9		1			7		6	
					1			4
	4	3						2

10. *Medium*

5		6				7		8
	2		1		7		3	
7								4
		1	6	9	3	8		
		9	2	7	5	3		
1								6
	7		8		9		5	
6		3				4		9

11. *Hard*

9		3		4				6
								5
	5	4			1			
1					3			8
		5				3		
3			6					7
			9			1	2	
8								
6				7		5		4

12. *Hard*

7			8					
				5		9		6
	3		2			7		
			5				6	3
		4		7		1		
8	2				3			
		8			5		4	
9		2		1				
					8			1

3.6 | Analyzing Arguments with Truth Tables

Truth Tables (Two Premises) • Valid and Invalid Argument Forms • Truth Tables (More Than Two Premises) • Arguments of Lewis Carroll

Truth Tables (Two Premises)   In Section 3.5 we used Euler diagrams to test the validity of arguments. While Euler diagrams often work well for simple arguments, difficulties can develop with more complex ones, because Euler diagrams require a sketch showing every possible case. In complex arguments, it is hard to be sure that all cases have been considered.

In deciding whether to use Euler diagrams to test the validity of an argument, look for quantifiers such as "all," "some," or "no." These words often indicate arguments best tested by Euler diagrams. If these words are absent, it may be better to use truth tables to test the validity of an argument.

As an example of this method, consider the following argument:

> If the floor is dirty, then I must mop it.
>
> The floor is dirty.
> _____
>
> I must mop it.

To test the validity of this argument, we begin by identifying the *component* statements found in the argument. They are "the floor is dirty" and "I must mop it." We assign the letters p and q to represent these statements:

> p represents "the floor is dirty";
>
> q represents "I must mop it."

Now we write the two premises and the conclusion in symbols:

$$\text{Premise 1: } p \rightarrow q$$
$$\underline{\text{Premise 2: } p \qquad\qquad}$$
$$\text{Conclusion: } q \quad .$$

To decide if this argument is valid, we must determine whether the conjunction of both premises implies the conclusion for all possible cases of truth values for p and q. Therefore, write the conjunction of the premises as the antecedent of a conditional statement, and the conclusion as the consequent.

$$[(p \rightarrow q) \quad \wedge \quad p] \quad \rightarrow \quad q$$

↑	↑	↑	↑	↑
premise	and	premise	implies	conclusion

Finally, construct the truth table for this conditional statement, as shown below.

p	q	$p \rightarrow q$	$(p \rightarrow q) \wedge p$	$[(p \rightarrow q) \wedge p] \rightarrow q$
T	T	T	T	T
T	F	F	F	T
F	T	T	F	T
F	F	T	F	T

Because the final column, shown in color, indicates that the conditional statement that represents the argument is true for all possible truth values of p and q, the statement is a tautology. Thus, the argument is valid.

The pattern of the argument in the floor-mopping example,

$$p \rightarrow q$$
$$\underline{p \qquad\qquad}$$
$$q \quad ,$$

is a common one, and is called **modus ponens,** or the *law of detachment*.

In summary, to test the validity of an argument using a truth table, follow the steps in the box.

Testing the Validity of an Argument with a Truth Table

Step 1 Assign a letter to represent each component statement in the argument.

Step 2 Express each premise and the conclusion symbolically.

Step 3 Form the symbolic statement of the entire argument by writing the *conjunction* of *all* the premises as the antecedent of a conditional statement, and the conclusion of the argument as the consequent.

Step 4 Complete the truth table for the conditional statement formed in Step 3 above. If it is a tautology, then the argument is valid; otherwise, it is invalid.

EXAMPLE 1 Using a Truth Table to Determine Validity

Determine whether the argument is *valid* or *invalid*.

If my check arrives in time, I'll register for the fall semester.

I've registered for the fall semester.

My check arrived in time.

SOLUTION

Let p represent "my check arrives (arrived) in time" and let q represent "I'll register (I've registered) for the fall semester." Using these symbols, the argument can be written in the form

$$p \rightarrow q$$
$$q$$
$$p \qquad .$$

To test for validity, construct a truth table for the statement $[(p \rightarrow q) \land q] \rightarrow p$.

p	q	$p \rightarrow q$	$(p \rightarrow q) \land q$	$[(p \rightarrow q) \land q] \rightarrow p$
T	T	T	T	T
T	F	F	F	T
F	T	T	T	F
F	F	T	F	T

The third row of the final column of the truth table shows F, and this is enough to conclude that the argument is invalid. ■

If a conditional and its converse were logically equivalent, then an argument of the type found in Example 1 would be valid. Because a conditional and its converse are *not* equivalent, the argument is an example of what is sometimes called the **fallacy of the converse.**

EXAMPLE 2 Using a Truth Table to Determine Validity

Determine whether the argument is *valid* or *invalid*.

If a man could be in two places at one time, I'd be with you.

I am not with you.

A man can't be in two places at one time.

SOLUTION

If p represents "a man could be in two places at one time" and q represents "I'd be with you," the argument becomes

$$p \rightarrow q$$
$$\sim q$$
$$\sim p \qquad .$$

The symbolic statement of the entire argument is

$$[(p \rightarrow q) \wedge \sim q] \rightarrow \sim p.$$

The truth table for this argument, shown below, indicates a tautology, and the argument is valid.

p	q	$p \rightarrow q$	$\sim q$	$(p \rightarrow q) \wedge \sim q$	$\sim p$	$[(p \rightarrow q) \wedge \sim q] \rightarrow \sim p$
T	T	T	F	F	F	T
T	F	F	T	F	F	T
F	T	T	F	F	T	T
F	F	T	T	T	T	T

The pattern of reasoning of this example is called **modus tollens,** or the *law of contraposition,* or *indirect reasoning.*

With reasoning similar to that used to name the fallacy of the converse, the fallacy

$$p \rightarrow q$$
$$\underline{\sim p}$$
$$\sim q$$

is called the **fallacy of the inverse.** An example of such a fallacy is "If it rains, I get wet. It doesn't rain. Therefore, I don't get wet."

EXAMPLE 3 Using a Truth Table to Determine Validity

Determine whether the argument is *valid* or *invalid.*

I'll buy a car or I'll take a vacation.

I won't buy a car.

I'll take a vacation.

SOLUTION

If p represents "I'll buy a car" and q represents "I'll take a vacation," the argument becomes

$$p \vee q$$
$$\underline{\sim p}$$
$$q \quad .$$

We must set up a truth table for the statement $[(p \vee q) \wedge \sim p] \rightarrow q$.

p	q	$p \vee q$	$\sim p$	$(p \vee q) \wedge \sim p$	$[(p \vee q) \wedge \sim p] \rightarrow q$
T	T	T	F	F	T
T	F	T	F	F	T
F	T	T	T	T	T
F	F	F	T	F	T

The statement is a tautology and the argument is valid. Any argument of this form is valid by the law of **disjunctive syllogism.**

EXAMPLE 4 Using a Truth Table to Determine Validity

Determine whether the argument is *valid* or *invalid*.

> If it squeaks, then I use WD-40.
>
> <u>If I use WD-40, then I must go to the hardware store.</u>
>
> If it squeaks, then I must go to the hardware store.

SOLUTION

Let *p* represent "it squeaks," let *q* represent "I use WD-40," and let *r* represent "I must go to the hardware store." The argument takes on the general form

$$p \rightarrow q$$
$$\underline{q \rightarrow r}$$
$$p \rightarrow r.$$

Make a truth table for the following statement:

$$[(p \rightarrow q) \wedge (q \rightarrow r)] \rightarrow (p \rightarrow r).$$

It will require eight rows.

So if you're an intellectual midget,

p	q	r	$p \rightarrow q$	$q \rightarrow r$	$p \rightarrow r$	$(p \rightarrow q) \wedge (q \rightarrow r)$	$[(p \rightarrow q) \wedge (q \rightarrow r)] \rightarrow (p \rightarrow r)$
T	T	T	T	T	T	T	T
T	T	F	T	F	F	F	T
T	F	T	F	T	T	F	T
T	F	F	F	T	F	F	T
F	T	T	T	T	T	T	T
F	T	F	T	F	T	F	T
F	F	T	T	T	T	T	T
F	F	F	T	T	T	T	T

This argument is valid because the final statement is a tautology. The pattern of argument shown in this example is called **reasoning by transitivity,** or the *law of hypothetical syllogism.* ■

🎥 In a scene near the beginning of the 1974 film *Monty Python and the Holy Grail,* an amazing application of **poor logic** leads to the apparent demise of a supposed witch. A group of peasants have forced a young woman to wear a nose made of wood. The convoluted argument they make is this: Witches and wood are both burned, and because witches are made of wood, and wood floats, and ducks also float, if she weighs the same as a duck, then she is made of wood and therefore is a witch!

Valid and Invalid Argument Forms
A summary of the valid and invalid forms of argument presented so far follows.

Valid Argument Forms

Modus Ponens	Modus Tollens	Disjunctive Syllogism	Reasoning by Transitivity
$p \rightarrow q$	$p \rightarrow q$	$p \vee q$	$p \rightarrow q$
p	$\sim q$	$\sim p$	$q \rightarrow r$
q	$\sim p$	q	$p \rightarrow r$

Invalid Argument Forms (Fallacies)

Fallacy of the Converse	Fallacy of the Inverse
$p \rightarrow q$	$p \rightarrow q$
q	$\sim p$
p	$\sim q$

Truth Tables (More Than Two Premises)

When an argument contains more than two premises, it is necessary to determine the truth values of the conjunction of *all* of them. Remember that if *at least one* premise in a conjunction of several premises is false, then the entire conjunction is false.

EXAMPLE 5 Using a Truth Table to Determine Validity

Determine whether the argument is *valid* or *invalid*.

If Eddie goes to town, then Mabel stays at home. If Mabel does not stay at home, then Rita will cook. Rita will not cook. Therefore, Eddie does not go to town.

SOLUTION

In an argument written in this manner, the premises are given first, and the conclusion is the statement that follows the word "Therefore." Let p represent "Eddie goes to town," let q represent "Mabel stays at home," and let r represent "Rita will cook."

$$p \rightarrow q$$
$$\sim q \rightarrow r$$
$$\underline{\sim r}$$
$$\sim p$$

To test validity, set up a truth table for the statement

$$[(p \rightarrow q) \wedge (\sim q \rightarrow r) \wedge \sim r] \rightarrow \sim p.$$

p	q	r	$p \rightarrow q$	$\sim q$	$\sim q \rightarrow r$	$\sim r$	$(p \rightarrow q) \wedge (\sim q \rightarrow r) \wedge \sim r$	$\sim p$	$[(p \rightarrow q) \wedge (\sim q \rightarrow r) \wedge \sim r] \rightarrow \sim p$
T	T	T	T	F	T	F	F	F	T
T	T	F	T	F	T	T	T	F	F
T	F	T	F	T	T	F	F	F	T
T	F	F	F	T	F	T	F	F	T
F	T	T	T	F	T	F	F	T	T
F	T	F	T	F	T	T	T	T	T
F	F	T	T	T	T	F	F	T	T
F	F	F	T	T	F	T	F	T	T

Because the final column does not contain all Ts, the statement is not a tautology. The argument is invalid.

Arguments of Lewis Carroll

Consider the following poem, which has been around for many years.

> For want of a nail, the shoe was lost.
> For want of a shoe, the horse was lost.
> For want of a horse, the rider was lost.
> For want of a rider, the battle was lost.
> For want of a battle, the war was lost.
> Therefore, for want of a nail, the war was lost.

Each line of the poem may be written as an *if . . . then* statement. For example, the first line may be restated as "if a nail is lost, then the shoe is lost." The conclusion, "for want of a nail, the war was lost," follows from the premises, because repeated use of the law of transitivity applies. Arguments used by Lewis Carroll often take on a similar form. The next example comes from one of his works.

Tweedlogic "I know what you're thinking about," said Tweedledum, "but it isn't so, nohow." "Contrariwise," continued Tweedledee, "if it was so, it might be; and if it were so, it would be, but as it isn't, it ain't. That's logic."

> ▌ **EXAMPLE 6** **Supplying a Conclusion to Assure Validity**

Supply a conclusion that yields a valid argument for the following premises.

> Babies are illogical.
> Nobody is despised who can manage a crocodile.
> Illogical persons are despised.

SOLUTION

First, write each premise in the form *if . . . then*.

> If you are a baby, then you are illogical.
> If you can manage a crocodile, then you are not despised.
> If you are illogical, then you are despised.

Let p be "you are a baby," let q be "you are logical," let r be "you can manage a crocodile," and let s be "you are despised." With these letters, the statements can be written symbolically as

$$p \rightarrow \sim q$$
$$r \rightarrow \sim s$$
$$\sim q \rightarrow s.$$

Begin with any letter that appears only once. Here p appears only once. Using the contrapositive of $r \rightarrow \sim s$, which is $s \rightarrow \sim r$, rearrange the three statements as follows:

$$p \rightarrow \sim q$$
$$\sim q \rightarrow s$$
$$s \rightarrow \sim r.$$

From the three statements, repeated use of reasoning by transitivity gives the conclusion

$$p \rightarrow \sim r,$$

leading to a valid argument.

In words, the conclusion is "If you are a baby, then you cannot manage a crocodile," or, as Lewis Carroll would have written it, "Babies cannot manage crocodiles." ▪

3.6 EXERCISES

Each argument is either valid by one of the forms of valid arguments discussed in this section, or it is a fallacy by one of the forms of invalid arguments discussed. (See the summary boxes.) Decide whether the argument is valid *or a* fallacy, *and give the form that applies.*

1. If Elton John comes to town, then I will go to the concert.
   If I go to the concert, then I'll call in sick for work.

   If Elton John comes to town, then I'll call in sick for work.

2. If you use binoculars, then you get a glimpse of the comet.
   If you get a glimpse of the comet, then you'll be amazed.

   If you use binoculars, then you'll be amazed.

3. If Kim Hobbs works hard enough, she will get a promotion.
   Kim Hobbs works hard enough.

   She gets a promotion.

4. If Johnny Forbes sells his quota, he'll get a bonus.
   Johnny Forbes sells his quota.

   He gets a bonus.

5. If he doesn't have to get up at 4:00 A.M., he's ecstatic.
   He's ecstatic.

   He doesn't have to get up at 4:00 A.M.

6. If she buys another pair of shoes, her closet will overflow.
   Her closet will overflow.

   She buys another pair of shoes.

7. If Kerry Wood pitches, the Cubs win.
   The Cubs do not win.

   Kerry Wood does not pitch.

8. If Nelson Dida plays, the opponent gets shut out.
   The opponent does not get shut out.

   Nelson Dida does not play.

9. "If we evolved a race of Isaac Newtons, that would not be progress."
   (quote from Aldous Huxley)

   We have not evolved a race of Isaac Newtons.

   That is progress.

10. "If I have seen farther than others, it is because I stood on the shoulders
    of giants." (quote from Sir Isaac Newton)

    I have not seen farther than others.

    I have not stood on the shoulders of giants.

11. She uses e-commerce or she pays by credit card.

    She does not pay by credit card.

    She uses e-commerce.

12. Mia kicks or Arnold pumps iron.

    Arnold does not pump iron.

    Mia kicks.

Use a truth table to determine whether the argument is valid *or* invalid.

13. $p \lor q$

    p

    $\sim q$

14. $p \land \sim q$

    p

    $\sim q$

15. $\sim p \to \sim q$

    q

    p

16. $p \lor \sim q$

    p

    $\sim q$

17. $p \to q$

    $q \to p$

    $p \land q$

18. $\sim p \to q$

    p

    $\sim q$

19. $p \to \sim q$

    q

    $\sim p$

20. $p \to \sim q$

    $\sim p$

    $\sim q$

21. $(\sim p \lor q) \land (\sim p \to q)$

    p

    $\sim q$

22. $(p \to q) \land (q \to p)$

    p

    $p \lor q$

23. $(\sim p \land r) \to (p \lor q)$

    $\sim r \to p$

    $q \to r$

24. $(r \land p) \to (r \lor q)$

    $q \land p$

    $r \lor p$

25. Earlier we showed how to analyze arguments using Euler diagrams. Refer to Example 4 in this section, restate each premise and the conclusion using a quantifier, and then draw an Euler diagram to illustrate the relationship.

26. Explain in a few sentences how to determine the statement for which a truth table will be constructed so that the arguments that follow in Exercises 27–36 can be analyzed for validity.

Determine whether each argument is valid *or* invalid.

27. Brian loves to watch movies. If Elayn likes to jog, then Brian does not love to watch movies. If Elayn does not like to jog, then Clay drives a school bus. Therefore, Clay drives a school bus.

28. If Hurricane Katrina hit that grove of trees, then the trees are devastated. People plant trees when disasters strike and the trees are not devastated. Therefore, if people plant trees when disasters strike, then Hurricane Katrina did not hit that grove of trees.

29. If the MP3 personal player craze continues, then downloading music will remain popular. American Girl dolls are favorites or downloading music will remain popular. American Girl dolls are not favorites. Therefore, the MP3 personal player craze does not continue.

30. Ashley Simpson sings or Ashton Kutcher is not a teen idol. If Ashton Kutcher is not a teen idol, then Fantasia does not win a Grammy. Fantasia wins a Grammy. Therefore, Ashley Simpson does not sing.

31. The Steelers will be in the playoffs if and only if Ben leads the league in passing. Bill coaches the Steelers or Ben leads the league in passing. Bill does not coach the Steelers. Therefore, the Steelers will not be in the playoffs.

32. If I've got you under my skin, then you are deep in the heart of me. If you are deep in the heart of me, then you are not really a part of me. You are deep in the heart of me or you are really a part of me. Therefore, if I've got you under my skin, then you are really a part of me.

33. If Dr. Hardy is a department chairman, then he lives in Atlanta. He lives in Atlanta and his first name is Larry. Therefore, if his first name is not Larry, then he is not a department chairman.

34. If I were your woman and you were my man, then I'd never stop loving you. I've stopped loving you. Therefore, I am not your woman or you are not my man.

35. All men are created equal. All people who are created equal are women. Therefore, all men are women.

36. All men are mortal. Socrates is a man. Therefore, Socrates is mortal.

37. Suppose that you ask a stranger for the time and you get the following response:

> "If I tell you the time, then we'll start chatting. If we start chatting, then you'll want to meet me at a truck stop. If we meet at a truck stop, then we'll discuss my family. If we discuss my family, then you'll find out that my daughter is available for marriage. If you find out that she is available for marriage, then you'll want to marry her. If you want to marry her, then my life will be miserable since I don't want my daughter married to some fool who can't afford a $10 watch."

Use reasoning by transitivity to draw a valid conclusion.

38. Calandra Davis made the following observation: "If I want to determine whether an argument leading to the statement

$$[(p \rightarrow q) \wedge \sim q] \rightarrow \sim p$$

is valid, I only need to consider the lines of the truth table which lead to T for the column headed $(p \rightarrow q) \wedge \sim q$." Calandra was very perceptive. Can you explain why her observation was correct?

In the arguments used by Lewis Carroll, it is helpful to restate a premise in if . . . then *form in order to more easily identify a valid conclusion. The following premises come from Lewis Carroll. Write each premise in* if . . . then *form.*

39. All my poultry are ducks.

40. None of your sons can do logic.

41. Guinea pigs are hopelessly ignorant of music.

42. No teetotalers are pawnbrokers.

43. No teachable kitten has green eyes.

44. Opium-eaters have no self-command.

45. I have not filed any of them that I can read.

46. All of them written on blue paper are filed.

Exercises 47–52 involve premises from Lewis Carroll. Write each premise in symbols, and then in the final part, give a conclusion that yields a valid argument.

47. Let *p* be "it is a duck," *q* be "it is my poultry," *r* be "one is an officer," and *s* be "one is willing to waltz."
   (a) No ducks are willing to waltz.
   (b) No officers ever decline to waltz.
   (c) All my poultry are ducks.
   (d) Give a conclusion that yields a valid argument.

48. Let *p* be "one is able to do logic," *q* be "one is fit to serve on a jury," *r* be "one is sane," and *s* be "he is your son."
   (a) Everyone who is sane can do logic.
   (b) No lunatics are fit to serve on a jury.
   (c) None of your sons can do logic.
   (d) Give a conclusion that yields a valid argument.

49. Let *p* be "one is honest," *q* be "one is a pawnbroker," *r* be "one is a promise-breaker," *s* be "one is trustworthy," *t* be "one is very communicative," and *u* be "one is a wine-drinker."
   (a) Promise-breakers are untrustworthy.
   (b) Wine-drinkers are very communicative.
   (c) A person who keeps a promise is honest.
   (d) No teetotalers are pawnbrokers. (*Hint:* Assume "teetotaler" is the opposite of "wine-drinker.")
   (e) One can always trust a very communicative person.
   (f) Give a conclusion that yields a valid argument.

50. Let *p* be "it is a guinea pig," *q* be "it is hopelessly ignorant of music," *r* be "it keeps silent while the *Moonlight Sonata* is being played," and *s* be "it appreciates Beethoven."
   (a) Nobody who really appreciates Beethoven fails to keep silent while the *Moonlight Sonata* is being played.
   (b) Guinea pigs are hopelessly ignorant of music.
   (c) No one who is hopelessly ignorant of music ever keeps silent while the *Moonlight Sonata* is being played.
   (d) Give a conclusion that yields a valid argument.

51. Let *p* be "it begins with 'Dear Sir'," *q* be "it is crossed," *r* be "it is dated," *s* be "it is filed," *t* be "it is in black ink," *u* be "it is in the third person," *v* be "I can read it," *w* be "it is on blue paper," *x* be "it is on one sheet," and *y* be "it is written by Brown."
   (a) All the dated letters are written on blue paper.
   (b) None of them are in black ink, except those that are written in the third person.
   (c) I have not filed any of them that I can read.
   (d) None of them that are written on one sheet are undated.
   (e) All of them that are not crossed are in black ink.
   (f) All of them written by Brown begin with "Dear Sir."
   (g) All of them written on blue paper are filed.
   (h) None of them written on more than one sheet are crossed.
   (i) None of them that begin with "Dear Sir" are written in the third person.
   (j) Give a conclusion that yields a valid argument.

52. Let *p* be "he is going to a party," *q* be "he brushes his hair," *r* be "he has self-command," *s* be "he looks fascinating," *t* be "he is an opium-eater," *u* be "he is tidy," and *v* be "he wears white kid gloves."
   (a) No one who is going to a party ever fails to brush his hair.
   (b) No one looks fascinating if he is untidy.
   (c) Opium-eaters have no self-command.
   (d) Everyone who has brushed his hair looks fascinating.
   (e) No one wears white kid gloves unless he is going to a party. (*Hint:* "a unless b" ≡ ~b → a.)
   (f) A man is always untidy if he has no self-command.
   (g) Give a conclusion that yields a valid argument.

COLLABORATIVE INVESTIGATION
Logic Problems and Sudoku Revisited

The logic problems and Sudoku in the Extension on pages 138–144 are fairly elementary, considering the complexity of some of the other problems found in the magazines mentioned. The problems here require more time and reasoning skills than the ones appearing in the Extension.

They are taken from *England's Best Logic Problems*, May 2004, and *Sudoku #13*, 2005.

The class may wish to divide up into groups and see which group can solve these problems fastest.

EXERCISES

Note: As an exception to our usual style, answers to these Collaborative Investigation Exercises are given in the back of the book.

1. **A Case of Foul Play** At the end of a shelf on a book-case is a pile of six murder novels published by a book club devoted to such works. From the clues given at the top of the next column, can you work out the titles and authors of the books numbered 1 to 6 in the stack, and work out the colour of its uniform style dust jacket? (*Note*: Women are Dahlia Dagger, Mary Hemlock, and Sandra Bludgeon, and men are Geoffrey Stringer, John Gunn, and Philip G Rott.)

Clues:

(a) *Murder in the Sun* is immediately below the novel by Mary Hemlock but somewhere higher in the pile than the book with the yellow dust jacket.

(b) Dahlia Dagger's contribution to the collection is entitled *Mayhem in Madagascar*; it is two below the green-covered book in the pile.

(c) The blue dust jacket belongs to the novel by Sandra Bludgeon, which occupies an even-numbered position on the shelf.

(d) The book with the red dust jacket is not *Lurking in the Shadows*.

(e) The brown dust jacket belongs to *A Killer Abroad*, which is by a female author.

(f) *The Final Case* occupies position 4 in the stack.

(g) The bottom book in the pile, which was not written by Geoffrey Stringer, has a black dust jacket.

(h) The author of the novel at the very top of the stack is John Gunn.

2. **Very Hard Sudoku**

8		3	7				9	
		6	8					
2								6
	2		1	8				9
				3				
4			6	5		2		
7								3
					1	8		
	5				8	7		1

CHAPTER 3 TEST

Write a negation for each statement.

1. $6 - 3 = 3$

2. All men are created equal.

3. Some members of the class went on the field trip.

4. If that's the way you feel, then I will accept it.

5. She applied and got a FEMA trailer.

Let p represent "You will love me" *and let q represent* "I will love you." *Write each statement in symbols.*

6. If you won't love me, then I will love you.

7. I will love you if you will love me.

8. I won't love you if and only if you won't love me.

Using the same statements as for Exercises 6–8, write each of the following in words.

9. $\sim p \wedge q$

10. $\sim(p \vee \sim q)$

In each of the following, assume that p is true and that q and r are false. Find the truth value of each statement.

11. $\sim q \wedge \sim r$

12. $r \vee (p \wedge \sim q)$

13. $r \rightarrow (s \vee r)$ (The truth value of the statement s is unknown.)

14. $p \leftrightarrow (p \rightarrow q)$

15. Explain in your own words why, if p is a statement, the biconditional $p \leftrightarrow \sim p$ must be false.

16. State the necessary conditions for
    (a) a conditional statement to be false.
    (b) a conjunction to be true.
    (c) a disjunction to be false.

Construct a truth table for each of the following.

17. $p \wedge (\sim p \vee q)$

18. $\sim(p \wedge q) \rightarrow (\sim p \vee \sim q)$

Decide whether each statement is true *or* false.

19. Some negative integers are whole numbers.

20. All irrational numbers are real numbers.

Write each conditional statement in if . . . then *form.*

21. All integers are rational numbers.

22. Being a rhombus is sufficient for a polygon to be a quadrilateral.

23. Being divisible by 3 is necessary for a number to be divisible by 9.

24. She digs dinosaur bones only if she is a paleontologist.

For each statement, write **(a)** *the converse,* **(b)** *the inverse, and* **(c)** *the contrapositive.*

25. If a picture paints a thousand words, the graph will help me understand it.

26. $\sim p \rightarrow (q \wedge r)$ (Use one of De Morgan's laws as necessary.)

27. Use an Euler diagram to determine whether the argument is *valid* or *invalid*.

    All members of that athletic club save money.
    Gregory Langlois is a member of that athletic club.

    Gregory Langlois saves money.

28. Match each argument in parts (a) – (d) with the law that justifies its validity, or the fallacy of which it is an example, in choices A–F.
    A. Modus ponens
    B. Modus tollens
    C. Reasoning by transitivity
    D. Disjunctive syllogism
    E. Fallacy of the converse
    F. Fallacy of the inverse

    (a) If he eats liver, then he'll eat anything.
    He eats liver.

    He'll eat anything.

(b) If you use your seat belt, you will be safer.
You don't use your seat belt.
_____

You won't be safer.

(c) If I hear *Mr. Bojangles*, I think of her.
If I think of her, I smile.
_____

If I hear *Mr. Bojangles*, I smile.

(d) She sings or she dances.
She does not sing.
_____

She dances.

Use a truth table to determine whether each argument is valid or invalid.

29. If I write a check, it will bounce. If the bank guarantees it, then it does not bounce. The bank guarantees it. Therefore, I don't write a check.

30. $\sim p \rightarrow \sim q$
$\underline{q \rightarrow p}$
$p \vee q$

CHAPTER 3 Introduction to Logic

3.1 Exercises **(Pages 103–104)**

1. statement **3.** not a statement **5.** statement **7.** statement **9.** statement **11.** not a statement
13. statement **15.** compound **17.** not compound **19.** not compound **21.** compound **23.** Her
aunt's name is not Hildegard. **25.** At least one dog does not have its day. **27.** No book is longer than this
book. **29.** At least one computer repairman can play poker. **31.** Someone does not love somebody sometime.
33. $x \leq 12$ **35.** $x < 5$ **37.** Answers will vary. **39.** She does not have green eyes. **41.** She has green
eyes and he is 56 years old. **43.** She does not have green eyes or he is 56 years old. **45.** She does not have
green eyes or he is not 56 years old. **47.** It is not the case that she does not have green eyes and he is 56 years
old. **49.** $p \wedge \sim q$ **51.** $\sim p \vee q$ **53.** $\sim(p \vee q)$ or, equivalently, $\sim p \wedge \sim q$ **55.** Answers will vary.
57. C **59.** A, B **61.** A, C **63.** B **65.** true **67.** true **69.** true **71.** true **73.** false
75. Answers will vary. **77.** Everyone here has done that at one time or another.

3.2 Exercises **(Pages 115–117)**

1. false **3.** true **5.** They must both be false. **7.** T **9.** T **11.** F **13.** T **15.** T **17.** T
19. It is a disjunction, because it means "$5 > 2$ or $5 = 2$." **21.** T **23.** F **25.** T **27.** T **29.** F
31. F **33.** T **35.** T **37.** T **39.** 4 **41.** 16 **43.** 128 **45.** seven **47.** FFTF **49.** FTTT
51. TTTT **53.** FFFT **55.** TFFF **57.** FFFFTFFF **59.** FTFTTTTT **61.** TTTTTTTTTTTTTFTTT
63. You can't pay me now and you can't pay me later. **65.** It is not summer or there is snow. **67.** I did not say
yes or she did not say no. **69.** $5 - 1 \neq 4$ or $9 + 12 = 7$ **71.** Neither Dasher nor Blitzen will lead Santa's sleigh
next Christmas. **73.** T **75.** T **77.**

p	q	$p \vee q$
T	T	F
T	F	T
F	T	T
F	F	F

79. F **81.** T

3.3 Exercises **(Pages 124–127)**

1. If you see it on the Internet, then you can believe it. **3.** If the person is Garrett Olinde, then his area code is 225.
5. If the soldier is a marine, then the soldier loves boot camp. **7.** If it is a koala, then it does not live in Iowa.
9. If it is an opium-eater, then it has no self-command. **11.** true **13.** true **15.** true **17.** false
19. Answers will vary. **21.** F **23.** T **25.** T **27.** If they do not raise alpacas, then he trains dogs.
29. If she has a ferret for a pet, then they raise alpacas and he trains dogs. **31.** If he does not train dogs, then they do
not raise alpacas or she has a ferret for a pet. **33.** $b \rightarrow p$ **35.** $p \rightarrow \sim r$ **37.** $p \wedge (r \rightarrow \sim b)$ **39.** $p \rightarrow r$
41. T **43.** F **45.** T **47.** F **49.** T **51.** T **53.** Answers will vary. **55.** TTTF **57.** TTFT
59. TTTT; tautology **61.** TFTF **63.** TTTTTTFT **65.** TTTFTTTTTTTTTTTT **67.** one
69. That is an authentic Persian rug and I am not surprised. **71.** The English measures are not converted to metric measures and the spacecraft does not crash on the surface of Saturn. **73.** You want to be happy for the rest of your life and
you make a pretty woman your wife. **75.** You do not give your plants tender, loving care or they flourish.
77. She does or he will. **79.** The person is not a resident of Oregon City or is a resident of Oregon. **81.** equivalent
83. equivalent **85.** equivalent **87.** not equivalent **89.** equivalent **91.** $(p \wedge q) \vee (p \wedge \sim q)$; The statement simplifies to p. **93.** $p \vee (\sim q \wedge r)$ **95.** $\sim p \vee (p \vee q)$; The statement simplifies to T.
97. The statement simplifies to $p \wedge q$. **99.** The statement simplifies to F.

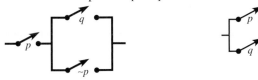

101. The statement simplifies to $(r \wedge \sim p) \wedge q$. **103.** The statement simplifies to $p \vee q$.

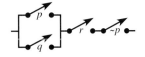

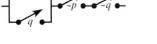

3.4 Exercises (Pages 132–134)

1. (a) If you were an hour, then beauty would be a minute.   **(b)** If beauty were not a minute, then you would not be an hour.   **(c)** If you were not an hour, then beauty would not be a minute.   **3. (a)** If you don't fix it, then it ain't broke. **(b)** If it's broke, then fix it.   **(c)** If you fix it, then it's broke.   **5. (a)** If it is dangerous to your health, then you walk in front of a moving car.   **(b)** If you do not walk in front of a moving car, then it is not dangerous to your health. **(c)** If it is not dangerous to your health, then you do not walk in front of a moving car.   **7. (a)** If they flock together, then they are birds of a feather.   **(b)** If they are not birds of a feather, then they do not flock together.   **(c)** If they do not flock together, then they are not birds of a feather.   **9. (a)** If he comes, then you built it.   **(b)** If you don't build it, then he won't come.   **(c)** If he doesn't come, then you didn't build it.   **11. (a)** $\sim q \rightarrow p$ **(b)** $\sim p \rightarrow q$ **(c)** $q \rightarrow \sim p$ **13. (a)** $\sim q \rightarrow \sim p$ **(b)** $p \rightarrow q$ **(c)** $q \rightarrow p$ **15. (a)** $(q \vee r) \rightarrow p$ **(b)** $\sim p \rightarrow (\sim q \wedge \sim r)$ **(c)** $(\sim q \wedge \sim r) \rightarrow \sim p$ **17.** Answers will vary.   **19.** If it is muddy, then I'll wear my galoshes.   **21.** If 18 is positive, then $18 + 1$ is positive.   **23.** If a number is an integer, then it is a rational number.   **25.** If I do crossword puzzles, then I am driven crazy.   **27.** If Gerald Guidroz is to shave, then he must have a day's growth of beard.   **29.** If I go from Park Place to Baltic Avenue, then I pass GO.   **31.** If a number is a whole number, then it is an integer.   **33.** If their pitching improves, then the Orioles will win the pennant.   **35.** If the figure is a rectangle, then it is a parallelogram with a right angle.   **37.** If a triangle has two sides of the same length, then it is isosceles.   **39.** If a two-digit number whose units digit is 5 is squared, then it will end in 25.   **41.** D   **43.** Answers will vary.   **45.** true   **47.** false **49.** false   **51.** contrary   **53.** consistent   **55.** contrary   **57.** Answers will vary. One example is: That man is Carter Fenton. That man sells books.

3.5 Exercises (Pages 137–138)

1. valid   **3.** invalid   **5.** valid   **7.** invalid   **9.** invalid   **11.** invalid   **13.** yes **15.** All people with blue eyes have blond hair.   **17.** invalid   **19.** valid   **21.** invalid   **23.** valid   **25.** invalid
   Dinya Norris does not have blond hair.

   Dinya Norris does not have blue eyes.

27. invalid   **29.** valid   **31.** Answers will vary.

Extension Exercises (Pages 141–144)

1. First, Piotr Knightovich, Yorki; Second, Ivan Rookov, Porki; Third, Boris Bishopnik, Gorki; Fourth, Yuri Pawnchev, Corki.   **3.** Ben Ashby, Jane Kenny, Dirk and Daisy, American; Hans Gruber, Sue Rogers, Merlyns, English; Peter Owen, Carol Dodds, Starr Twins, own composition; Steven Thorp, Nancy O'Hara, Rose and Thorn, Irish.

5.
7	2	6	4	9	1	5	3	8
9	4	5	8	6	3	2	1	7
8	1	3	7	5	2	4	9	6
6	8	1	3	2	4	7	5	9
2	9	7	6	1	5	3	8	4
3	5	4	9	8	7	1	6	2
4	7	9	1	3	8	6	2	5
5	3	8	2	4	6	9	7	1
1	6	2	5	7	9	8	4	3

7.
2	7	5	3	8	4	6	1	9
8	3	6	5	9	1	4	2	7
4	1	9	7	6	2	8	3	5
3	4	7	2	5	8	1	9	6
6	2	8	1	4	9	7	5	3
5	9	1	6	7	3	2	4	8
9	5	4	8	1	6	3	7	2
7	8	2	4	3	5	9	6	1
1	6	3	9	2	7	5	8	4

9.
1	8	2	5	7	9	3	4	6
5	3	4	8	1	6	2	9	7
7	6	9	2	3	4	8	1	5
4	1	8	7	9	2	6	5	3
3	7	6	1	8	5	4	2	9
2	9	5	4	6	3	7	8	1
9	2	1	3	4	7	5	6	8
8	5	7	6	2	1	9	3	4
6	4	3	9	5	8	1	7	2

11.
9	8	3	2	4	5	7	1	6
2	6	1	3	9	7	8	4	5
7	5	4	8	6	1	9	3	2
1	7	6	4	5	3	2	9	8
4	9	5	7	2	8	3	6	1
3	2	8	6	1	9	4	5	7
5	4	7	9	8	6	1	2	3
8	1	2	5	3	4	6	7	9
6	3	9	1	7	2	5	8	4

3.6 Exercises (Pages 151–154)

1. valid by reasoning by transitivity   **3.** valid by modus ponens   **5.** fallacy by fallacy of the converse **7.** valid by modus tollens   **9.** fallacy by fallacy of the inverse   **11.** valid by disjunctive syllogism   **13.** invalid **15.** valid   **17.** invalid   **19.** valid   **21.** invalid   **23.** invalid

25. Every time something squeaks, I use WD-40.
Every time I use WD-40, I go to the hardware store.

Every time something squeaks, I go to the hardware store.

27. valid

29. invalid　**31.** invalid　**33.** valid　**35.** valid　**37.** If tell you the time, then my life will be miserable.
39. If it is my poultry, then it is a duck.　**41.** If it is a guinea pig, then it is hopelessly ignorant of music.　**43.** If it is a teachable kitten, then it does not have green eyes.　**45.** If I can read it, then I have not filed it.　**47. (a)** $p \rightarrow {\sim}s$
(b) $r \rightarrow s$　**(c)** $q \rightarrow p$　**(d)** None of my poultry are officers.　**49. (a)** $r \rightarrow {\sim}s$　**(b)** $u \rightarrow t$　**(c)** ${\sim}r \rightarrow p$
(d) ${\sim}u \rightarrow {\sim}q$　**(e)** $t \rightarrow s$　**(f)** All pawnbrokers are honest.　**51. (a)** $r \rightarrow w$　**(b)** ${\sim}u \rightarrow {\sim}t$　**(c)** $v \rightarrow {\sim}s$　**(d)** $x \rightarrow r$
(e) ${\sim}q \rightarrow t$　**(f)** $y \rightarrow p$　**(g)** $w \rightarrow s$　**(h)** ${\sim}x \rightarrow {\sim}q$　**(i)** $p \rightarrow {\sim}u$　**(j)** I can't read any of Brown's letters.

Collaborative Investigation　**(Page 155)**

1. 1, *Death in Beijing*, John Gunn, red; 2, *A Killer Abroad*, Mary Hemlock, brown; 3, *Murder in the Sun*, Geoffrey Stringer, green; 4, *The Final Case*, Sandra Bludgeon, blue; 5, *Mayhem in Madagascar*, Dahlia Dagger, yellow; 6, *Lurking in the Shadows*, Philip G Rott, black.

Chapter 3 Test　**(Pages 156–157)**

1. $6 - 3 \neq 3$　**2.** Some men are not created equal.　**3.** No members of the class went on the field trip.
4. That's the way you feel and I won't accept it.　**5.** She did not apply or did not get a FEMA trailer.　**6.** ${\sim}p \rightarrow q$
7. $p \rightarrow q$　**8.** ${\sim}q \leftrightarrow {\sim}p$　**9.** You won't love me and I will love you.　**10.** It is not the case that you will love me or I will not love you. (Equivalently: You won't love me and I will love you.)　**11.** T　**12.** T
13. T　**14.** F　**15.** Answers will vary.　**16. (a)** The antecedent must be true and the consequent must be false.　**(b)** Both component statements must be true.　**(c)** Both component statements must be false.　**17.** TFFF
18. TTTT (tautology)　**19.** false　**20.** true

Wording may vary in the answers for Exercises 21–25.　**21.** If the number is an integer, then it is a rational number.
22. If a polygon is a rhombus, then it is a quadrilateral.　**23.** If a number is divisible by 9, then it is divisible by 3.
24. If she digs dinosaur bones, then she is a paleontologist.　**25. (a)** If the graph helps me understand it, then a picture paints a thousand words.　**(b)** If a picture doesn't paint a thousand words, then the graph won't help me understand it.
(c) If the graph doesn't help me understand it, then a picture doesn't paint a thousand words.　**26. (a)** $(q \wedge r) \rightarrow {\sim}p$
(b) $p \rightarrow ({\sim}q \vee {\sim}r)$　**(c)** $({\sim}q \vee {\sim}r) \rightarrow p$　**27.** valid　**28. (a)** A　**(b)** F　**(c)** C　**(d)** D　**29.** valid
30. invalid

PERMUTATIONS

The number of permutations of n elements taken r at a time, where $r \leq n$, is

$$_nP_r = \frac{n!}{(n-r)!}.$$

COMBINATIONS

The number of combinations of n elements taken r at a time, where $r \leq n$, is

$$_nC_r = \binom{n}{r} = \frac{n!}{(n-r)!r!}.$$

BINOMIAL PROBABILITY

If p is the probability of success in a single trial of a binomial experiment, the probability of x successes and $n - x$ failures in n independent repeated trials of the experiment is

$$_nC_r p^x (1-p)^{n-x}.$$

MEAN

The mean of the n numbers, $x_1, x_2, x_3, \ldots, x_n$, is

$$\bar{x} = \frac{x_1 + x_2 + \cdots + x_n}{n} = \frac{\Sigma(x)}{n}.$$

SAMPLE STANDARD DEVIATION

The standard deviation of a sample of n numbers, $x_1, x_2, x_3, \ldots, x_n$, with mean $\bar{x}$, is

$$s = \sqrt{\frac{\Sigma(x-\bar{x})^2}{n-1}}.$$

BINOMIAL DISTRIBUTION

Suppose an experiment is a series of n independent repeated trials, where the probability of a success in a single trial is always p. Let x be the number of successes in the n trials. Then the probability that exactly x successes will occur in n trials is given by

$$_nC_r p^x (1-p)^{n-x}.$$

The mean μ and variance σ^2 of a binomial distribution are, respectively,

$$\mu = np \quad \text{and} \quad \sigma^2 = np(1-p).$$

The standard deviation is

$$\sigma = \sqrt{np(1-p)}.$$

The **derivative** of the function f is the function denoted f' whose value at the number x is defined to be the number

$$f'(x) = \lim_{h \to 0} \frac{f(x + h) - f(x)}{h},$$

provided this limit exists.

RULES FOR DERIVATIVES

Assume all indicated derivatives exist.

Constant Function   If $f(x) = k$, where k is any real number, then

$$f'(x) = 0.$$

Power Rule   If $f(x) = x^n$, for any real number n, then

$$f'(x) = n \cdot x^{n-1}.$$

Constant Times a Function   Let k be a real number. Then the derivative of $y = k \cdot f(x)$ is

$$y' = k \cdot f'(x).$$

Sum or Difference Rule   If $y = f(x) \pm g(x)$, then

$$y' = f'(x) \pm g'(x).$$

Product Rule   If $f(x) = g(x) \cdot k(x)$, then

$$f'(x) = g(x) \cdot k'(x) + k(x) \cdot g'(x).$$

Quotient Rule   If $f(x) = \dfrac{g(x)}{k(x)}$, and $k(x) \neq 0$, then

$$f'(x) = \frac{k(x) \cdot g'(x) - g(x) \cdot k'(x)}{[k(x)]^2}.$$

Chain Rule   Let $y = f[g(x)]$. Then

$$y' = f'[g(x)] \cdot g'(x).$$

Chain Rule (Alternative Form)   If y is a function of u, say $y = f(u)$, and if u is a function of x, say $u = g(x)$, then $y = f[g(x)]$, and

$$\frac{dy}{dx} = \frac{dy}{du} \cdot \frac{du}{dx}.$$

Generalized Power Rule   Let u be a function of x, and let $y = u^n$ for any real number n. Then

$$y' = n \cdot u^{n-1} \cdot u'.$$

Exponential Function   If $y = e^{g(x)}$, then

$$y' = g'(x) \cdot e^{g(x)}.$$

Natural Logarithmic Function   If $y = \ln |g(x)|$, then

$$y' = \frac{g'(x)}{g(x)}.$$